People and Progress

by WILLIAM S. GRAY *and* MAY HILL ARBUTHNOT

BASIC READERS

The 1947-48 Edition

CURRICULUM FOUNDATION SERIES
REG. U.S. PAT. OFF.

Scott, Foresman and Company

CHICAGO   ATLANTA   DALLAS   NEW YORK

Copyright, 1947, by Scott, Foresman and Company

Previous Editions Copyright, 1930, 1931, 1936, 1940, 1943, by Scott, Foresman and Company

PRINTED IN THE UNITED STATES OF AMERICA

Contents

Young Americans Today

	PAGE
Ronnie and the Mystery Horse..BELLE COATES..........	8
Marion Andrews, Lifesaver......MILDRED AUGUSTINE.....	17
Who's Scared of Bears?........ELEANOR HAMMOND......	24
High Water in Arkansas........CHARLES J. FINGER......	32
The Junior Team's Bargain.....CHESLEY KAHMANN......	41

Early Adventures in Progress

News for the Gazette..........FRANCES CAVANAH......	52
Yankee Clipper Ship..........CORNELIA MEIGS........	61
All Aboard!..................JEANETTE C. NOLAN......	70
Can't a Machine Do It?........GRACE HUMPHREY.......	79
Newfangled Notions...........CAROLINE D. EMERSON....	90
The Horseless Carriage.........EMMA GELDERS STERNE...101

Man-made Wonders of Today

PAGE

Coast Guard to the Rescue..... HENRY B. LENT 114
Smoke Jumper............... MARGARET McKAY 120
Miracle of the Air............ FREDERIC N. LITTEN 125
The Night Express........... RAY STANNARD BAKER 139
A Fireman's Bag of Tricks..... HOWARD M. BRIER 148

Fun and Fancy

The Caliph's Clock............ JOHN BENNETT........... 158
Rhyming Ink................ MARGARET AND MARY BAKER . 174
The Story of Dr. Dolittle...... HUGH LOFTING 183
Ben and Me................. ROBERT LAWSON 194

World Neighbors

Pepperfoot Earns His Name.... ROBERT DAVIS 210
The Immortal Railroad........ RUTH E. KENNELL 225
A Letter for Nikias........... JOSEPHINE BLACKSTOCK 236
End of a Quest............... ALICE C. DESMOND 248
The Good River.............. PEARL S. BUCK 257

The World of Nature

Adventures of Chut........... DOROTHY COTTRELL 276
Enchanted Island............. VON HAGEN AND HAWKINS... 290
Sharp Wits in Bronze Armor... JULIE CLOSSON KENLY 305
The Shining Gateway......... HUBERT EVANS........... 313
The Wild Goat's Kid.......... LIAM O'FLAHERTY 326

Defenders of Freedom

		PAGE
Thomas Jefferson	SONIA DAUGHERTY	342
Lafayette Meets His Hero	JEANETTE EATON	355
Simón Bolívar, Liberator	MARION LANSING	363
First Lady of China	BASIL MATTHEWS	373

Stories That Never Grow Old

Robin Hood	ENGLISH LEGEND	388
Tom and the Treasure Chest	HOWARD PYLE	404
The King of the Golden River	JOHN RUSKIN	425

Young Americans Today

Ronnie and the Mystery Horse

"What will you do now, Ronnie?" gasped Beth as the roan pony from Bar K ranch dashed away after spilling Ronnie Gainor into the sagebrush. "You'll have to get another horse to enter the relay race at the ranchers' picnic this afternoon."

"Yes, I know," said Ronnie, brushing his gaily colored shirt as he watched the borrowed pony disappear toward home in a cloud of dust. "There isn't time to ride ten miles to get the roan back. I must find another horse to use with Star and Sprint."

With Beth for his audience, Ronnie had been practicing for the relay, making the change from Sprint to the roan. But on returning to the Gainor corral, the roan, shying at a gopher, had thrown Ronnie into the sagebrush and run away.

Determinedly Ronnie set his freckled jaw. "I'm going to ride in the relay race, Beth. I'm going to win the prize twin calves so that I can help Dad start a new herd in place of the cattle he lost last winter in the blizzard."

"I know, Ronnie," Beth said gently. They had talked of little else all summer—this Western boy and the girl from the neighboring ranch.

The race was at two o'clock. It was now nearly noon. Both Beth and Ronnie knew that every horse for miles around had been bargained for by some boy who was riding in the relay. There was practically no chance of finding another suitable horse to take the place of the runaway roan pony.

Suddenly Beth smiled triumphantly. "Here's my horse! You can ride Dude."

"Him!" Ronnie gave the horse a scornful glance and almost laughed. "Dude wouldn't do at all."

"Dude can *run*," Beth protested loyally. "He has long legs."

"But he's too old, Beth. Like as not he'd lie down on the race track, just as he lay down at your gate last spring when the spice peddler drove up with him. That's why the peddler gave him to you and bought a better horse from my dad. Dude's no good for anything—except," Ronnie added quickly, with a good-natured smile lighting up his freckled face, "to curry and feed and pet and maybe ride a mile or two. He wouldn't do for a relay race."

"He *might* do," the girl still insisted stubbornly. "No one knows what old Dude is good for. He's a mystery horse. We don't know anything about him, except that he's over ten years old by his teeth."

"And that he lies down when he's tired and starts to run whenever anyone on horseback comes near," said Ronnie. "Those are bad habits in a horse."

"Maybe," said Beth, thinking that one or two bad habits didn't necessarily spoil a good horse.

Ronnie began pacing up and down. "I'll *have* to get another horse," he muttered.

At last Beth said, "Charlie Long over in Clay County is sure to ride his pinto pony to the picnic. Maybe you could borrow her."

Ronnie brightened. "Maybe I could. Thanks, Beth! You always help me out of my troubles."

As Beth started away on Dude, Ronnie rushed toward the ranch house, shouting back jubilantly, "I'll be seeing you at the picnic!"

Beth, riding old Dude, was late in arriving at the picnic. The foot races and greased pig contest were over. It was about time for the relay race.

In this race each boy was to enter three ponies. On one of these he would start the race. His other two ponies were to be held by a keeper near the inner edge of the track. Then, after the boys had raced their first ponies once around the track, they were to dismount swiftly, change the saddles to their second ponies, and ride them around. In the third lap, they were to ride the third and last ponies.

It was dismounting, resaddling, and remounting that called for skill in a rider. Not a movement could be wasted, not a second lost. The ponies themselves must be swift and sure-footed. The boy who came in first on his third horse would win the prize calves that were now being led out—twin red heifers with pure white faces. Everybody was applauding.

"Oh, I do hope Ronnie wins them," breathed Beth as she watched from the edge of the cottonwood grove near the race track. She tried to find Ronnie with Star and Sprint and the borrowed pinto among the group of boys and ponies, but Dude was nervous and needed all her attention. His ears pricked up; his long white body quivered with the urge to run as Beth guided him away from the ponies to the far edge of the grove.

Already the boys were leading their ponies up to the circular track that had been laid out like a great wheel on the prairie in front of the giant cottonwoods. Dude, with his head higher than usual, looked eagerly toward the ponies. His funny, loose-hanging lower lip went up and down—pup-pup—as he trotted briskly along, picking his long-legged way over the gopher holes.

"Funny old Dude," said Beth lovingly. "What were you raised to be? Army horse, fire horse, or circus horse as Dad says? But what does it matter as long as you are *my* horse?"

As she tied the old horse to a tree, Beth heard the starter's shrill whistle and saw the procession of riders file up to the line. She hurried toward the track to cheer for Ronnie. Where was he?

At that instant he came running through the trees.

"Why aren't you in the race?" asked Beth.

Ronnie bit his lip to hide its trembling as he said, "Charlie Long hasn't come yet with his pony."

"Oh, Ronnie!" Beth cried in disappointment. Her eyes swept the crowd and the prairie beyond. All of a sudden she exclaimed, "Oh, there's Charlie at the creek, watering his pony. Go back, Ronnie, and start the race with Star and Sprint. I'll have another horse there in three minutes." With that promise Beth darted away.

At the creek she discovered Charlie Long looking anxiously at his pony's left forefoot. "Got a stone in her foot," he explained as Beth ran up. "She limped so much I thought I'd never get here."

Beth smothered a sob. There was no use asking Charlie to lend his pony now. There wasn't time enough to get the stone out before the race. Beth had promised Ronnie a horse in three minutes, and across the way the boys were starting their ponies around the first lap.

In the lead Beth saw Ronnie's bright silk shirt above Star's lowered head. Ronnie would certainly win the calves—if he could get another horse!

Now the riders were coming in at the finish of the first lap. There was a flash of quick young arms as the boys leaped to the ground; a gleam of brown saddles being changed swiftly from the first ponies to the second ones. Ronnie started on the second lap with Sprint far ahead of the others. The crowd was cheering him wildly.

Beth knew that Ronnie would be around the track again in less than two minutes. There must be another horse waiting for him to ride. What horse? But why ask? There was only one other horse to be had—Dude!

A moment later the frantic girl was leading the high-headed, long-legged old white horse out of the cottonwood grove toward the place where the keepers were holding the last relay of ponies.

Ronnie, riding Sprint, was leading the other riders swiftly around the second lap.

Again Ronnie came in first. He was off his horse, the saddle with him. Without looking, he turned to throw it on Charlie's pinto. He was sure the pinto would be right there, for Beth had promised. She had never failed him. But his saddle fell expertly over a white back instead of a spotted one. Ronnie blinked. What was this? A *white* horse—old Dude!

Beth, holding the quivering Dude, saw Ronnie's dejected look. "Hurry, Ronnie!" she gasped. "Dude is all there is. Charlie Long's pony is lame."

But Ronnie could only stare at Dude. He was ashamed. He was beaten. Dude began to toss his head; his funny, loose-hanging lower lip worked up and down—pup-pup-pup! Beth could hardly hold him. One boy started on the last lap. Then another. The crowd cheered. Ronnie didn't seem to care.

"Hurry, Ronnie!" Beth pleaded.

"Oh, all right," Ronnie agreed grudgingly. He cinched the saddle tight and vaulted into it. The spectators would laugh at him, but he would carry through. He wouldn't be a quitter.

There were four ponies ahead of them as Dude and Ronnie started on the last lap. The crowd shouted good-naturedly at the bony, long-legged old horse trailing behind the fleet ponies.

Soon there were only three ponies ahead. Then two. Then one. Old Dude was overtaking the ponies as surely and easily as a stately old stork might overtake a flock of fluttering chickadees. All the bottled-up restlessness in his long bony body seemed to have broken loose in his flying feet.

The spectators gasped and began to cheer him. The next instant the relay race was over. Ronnie had won it. Someone was leading the twin calves up to him.

Raising his old sombrero in a gesture that said thank you, Ronnie slid off Dude's back to take the halters of the prize calves. Beth was there, reaching for Dude's reins, whispering proudly to him.

"It wasn't a bad habit after all—was it, Dude—your wanting to run when you saw horseback riders? You were only showing us what you were born to be—a race horse."

Then Ronnie stood there facing her with his two calves. He was wild with joy, but he was humble, too. He wanted to tell Beth that he was sorry for the things he had said about her horse, but he didn't know how to say it.

Shyly he shoved one calf toward her. "You take it, Beth. For letting me ride old Dude."

Beth stared at him with shining eyes. He was giving her half of the start of his new herd! She answered him gently, "Oh, no, thank you, Ronnie. Dude is enough for me!"

Marion Andrews, Lifesaver

Big Bob Walker, the lifeguard at Lakeside Beach, glanced out over the water where only a few of the most enthusiastic bathers were swimming.

"Two more weeks will finish the season," Bob remarked to the girl beside him.

"And then you'll be leaving?" Marion Andrews spoke regretfully, for when Big Bob returned to college, it meant the end of the swimming lessons he had been giving her. During the two summers that he had been a guard at Lakeside he had taught her lifesaving and greatly improved her racing stroke, the crawl.

"I'm staying for the water carnival," Bob said. "You'll be in the swimming races, I suppose?"

A look of disappointment came into Marion's eyes for an instant. Then she smiled.

"I'm helping to decorate the floats, and I'm to be in one of the water pyramids."

"But aren't you swimming in the races, or diving, or taking part in the canoe tilts?"

"I'm not good enough, Bob. You see, I've been practicing lifesaving most of the summer, and my diving isn't good. My racing stroke isn't so bad, but there are three other girls who are larger than I am, and they make better time than I do; so they will swim in the races."

The Seals Club, to which Marion belonged, gave a water carnival each summer at Lakeside Beach, and this event usually marked the end of the summer season. The carnival was sure to be thrilling, and hundreds of people would crowd the beach to watch the spectacular stunts. Only the very best swimmers and divers took part in the contests.

"I wish I had worked on my diving this summer," Marion said a trifle enviously. "Martha Daniels is to do fancy high diving, and she will carry off all the honors."

"Perhaps she will," Bob said. "But personally, I'd rather be a good swimmer. It doesn't help any to know how to dive when a drowning man gets you by the neck."

"I think I'll try a high dive, now," said Marion. "I'm scared to death of diving from that tower, but I want to see if I have the nerve to do it."

It was fear of striking the water flat, and not fear of the distance from the diving tower to the water, that made the girl hesitate. As she had often said, "Even soft water is hard, if you hit it flat."

"Oh, well, here I go." Marion swam to the float, climbed the tower, poised for only an instant, and then dived without allowing herself time to think. She felt her feet going over as she neared the water, and she tried to obey the shouted warning from Bob, "Head up, Marion."

As she struck the water, she seemed to feel every pound of her body's weight; her feet flopped over, twisting her back slightly. She came to the surface of the water and swam slowly back to where Bob stood.

"Too bad, Marion! That must have hurt. Keep your head up, or you'll flop over every time."

"I think I'll call it a day. I'm willing to let Martha Daniels have the diving honors," Marion said as she started away.

On carnival day an enthusiastic crowd of people was assembled along the shore of the lake. Marion was at the clubhouse at an early hour, for she did not mean to miss a single feature of the program. First came the swimming races and then a game of water baseball. Comedy was furnished by a tub race, a canoe tilt, and an old-clothes race.

Next came the floating pyramids, in which Marion took part. Together with twenty other girls in black bathing suits and crimson caps, she swam out into the water. The girls arranged themselves in rows, holding hands, and floated across the lake. From the shore, the effect was that of a moving pyramid of crimson dots.

When it came time for the fancy diving, Marion found a place on the float beside the diving tower. Martha Daniels was the star diver of the club, and all eyes were on her as she stood ready at the edge of the platform. For a moment Marion removed her eyes from the girl and glanced down at the water. She gave a sudden start and leaned forward to get a clearer view. Below the surface was the indistinct outline of an object that had not been there before, and instantly Marion guessed what had happened.

During the storm last night a heavy limb from a tree must have drifted under the diving float and caught there. Now, jarred loose by a sudden lurch of the crowded float, one end of the log had swung out to the place where Martha would surely hit the water. Fear paralyzed Marion for the moment; then she cried out in warning, "Stop!"

Martha did not hear. She poised on the edge and sprang upward and out, spreading her arms for the swan dive. For a moment her body seemed to be suspended in air; then she shot downward. She struck the water, and what would have been a perfect dive ended in an awkward flop.

Quick as a flash, Marion slid from the float. A dozen powerful strokes brought her to the spot where she had seen Martha go under. She peered down into the water and caught a glimpse of a huddled form. Drawing her body into a ball, she ducked her head, straightened her body with a sudden snap, and shot through the water in a perfect surface dive.

Marion kept her eyes open, and the moment that she was well below the surface, began to swim toward the dark form. Her hand reached out and clutched Martha by the strap of her bathing suit. Wasting not an instant, she swung the girl's limp body into position for the cross-chest carry, and, with one arm free, began to kick her way to the surface. She was nearly out of breath, but not for a minute did she think of releasing the body that hung like a dead weight upon her.

Then, just as it seemed that she could no longer hold her breath, her head emerged and she gulped in the fresh air. Before Marion could take a stroke toward shore, Bob had reached her to take charge of Martha.

"Keep back, everybody!" Big Bob warned as he carefully stretched Martha on the sand. "Give her a chance for air."

Members of the Seals Club and other swimmers formed a protecting circle about the unconscious girl and held curious and frightened persons from crowding in upon her. A hurried examination told the lifeguard that Martha's outstretched hands had struck the log first, and that she had suffered only a glancing blow upon the head. One arm hung limp, and it was evident that it was broken.

"She's coming around now," Bob announced after he had worked with her for a few minutes. "We'll get a car and take her to the hospital, where she can have medical treatment. She'll be all right as soon as the broken bone is set."

When Bob had seen Martha off to a hospital, he returned to the beach, for his duty as lifeguard made it necessary for him to be within calling distance. The crowd was melting away, but a few people were still standing near the float where the accident had taken place. Bob glanced searchingly up and down the beach. As he turned toward the clubhouse, he saw Marion hurrying away in the opposite direction.

"Hello there, Marion. Come here. What do you mean by running off when everyone wants a chance to congratulate you?"

Marion opened her gray eyes wide; then a flush of pleasure came over her face. Big Bob, seeing her surprised look, knew that she had not counted upon being the heroine of the day. He laughed.

"Why, Marion, you funny kid! Don't you know that your rescue of Martha was the most thrilling event of the carnival? You had the biggest part of the whole show. And if you think you can sneak home without anyone's telling you so—well, you're mistaken!"

Who's Scared of Bears?

It was Don Brown who had suggested the idea. If Bill Jenkins, the new boy in town, wanted to join the Centerville Detective Club, he must pass a test to prove his courage. It hadn't taken long to decide that a trip after dark to the deserted shack in Bear Swamp was the perfect test, and now the club members had the shack prepared for Bill's trial.

A choice collection of fireflies had been brought in from the woods, and their tiny, flickering lights made weird spots of color against the damp, mossy walls. Lifelike bats had been cut from black paper, and a stuffed owl added to the ghostly scene.

"It's spooky, all right," Don chuckled, "and this paper skeleton left from my Halloween party makes it a lot spookier."

The paper skeleton was suspended on a string, and the draft created by opening the door would cause the skeleton to sway as if it were walking. An oatmeal container with marbles in it was attached to the door by a cord in such a way that it would move along the floor as the door opened. The marbles rolling about would give the effect of a ghostly rattle guaranteed to chill anyone's bones. A carved box, that Bill was to take back as proof that he had been there, was hidden among some fir cones.

Everything was ready, and it remained only to go back to town and give Bill his instructions.

Bill had already been notified that his application for membership in the club would be accepted if he passed a test to show that he had the courage needed by a good detective. So that evening after dinner he appeared in the Browns' garage, which the boys used as a club room, to get his instructions.

"You are to go out to an old shack in Bear Swamp after dark tomorrow and bring back the carved wooden box that is hidden there," Claude Spencer, the club president, directed Bill. "You must go alone and bring back the box and give it to us here at the club room. You know where Bear Swamp is, don't you?"

"Yes, I know. It's out on the Cedar Mills road," Bill said. But he looked troubled.

"You aren't scared to go out to that old shack after dark, are you?" Claude asked hopefully.

"I guess not," replied Bill. "But are there really bears in that swamp?"

Claude and Don exchanged amused glances.

"Oh, not *many*," Don chimed in. "Sometimes a few come down to eat huckleberries in the swamp."

"A man met a black bear on the fourth hole of the golf course on the other side of the swamp one day," Jim Cody remarked, neglecting to say that this incident had occurred ten years before.

"There won't be any bears in the old shack," Ted Martin said. "And if you do meet one on the trail up the creek—well, you're smart enough to figure out a way to escape, aren't you?"

"A detective must be smart," Stan Jones added. "But maybe you'd rather not join our club?"

Bill Jenkins gulped, but he said, "Oh, sure I want to join. Who's scared of bears?"

So matters were settled. On the following night Bill was to make the lonely journey to the deserted old shack a mile from town. He was to obtain the box hidden there and bring it back to the club room that same night.

"He'll think he's run into something worse than a bear when he sees those fireflies lighting up that paper skeleton," Ted said. "I'd give a dollar to see him then."

Jim slapped his knee. "Why shouldn't we see him?" he asked. "Why not go out and hide in the bushes back of the shack, where we can look in through the window? We can see the whole show."

"That's a good idea," Don agreed. "Besides, if Bill gets too scared, we can come out and keep him company—tell him it's all just a joke."

By seven o'clock next evening the boys were making their way toward the old shack in order to be there before Bill arrived. They hid in the bushes at the edge of the woods and waited.

To the eager boys the wait seemed endless. The last rays of sunset faded, and soon the evening star glowed bright and clear above the murmuring reeds in Bear Swamp.

"Won't Bill ever get here?" Ted whispered.

"Maybe he isn't coming," Stan suggested.

"But he said he'd come, and he seemed anxious to get into the club," Ted whispered back.

Minutes passed. The thin crescent of a new moon shone above the shadowy fir trees. The watchers peered from their hiding places. They were tired of waiting, and the woods was growing very dark and full of mysterious noises.

At last there came a sharp crackling of twigs. "He's coming!" Claude whispered hoarsely.

They strained their eyes to see the approaching figure. Suddenly Ted grasped Stan's arm hard. "Look! Wh—what is that?" he stuttered.

For a minute Stan was too startled to answer. "It's—it's a bear!" he finally gasped.

It was certainly a huge black furry form waddling through the tall grass. The moonlight showed bright yellow eyes and a mouth edged with white teeth. The bear turned its head this way and that as if scenting the evening air. Finally it made for the clump of bushes where the boys were hiding.

"Come on!" Jim yelled. "It's coming right at us!" He turned to run and collided with Claude. The boys raced pell-mell toward the shack. In their wild flight Ted tripped on a tree root, and Stan sprawled on top of him.

But somehow all five boys tumbled inside the shack and slammed the door. Ted got to his feet, rubbing his knees, and peeped out the window. "It's going away," he reported in a tone of relief. "I guess all that racket scared him."

For a few minutes after the bear had disappeared, the boys huddled together in the shack. Then cautiously they opened the door and peered out.

"It's gone," Ted whispered.

"I guess Bill isn't coming to the shack," Jim said a trifle shamefacedly. "It isn't any use waiting for him." And without another word the conspirators made for home at top speed.

But when the club members arrived at the garage the next morning to discuss the matter further, they found the carved box inside the door. There was a note under it saying:

> Can you fellows come up to my house Saturday afternoon to try out my new airplane model? There will be some chocolate pie.
>
> Bill

The boys looked at each other in surprise. "So Bill went out to the shack after all," Ted said in an awed tone. "I don't suppose he saw the bear."

No one mentioned the trick they had tried to play on Bill. But they agreed unanimously to accept his invitation.

When they arrived at Bill's home, there was something on the floor before the fireplace that made them all stare. It was a huge black bearskin rug with yellow glass eyes and a most lifelike red mouth edged with pointed white teeth.

"You don't suppose——" Ted glanced at Stan, and Stan looked at Don. "You don't suppose Bill and that rug——"

Don stooped and picked up something from the rug. It was a dry pine needle. There was also a slight smudge of swamp mud on a hind claw. A boy on all fours with a bearskin rug over his back might be mistaken for a real bear—by moonlight.

"And we asked if Bill is really smart!" Don laughed. "He's smart enough for our club any day!"

Bill, who had followed the boys into the room, laughed out loud. "I guess you're pretty smart detectives yourselves," he said, "and I'm proud to get into your Detective Club."

High Water in Arkansas

Proctor K. North, Tad's father, owned the ferryboat that went back and forth between Proctor's Landing and the other side of the Arkansas River. It was not much of a craft to look at, being little more than a roughly made platform built on two flatboats. It was propelled by a little gasoline engine on a smaller flatboat lashed alongside. Except on school days Tad ran the engine.

It was early spring—the time of high water in Arkansas. The lower branches of the willows along the riverbanks were burdened with floating sticks, cornstalks, and odds and ends. All morning things had been drifting down; once a haystack, then a hencoop with two bedraggled hens for sailors, then a mile-long tangle of cornstalks. Hourly the river rose, became yellower and yellower, noisier, angrier, wider.

About eleven o'clock Proctor K. said, "I guess we'll call it a day, Tad, and lay up."

"Meaning it's dangerous?" asked Tad.

"Not what I call plumb dangerous, Tad; only the way I look at things is that a pocketful of caution is worth more'n a hundred sacks of take-a-chance. What is not wisdom is danger."

Tad nodded, then asked, "What about Sim's delivery truck, the bread, and all that?"

"If he comes within the next hour, of course we'll take him over. If he doesn't get here by then, why, folks'll have to bake for themselves the way they did when I was a boy."

But in spite of bad roads, Sim was only a half hour late, and, as usual, his dog, Susie, announced their coming with joyous barks. She capered about the deck as soon as the truck was aboard and barked frenziedly at the water.

"Maybe I ought to tie her up for once; she's that excited," said Sim doubtfully.

Tad, testing his engine, thought it would be a pity to tie Susie, seeing how she enjoyed everything.

Sim walked across the gangplank to lend a hand to Proctor K., who was preparing to cast off the line. Then things happened. A rabbit appeared on the top of the levee. Susie gave a sharp hunting cry, scampered across the gangplank, and started up the levee in happy chase.

Tad looked up to see the dog racing like mad along the top of the bank and heard Sim say, "Oh, pshaw! I knew I ought to have tied her."

Sim went running up the riverbank after Susie, and Proctor K., after taking a half hitch round the post with the mooring line to hold the ferryboat, followed. That was the moment when the second thing happened.

Downstream came rolling the stump of a tree, its wicked-looking roots protruding above water, ready to do mischief. One root, reaching high, caught the rope and dragged it under water just as the end of the stump collided with the ferryboat and drove it sideways.

Tad seized an oar to prevent being driven against the bank. At the same instant he saw the post to which the rope was tied, dragged out of the soft earth and start riverward.

Before he realized what had happened, twenty feet of raging yellow water separated the ferryboat from the riverbank. Tad saw Sim on the bank with Susie under his arm, saw Proctor K. at the water's edge, saw the willows sliding strangely northward, and Sim and Proctor K. sliding with them. Then he knew he was adrift, and panic seized him. But his panic was for a moment only. In a flash he had his engine going, but almost immediately he knew how useless it was. The ferryboat was in the grip of the current and already in mid-river, sweeping rapidly downstream.

What is not wisdom is danger, his father's motto, ran through Tad's mind. So he stopped the motor. He would take a chance on the boat's being carried along to a point nearer the bank. He must not waste gasoline which might come in useful later on.

"Tad, you've got to think straight now," he told himself.

He took off his coat and covered the engine. Tad felt that if *he* got wet it would do no harm, but the engine was a different matter. Next he picked up the mooring line which was trailing in the river, hauled it in, and coiled it ready for use. With these things in order, he climbed to the roof of the delivery truck to take observations. It was then that he realized he was not alone on the flooded river.

Ahead was a shantyboat, a sort of little Noah's Ark. It was one of those floating houses in which people live who gather shells for button factories. He saw a Negro woman waving a white cloth, and on the roof of the ark were three children.

Then Tad became breathless. Ahead, in the line the shantyboat would take, was a long and wicked-looking wave. Tad knew what would happen. The shantyboat would catch the wave broadside on; it would tilt, and the deluge of water piling against it would cause the boat to capsize. All that came to him in a second. Suddenly Tad became active. Down he leaped to his engine and started it. Back he ran to the steering oar and tugged to change the course, so that the drift of the ferry would take it near the shantyboat.

"Catch! Make fast!" shouted Tad as he flung the mooring line.

He saw the woman bend forward to catch the flying rope, saw how she caught it, how she gave it a swift turn around a post, and he knew that the trick was done. The boats were now fast to each other. The rest was up to Tad.

Getting the ark alongside and holding it there while the woman and three frightened children got on board the ferry was easy. Then Tad shut his engine down, and there were joyful thanks.

Also there were rejoicings when Tad, wondering if it was honest to do so, opened the door of the truck and took out bread and cakes for the children. They stuffed rather than ate, so ravenous they were.

"Two days they got never a bite!" said Nancy, the mother. She munched a cake herself, and then she turned to Tad and asked, "You all alone on this rescue boat, Mister Captain?"

So Tad had to explain. "This is no rescue boat," he said. "I'm adrift just like you. An accident."

"Accident? What you mean, Mister Captain?" She persisted in giving him that title. "Don't you see Heaven sent you down the river to us? 'Twas all arranged, Captain. Two bends in the river, and we'll come to Cypress Island, where I was in the high water in '32. The Lord's a-sending us there."

What with the swirling waters and the islands of wreckage, they were almost upon Cypress Island before Tad realized they were even near it. If the little engine could force the ferryboat out of the raging current into the still water behind the island, there was hope. The next minute or two meant quick work.

Tad sent Nancy to the steering oar. Then opening the rear door of the delivery truck, he bundled the children inside where they would be safe, stepped to the flatboat alongside, and started the engine.

Immediately they were racing through the wild waters at high speed.

Once the ferryboat pivoted on a hidden snag and almost pulled the shantyboat on its side. Once the engine fluttered, as if it had done its best and, wearied, could do no more.

But they won.

The ferryboat slid into calmer water in the lee of the island, and into the river, waist-deep, ran some of the islanders who were marooned there.

"You've made it," yelled one of the men, a tall, bronzed fellow.

They laid hands on the ferryboat and pulled it inshore, while the engine chug-chugged bravely.

"More mouths to fill and nothing much to give them," said one islander hopelessly.

"I tell you the Lord knows His business and never does things halfway," declared Nancy, and to Tad's dismay, she pointed to the food in the delivery wagon.

The marooned people were willing to believe her a little later when, with a blazing fire for comfort, all of them were feasting on Sim's bread and cakes, milk, cheese, crackers, bacon, canned pork and beans, salmon, and much more. When one of the men wondered who was going to repay Sim, Nancy relieved her own mind, even if she did not relieve Tad's, by repeating, "The Lord never does things halfway! It'll come out all right." And as it turned out, Nancy was a good prophet.

A relief boat sent by the Red Cross arrived five days later. The rescue workers on that motorboat expected to find famished people on Cypress Island. Instead, there were fifteen well-fed and comfortable persons, a brave flag fluttering on a newly erected flagpole, and things in general wearing the air of a picnic rather than a flood disaster.

The relief supervisor congratulated Tad on his good work, and a newspaper reporter talked about a medal. But when he pushed the boy in front of the microphone of a broadcasting set, Tad only said, "I really didn't do anything. It just all came about the way it did."

The Junior Team's Bargain

The Junior Football Team, all present except the star player, Joe McMahon, trudged down the main road from Dover Village and headed for the McMahon farm. Dressed in odds and ends of football equipment and carrying well-filled packages of sandwiches and cookies, the team was walking fast and walking with a purpose.

"Wait until Joe hears this!" Brick Evans said for the dozenth time, patting his chest. Stuffed beneath his scarlet jersey was a letter from the nearby Frankville School challenging the Dover Juniors to their first big game. But more than a mere game was at stake. The Juniors had to prove that they deserved to be called a real team. Somehow they had to convince the whole town that no longer were they a harum-scarum bunch of babies. They were a team. Even the high-school boys would have to admit it, now that they had an out-of-town game, especially if the Juniors should win in their first real contest.

It was Saturday, and since Joe had no telephone, the only way to acquaint him with the big news was to walk the two miles out to the McMahon farm. It wasn't a waste of time, Brick pointed out, because they could practice signals and passing on the way. They could eat a picnic lunch and then have plenty of time afterward for a practice game in McMahon's pasture.

"With Joe on the team, we'll have a good chance to beat Frankville," Ed Jackson said. The others nodded. There wasn't any question about Joe's being the best player on the Junior Team, even if he was the newest member. Joe had an uncanny way of side-stepping even the most persistent tackle, and he could snare a forward pass out of the air as easily as if the ball were an apple falling from a tree.

However, Joe did have one handicap. He seldom had time to practice. His farm chores kept him so busy that an hour before school each weekday was all he could spare.

The Juniors strode along, jubilant at the prospect of a whole afternoon of practice with Joe and of the improvement their team would make.

When the boys reached the farm, they spied Joe and his father in a field, digging potatoes.

"Hi, Joe! We have a game with Frankville a week from Saturday," cried Brick, waving the letter.

Reaching Joe's side, he read the challenge aloud, expecting his friend to be greatly excited. Instead there was a look of dismay on Joe's face.

"What's Joe got to do with your football team?" asked Mr. McMahon, leaning on his digging fork.

"What's he got to do with it?" asked Brick. "Why, he's our star player!"

"Joe is ninety per cent of the Junior Team!" added Ed Jackson.

"Is this true?" Mr. McMahon asked Joe sternly.

In the next few minutes the story came out. For weeks Joe had been getting up an hour and a half earlier than usual to do his share of the chores before going to school for football practice. All this time Mr. McMahon had thought, without Joe's actually telling him so, that the boy had done this in order to have more time for schoolwork.

"So it was just for football!" Mr. McMahon exclaimed. "I don't like the idea of town boys——"

But he was interrupted by Joe, who said quickly, "Listen, Dad! I'll give up football if you won't blame the boys."

"All right," said his father. But still he gave his opinion of town boys in general—sissies, he called them, who never did a lick of work and hadn't anything more important on their minds than a namby-pamby game like football.

"Sissies! Namby-pamby!" Brick thought to himself. He thought of how the high-school team had to train in order to toughen up before going into a game. He thought of how his own team worked.

"Well, good-by," Brick said to Joe. He turned away, followed by the rest of the forlorn team.

Joe started after them. "You see," he explained, "it's only because there's so much work that Dad feels the way he does. We can't get help, and there are a million things to do—sheep, cows, horses, pigs, and chickens to tend to, and the farm itself."

"If you can't play," said Brick, "the team might just as well quit right now!"

"Well," sighed Joe, "I guess I was crazy to think I could ever be on the team when there is so much work to be done before winter. So long, fellows."

The boys waved to Joe and turned toward town. For a while they walked along without a word. Brick was turning the whole matter over in his mind. Suddenly he hit on an idea, and the team went into a huddle while he explained his plan.

When he concluded, new hope was on everyone's face. Back up the road marched the team and straight into the field where Joe and his father were still hard at work digging potatoes.

"Mr. McMahon," asked Brick, "could Joe play football if you could get all the fall work done?"

"Yes, indeed!" answered Mr. McMahon. "When the work is done, he can play all he wants to!"

"It's a bargain!" said Brick. "Give us forks. We'll pitch in and dig these potatoes in no time."

"I've a good notion to let you tackle it!" said Mr. McMahon. "Get them started, Joe."

Joe brought out extra forks and baskets, and his friends grasped them with grim determination. Joe's father assigned two boys to a row, one boy to dig potatoes and the other to pick them up.

"*Sissies! Namby-pambies!*" most of the boys were snorting to themselves as they started work, vowing silently to show just how industrious and efficient town boys could be.

Brick wielded his potato fork energetically as he tackled his row.

"Don't jab like that, my boy!" Mr. McMahon shouted as Brick's fork split a big, smooth potato in two. Then he patiently showed the diggers how to stick the fork into the ground so that not a single potato would be damaged.

"Look!" he called to Bob Gray. "You're leaving half the potatoes in the hill!"

It wasn't so easy as it looked, but Bob learned rapidly, and so did the other boys. In a short time they were doing the work nearly as well as Joe and his father, though not so fast.

Joe, who was next to Brick, said, "It's mighty nice of you fellows to help with the work."

Brick's back was already aching, but he said, "Oh, what's a patch of potatoes, anyhow? We have a game with Frankville, and that's what counts!"

With ten extra boys working, the bushel baskets were soon filled, and Mr. McMahon went after the wagon to haul the potatoes from the field.

"Do you have to work as hard as this all the time, Joe?" asked Brick.

"Yes, but I'm used to the work," answered Joe. To prove it, he dug his fork into the ground, brought up a hill of potatoes, and shook off the dirt with what seemed no effort at all.

"Any work that you're not used to makes your muscles sore," Joe went on. "You feel it at first, but you get over it. What I mean is that I'm used to farmwork, and you're not."

Although Brick felt like lying down and never getting up again, he said, "Well, just because we feel it a little is no sign we're quitting!"

"Who said anything about quitting?" cried Bill, smothering a groan. The others echoed his words. They were all doing their utmost to demonstrate that town boys could work.

Soon Joe's father returned with the horse and wagon and began to load the potatoes rapidly. When the wagon was full, Joe and Brick drove it to a shed and spread the potatoes out to dry.

Shortly after the two boys got back to the field, Mr. McMahon said, "It's dinner time!"

The town boys dashed toward the big elm tree where they had left their lunch packages. But Mr. McMahon called out, "You're coming to the house. My help always eats at my table."

"But there're ten of us!" Brick protested.

"Country food stretches," said Mr. McMahon. "I told my wife that you are here. Bring your sandwiches if you want to, but come on."

The boys, whose appetites had been whetted by their unaccustomed exertion, trooped willingly after him. Soon they were seated at the table.

The boys took one look at the heaped dishes of tempting food, and all their doubts vanished as to Mrs. McMahon's ability to feed ten extra boys.

There were meat pies and baked potatoes and a dish of string beans swimming in milk and butter. There were hot corn-meal muffins and three kinds of jam to go with them.

"Now, help yourselves," Mrs. McMahon invited cordially. "And if you don't see what you want, just ask for it. Don't be bashful."

The boys needed no urging. As Brick started on his second plateful, he began to feel better, and he could see spirit coming back into the others, too.

When at last Mr. McMahon slid his chair back from the table, Brick jumped to his feet, saying, "I guess we can finish that potato patch by dark."

"The bargain wasn't just to finish the potatoes," said Mr. McMahon. "It was to *get the fall work done*, and the potatoes are only a small part of what has to be done around here before cold weather."

Brick gasped, and so did the rest of the team.

"We'll come out every day after school," Brick pleaded earnestly. "But we must have Joe for the Frankville game—and all the other games. He has tough muscles, and he doesn't get winded like the rest of us, and——"

Suddenly he realized that Joe's toughness and endurance were the result of regularly doing these farm chores. He had been in a sort of training, like the high-school track and football training. If the whole Junior Team had been in training—if they all could develop muscles like Joe's—why, Frankville wouldn't have a chance.

"Mr. McMahon," Brick said, "we'd be glad to come here all the spare time we have. We need a regular workout. It'll put us in shape for football!" Recalling what Joe's father had said about football's being a namby-pamby game, he added, "You have to be tough to play good football!"

"Really tough," said Bill, shaking his head for emphasis.

"As tough as nails," Ed Jackson put in.

"We never thought of football that way, did we?" said Mrs. McMahon to her husband.

Mr. McMahon looked from boy to boy. "You'd work your heads off for football, wouldn't you?" he said, as if he couldn't quite believe it.

"Yes, we would!" shouted ten enthusiastic voices.

"Well, if you town boys really want to toughen up, I'd be the last to prevent you," Mr. McMahon began, tilting back his chair as a slow smile spread over his face. "It's a bargain. You don't have to come every day. Two or three times a week will be enough to get the work done, and it won't always be digging potatoes. There's a lot of other things to do. From now on, Joe can be on your team, and welcome. And I'll pay you something besides."

Brick whirled to face his teammates. "How about a cheer, fellows?" he shouted. "What's the matter with Mr. McMahon?"

The answering cheer fairly made the silverware on the table dance.

"He's all right!" ten voices yelled in unison.

"Who's all right?"

"Mr. McMahon!"

Shouting like Indians, the eleven boys burst out of the house and tore back to the field. The way they tackled those potatoes showed how they expected to tackle Frankville a week from Saturday.

Early Adventures in Progress

News for the Gazette

Timothy Waring was an apprentice to the editor of the *Fielding Gazette*. Timothy's contract said that he must work in Mr. Fielding's print shop until his eighteenth birthday, but though that was six long years away, Timothy didn't mind. He was proud to have a part in printing one of the few newspapers published in the American Colonies in 1776.

More than anything in the world Timothy wanted to become the editor of a newspaper, as his hero, Benjamin Franklin, had been, and nowhere could he learn his trade better than in the place he was now. Already he could set type and run the printing presses, and he was looking forward to the day when he would have enough experience to gather news and write it up for the paper.

One hot afternoon in early July Mr. Fielding turned from the case where he was setting type to answer the question of his embarrassed helper.

"What, Timmy?" he said, staring. "You want a day off during the week? A fine apprentice you are!"

"Oh, no, sir, not a day off," said Timothy, twisting his leather apron in his hot hands. "I wouldn't have to leave until five, after the paper has gone to press. I can walk home in three hours. Then in the morning I'll get up before dawn and be back here in plenty of time to deliver the papers. You see, sir, now that John is away at the war, I'm the eldest—and it's Mother's birthday—and I always have helped her celebrate it before——"

Mr. Fielding nodded slowly as he looked down into the eager, freckled face.

"Well, yes, I'll let you off, but don't be asking favors like this too often. If you'll take good care of my mare, Nellie, you may ride her; but see to it that you are back promptly at seven in the morning." Mr. Fielding reached into his pocket and laid a coin in Timothy's hand. "You deserve it. You've been a good lad. And now run along. There's no need to wait, because I'll hold the press until midnight. A postrider may come with news from the convention in Philadelphia.

I've a feeling in my bones that the Declaration of Independence has been signed. I've left a space vacant on the front page for the story, and I'll hold the space until midnight. It won't be my fault if tomorrow my subscribers don't read the best piece of news they've heard in all their lives."

Timothy stopped short in the act of taking off his apron. "Then you think a postrider might still come to town with the news tonight?"

"Aye, that I do," was the firm answer. "So run along."

In a short time Timothy was riding toward home. Nellie seemed to understand that she was carrying him to some very special celebration, for she cantered steadily along the yellow ribbon of road in spite of the dust and the heat. But the boy had forgotten for the moment that he was homeward bound. He had even forgotten the new scissors he carried as a birthday gift to his mother.

He was thinking of the same thing that most people in the thirteen colonies were thinking of at that time. Each colony had sent delegates to a convention in Philadelphia to consider an important paper called the Declaration of Independence. If they all signed, it meant that they declared the colonies free and independent of England. There were folks who thought the delegates would never dare to sign their names to the paper, for they would be considered guilty of treason by England. And if the American Revolution failed, what would be their punishment?

"It takes brave men, Nellie, to run a risk like that," said Timothy. "Oh, I hope a postrider comes tonight in time for Mr. Fielding to print the story in tomorrow's paper."

All week the town had waited anxiously for word from Philadelphia. There were no telegraph wires or radios or telephones in those days to carry the news. Instead, reliable messengers on swift horses rode from town to town. It was known throughout the colonies that, as soon as a decision had been reached by the delegates in Philadelphia, postriders would be sent in every direction. The days had dragged on, and the suspense had grown harder and harder to bear as no messenger appeared.

But when Timothy reached home, he forgot the plight of the colonies in the warmth of his mother's greeting. She had not expected him so early and was delighted with the scissors he brought. Tom, the younger brother, helped him rub down the mare, while Towser, the pup, barked joyfully at his heels, and sister Jenny bombarded him with endless questions. Then there was time for the boys to swim in the creek before supper.

The creek was quite a distance from the house, across the oat field, but still within hearing of the supper bell. After a half hour of cool splashing, the boys heard the bell, and dressing hurriedly, picked their way over the new oats back to the house.

"I declare," said Timothy sheepishly as he entered the kitchen, "I left my shoes and socks down by the creek! What do you think of that?"

Tom and Jenny laughed gleefully, for Tim's forgetfulness of shoes and socks seemed to prove to them that he was still a country boy at heart. Until now they had been feeling a little in awe of his new dignity as apprentice to an editor.

"Eat your supper, Timmy," said his mother. "There will be time afterward to fetch your shoes."

The food smelled delicious and looked even better. There were hot biscuits, chicken, and a birthday cake that Jenny had baked as a surprise.

Timothy's tongue was loosened, and Mr. Fielding would never have known him for his quiet apprentice.

"My apprenticeship will be up when I'm eighteen," he boasted, spreading a hot biscuit with blackberry jelly, "and then I'm going to be an editor and have my own newspaper."

"An editor at eighteen?" scoffed Jenny.

"Benjamin Franklin was—when he was seventeen," Timothy argued.

"But, son," his mother reminded him, "it takes a great deal of money to own a newspaper."

"Well, Benjamin Franklin owns his paper, and he didn't have much money to start with. Mr. Fielding says I'll make a good newspaper man. He's teaching me everything about a newspaper. I wish I could do something for him."

After supper their conversation turned to the Declaration of Independence. Darkness came before they realized it as they sat together on the doorstep talking of the hope that beat high in the heart of every patriot. Only when they were going to bed did Timothy remember his shoes. He must get them. They were the only shoes he had ever owned.

"I don't want you boys trampling the oats in the dark," said their mother. "You'd better go around by the road and take a lantern with you."

It was a good suggestion, for they could scarcely see three feet ahead. The road was deserted, and there was no sound except the rustling of trees, the occasional chirp of a drowsy bird, and the soft swish of an owl's wings in the darkness.

The boys were following the ditch that ran along the side of the road. Holding their lantern low to light their path, they approached the bridge that would take them across to a lane that led to the creek. But just as they reached the bridge, the quiet was broken by a loud groan.

"What's that?" asked Timothy, lifting his lantern high over his head. The light revealed nothing, but another sound came from the direction of the ditch—a few mumbled phrases which they could not understand. Tom slipped a cold hand into his brother's. But frightened though they were, neither thought of turning back. They stepped forward cautiously, and by the light of their lantern they saw a horse that had fallen into the ditch, with his rider pinned beneath him.

Tom hurried home for his mother and sister, and the four of them succeeded in dragging the man out from under his horse. Somehow they carried him to the house, and under the kindly care of Mrs. Waring, he revived. He did not seem seriously injured, but he was unable to continue his journey that night.

"I must go to the *Fielding Gazette* office!" he cried. "I am a postrider from Philadelphia." He tried to rise, but fell back on the pillows.

"Tell me the news," cried Timothy. "I'll ride with it at once to the editor of the *Gazette*." And he scarcely breathed while the man told his story.

Thus it happened that Timothy and Nellie made the journey back to town that dark night with neither moon nor stars to guide them. It was not the ride that every boy dreams of taking sometime—a wild gallop for freedom or a swift, thrilling dash to a rescue. It was a slow, patient jog along an unseen road, while the moaning calls of a whippoorwill and a screech owl made the darkness frightening.

Timothy had an urge to give Nellie a kick, but he recalled the fate of the postrider's horse. He proceeded slowly and cautiously, and that was a far braver thing than riding at breakneck speed.

Later an astonished Mr. Fielding saw a barefoot boy burst into his office.

"It's signed!" cried Timothy. "The Declaration of Independence has been signed!"

Without a word the editor walked to the type case and began setting up the story as Timothy told it to him.

Next morning the subscribers of the *Gazette* read the great news with rejoicing. To Timothy's surprise there was an item about his part in bringing the news. Also, the item said that his master, as a token of trust, intended to make Timothy his heir, and that he would become a partner on the *Gazette*.

"Oh, Mr. Fielding, thank you!" The boy flushed and wriggled his toes with embarrassment.

"It's about time you said thank you," remarked Mr. Fielding gruffly, although he knew Timothy had read the item only a moment before. Then a twinkle came into his eyes as his gaze traveled to Timothy's bare feet. "Come, son. Let's go down to the shoemaker. I think my new partner needs a pair of shoes."

Yankee Clipper Ship

Jonathan Adams and Humphrey Reynolds spent most of their waking hours in each other's company. For hours they would sit on the wharf watching the ships come sailing up the bay—flying visions of square white sails and darkly outlined rigging that were seen a hundred years ago.

"I am going into the Navy," Humphrey would say. "I intend to sail the fastest and finest ship of the whole fleet to the ends of the world and back. And I will have you for a chief officer, Jonathan."

"No," Jonathan would return seriously. "I get ill when I go to sea, and I don't like hardtack and salt pork. No, I will stay at home in my father's shipyards, and some day I will build ships that are real ships and not just tubs like these."

From "The Tree of Jade" in Cornelia Meigs' *Pool of Stars*. By permission of The Macmillan Company.

They parted when they were seventeen and did not meet again for years; for Humphrey went into the Navy as he had planned, and Jonathan, with mallet and chisel in hand, was hard at work in his father's shipyard. In time he became master of the entire business, while Humphrey was sailing on those far voyages of which he had often dreamed.

Jonathan had his dreams also, but now he did not speak of them. He only toiled away at building the heavy, sturdy vessels that carried America's trade overseas. Honest ships they were and reliable, as sure of coming to port as if they belonged to the later age of steam. But oh, how long it took them to cross the sea! Twenty-three days!

When alone in his dingy office, with the door shut, Jonathan would push aside the clutter of plans and drawings and would get out the model of a strange vessel, slender and graceful, with a hull like that of a racing yacht. He would set it upon a bench and stand there staring at it, sometimes for hours at a time.

One day when he was musing dreamily over his model, there came a knock at the door, followed quickly by an impatient second one and a thunderous third, all during the moment that it took the shipmaster to put his model out of sight. The door opened, and in strode a tall, sunburned man in blue uniform. It was Captain Humphrey Reynolds, come to see his old comrade, bringing a roll of government papers under his arm.

"Congress has decided to increase the Navy," the young officer explained, "and the orders are going out to build twelve ships in haste. One of the contracts is to come to you, if you will take it. They are even in such need that they have not laid down the specifications to the last bolt and rope's end. So the shipbuilder and the naval officer who commands this ship can really have something to say about the design."

He looked at his old friend steadily and saw a slow smile of deep, unspoken delight dawn upon the shipbuilder's face. Jonathan Adams' hard hands did not often tremble, but they shook a little now as he brought out his model.

"I have been thinking about a design such as this since I was ten years old," he said, "and the chance to build it has come at last. I will make the Navy a real ship, Humphrey, and the whole world will open its eyes when you sail her."

She grew up quickly on the ways, that ship of theirs, with her bowsprit standing far out, while people watched the workmen toiling up and down her timbered sides. Old naval officers, some of whom had seen the ships of the Revolutionary War, shook their heads unbelievingly.

"Look at that sharp bow and narrow hull," one man would say. "Such a craft will never be seaworthy. Why can't these young fellows stick to the models we have tried out for them?"

"This whole ridiculous affair will capsize in the first good puff of wind," another would comment.

The day of the launching came. And then news reached Humphrey's ears that sailors, wharfmen, and naval officers were saying that the new ship, the *West Wind*, would never withstand a storm.

"They are the men," Humphrey scoffed, "who would still sail vessels like Noah's Ark, if such people as Jonathan Adams did not have the courage to build something new. The *West Wind* will teach shipmasters something, once she sets sail for the Mediterranean Sea and its swarms of pirates."

The young United States and other countries had bought safety from the lawless pirates in North Africa by sending them gifts and money. But finally the United States had refused to pay tribute and had sent a fleet of warships that bombarded the pirate seaports of Algiers, Tripoli, and Tunis. Afterward the United States Navy had policed the Mediterranean, and it was thither the *West Wind* was to sail with important dispatches for the Commander of the Mediterranean Fleet.

At last the ship was ready, a rare and beautiful sight with her slim hull, her row of guns, and her towering masts with their sails of silvery canvas. She sailed at daybreak of an April morning, a ghostly, fairylike thing, slipping away in the gray light and the mist of dawn. Jonathan stood on the dock to watch her go, staring fixedly after his winged dream flying at last across the Atlantic.

The weather was stormy and the winds fitful, but the storms lent the *West Wind* wings so that the crew's anxiety gave way entirely to pride in the speed that she was making. There was a certain grizzled old sailor, however, who openly refused to believe the evidence of the ship's speed. "Twenty-three days is the best she'll do," he vowed over and over again. Yet, on the nineteenth day of their passage, a gusty afternoon of early May, it was he who came to Captain Reynolds, round-eyed with amazement, to report, "There's land been sighted, sir. It—it looks like Gibraltar."

So that Yankee clipper ship came through the gates of the Mediterranean, a gentle breeze behind her, a swift, slender hull under a cloud of snowy canvas. The *West Wind* had set a record!

"That was only a trial," Humphrey kept saying, "when we were learning to handle her. On the voyage home—we will save additional time."

That voyage was soon to be, for the vessel was to carry Navy dispatches and reports back to the United States from Tripoli. The day before she was to sail, word came from the ruler of Tripoli that he was sending his Minister of State to make the ship a friendly visit.

The stout, dusky Arab official came aboard, gorgeous in his satins and precious jewels. After appropriate greetings and an inspection tour of the ship, he put one hand within his robe and laid a handful of gold coins on the oak table in Captain Reynold's cabin.

"A gift from my ruler to you," he said.

"But what for?" Humphrey asked.

"A mere token sent with the message that the ruler of Tripoli begs you to be a little blind if you should see a vessel of ours in pursuit of some French or British trading vessel."

"We drive no bargains to be paid for in stolen coin," returned the Captain hotly. "Have you not yet learned what America thinks of pirates?"

"The Atlantic is broad," the Arab commented slyly, "and America is far away."

"You do not seem to realize," Captain Reynolds replied, "that with this ship we have shortened the voyage by four days, and will, when we set sail again, lessen it by more than that. Every seacoast will ring with the news that the *West Wind* has crossed the ocean in eighteen days."

"Eighteen days!" scoffed the other. "That is past belief. Ships move by sails, not wings!"

"Eighteen days," repeated Humphrey. "And a thousand miles nearer to you thieving pirates!"

Humphrey brought his hand down upon the table with such force that the coins went rolling to the floor, and the dignified Arab was forced to go groveling on his hands and knees to pick them up. When he arose, Humphrey was standing by the door, holding it open.

The Arab departed in a show of offended dignity and was rowed ashore. Then Captain Reynolds turned to the preparations for getting under way.

In the days that followed, whatever else went wrong, the wind never failed. Lines parted, tackle jammed, and sails were carried away; but still the wind held. Seven days, eight days, nine days—they were halfway across, and excitement had begun to run high.

At the end of the ninth day, while the *West Wind* was wallowing in a high sea, it was discovered that the water kegs had broken loose. The greater part of the precious water supply had leaked away!

"Now our need to make port is all the greater," Captain Reynolds said grimly, as the small ration of water for the day was measured out to each man, including himself.

Days passed while the men became weak and sluggish at their work, but still a stiff breeze held, and the *West Wind* did not falter. They passed no ship from which they could obtain water; their only hope lay in making port. They turned northward, lost the trade winds, seemed for a terrible moment to be hanging becalmed; but a fresh breeze caught them and bore them on toward home.

They were like pale ghosts of a ship's crew that dawn when the lookout's husky call of "Land-ho!" announced the shores of Maryland. *Eighteen days from Gibraltar and all records broken at last!* The Yankee clipper's speed had brought America a thousand miles nearer her neighbors across the sea.

All Aboard!

On the hot summer morning of August ninth, 1831, a great crowd was pressing through the Albany streets to see one of America's newest miracles. Derek was in that eager throng. He squeezed and ducked and pushed and prodded till at last he saw it—the iron horse.

There it was, the demon machine, puffing and panting on the track. It was the *DeWitt Clinton*, which that day would haul its big load the whole seventeen miles from Albany to Schenectady, and what was more, all the way back.

The *DeWitt Clinton* had enormous wheels and a smokestack rearing loftily above the steam boiler.

An important-looking man stood on a tiny platform behind the locomotive. His job was to operate it.

A car behind the engineer held a pile of wood and two big water barrels draped with a leather hose. Then came three vehicles which resembled stagecoaches, linked to the fuel-car and to each other by a chain. Each coach could accommodate eight or nine passengers, with additional seats on top. Attached to the final coach was a string of flatcars, intended for freight or baggage, but set that day with wooden benches for the guests invited to take the grand tour to Schenectady.

Derek noticed all details of the train and imagined the delight of riding on it. Strolling alongside it, he trod on the toes of someone's polished boots.

71

"Excuse me, sir," Derek apologized to the owner of the shiny boots, who was fashionably dressed and bareheaded. In the crook of his left arm he balanced his big beaver hat. He was sketching on a paper spread over the hat crown.

"What are you drawing, sir?" Derek asked.

The artist plied his pencil in silence for a moment. Then he said, "You realize, perhaps, that this August ninth, 1831, is a historic occasion?"

"Because of the train?" asked Derek.

"Precisely. The first official trip of the *DeWitt Clinton* will be written into the history of America—and with it the name of William Brown."

"Are you William Brown?"

"At your service," the man bowed. "And you?"

"Derek Dexter. I'm twelve. I live in Albany with my grandparents."

"You're a passenger for Schenectady?"

Derek grinned. "Oh, no. I'd love to go, but I can't. Tell me, sir, are you going?"

"I wouldn't miss it for the world!"

Mr. Brown thrust the paper into the pocket of his satin waistcoat. Then pointing out a flatcar, he said, "Yonder is my bench. You have my permission to sit there for a moment—just for fun."

An excellent suggestion! Derek soon was perched on the flatcar. About him bobbed the passengers going on that historic trip, dignified gentlemen with long whiskers and plush hats; ladies in voluminous dresses with sunshades and flowery bonnets.

The captain of the train was busily collecting the fares. He talked with Mr. Brown, who gestured toward Derek. Then the captain clambered to a stool on the fuel car.

All at once the blast of a whistle drowned out all conversation; sudden fear gripped travelers and spectators. Derek leaped up. "I must get off!" he cried.

The whistle shrilled again; the engine wheezed and grunted and with a terrific lurch began rolling. As the slack in the chains was taken up, the coaches rolled, too—slowly, one at a time, and then the flatcars.

The result was wild confusion. Coaches and cars collided and banged; every passenger was dislodged and thrown into the lap of the person behind him. Men roared astonished protests; women shrieked in horror. The engineer tottered and clung to his throttle; the captain, clutching an iron bar, hung suspended like a monkey on a trapeze.

But the train was moving forward. Derek, picking himself up from the tangle of people and overturned benches, tugged at Mr. Brown's wrists.

"I must get off. I told Grandmother——"

Before the words were fairly out of his mouth, a new excitement threatened. The engine belched forth showers of sparks from the giant smokestack. The wind was carrying the sparks in a fiery deluge which dropped on the ladies' fluffy clothing and the silky; flowing whiskers of the men. Cotton cloth flared into jets of crimson. Wool smoldered. A beautiful velvet bonnet burst into flames and was snatched from the head of its terrified wearer.

Everyone was in a panic, smothering the fires.

Derek pounded Mr. Brown's blazing shirt collar. Mr. Brown in turn pounded Derek. Everybody around them slapped someone else, rescuing a friend from disaster.

But the train went on. The engineer resolutely sent his iron steed over the rails. The shower of sparks did not cease, but it diminished.

All the passengers were badly singed; their garments tattered and blackened. In spite of this, they laughed. They had expected an adventure, and they could become accustomed to the agile dodging that was necessary to prevent any serious damage.

Only Derek was subdued and sober. With every minute he was farther from Albany. Grandmother would be searching for him, worried and perhaps angry. What could he do? He peered anxiously up the ribbon of track.

A water tank was coming into view. Mr. Brown said they would stop to take on water.

The engineer had been doubtful of his brakes, and he applied them powerfully. What happened then was an exact repetition of the starting performance, but in reverse. The engine balked and was banged by the fuel-wagon; the fuel-wagon was bumped by the coaches; the coaches were jolted by the trailing flatcars. The whole train shuddered and stopped.

"Something must be wedged in between the cars to avoid the perils of starting and stopping," declared Mr. Brown. "Fence rails will do. Who'll volunteer to help tear down that fence over there?"

Derek volunteered along with the men, and with Mr. Brown leading, they all tumbled out and set to work.

When the rails were in place, the captain tooted his whistle, and the travelers scrambled aboard.

Easily, without jarring a bit, the train was off.

"The worst is past," Mr. Brown said consolingly to Derek. "Isn't this comfortable?"

"I ought to be at home," Derek muttered.

"You ought," agreed the artist, smiling. "But what can't be cured must be endured. So why not be happy? I'll guarantee that fifty years from today you'll have no regrets."

Derek considered the advice. He couldn't be *quite* happy. And yet the riding was lots of fun!

After that pause at the water tank, the *DeWitt Clinton* chugged triumphantly through the open fields, where astonished cattle eyed it distrustfully, frightened colts squealed, dogs barked, and farmers leaned on their plows to stare in amazement.

With all this delay, the trip took one hour and forty-five minutes. At Schenectady more than a thousand citizens were assembled in a welcoming committee. During the two-hour interval there were enthusiastic speeches and refreshments.

The return trip was calm and took just thirty-eight minutes. The passengers said that the railroad was proving its worth and would speed the progress of the nation. They joked and sang.

As the engine braked to a stop, Derek was silent.

"Do you want me to go to your grandmother and explain your absence?" Mr. Brown asked.

"No thank you." Derek couldn't let the artist share his scolding. "Good-by, sir." And Derek raced homeward.

"Well!" Grandmother said, looking up as Derek stepped in the door. "So you went on a journey?"

"I—I didn't mean to. But I did enjoy it."

"Didn't mean to? Why, you let that artist pay your fare. Deacon Pierce was on the platform and heard him talking to the train captain about you."

Derek gulped. That idea hadn't occurred to him.

"Grandfather is at the hotel now," Grandmother said, "to repay that artist fellow. We Dexters don't accept such favors. We pay our own way. Your supper's on the table. I saved it for you."

Derek dawdled over the milk and gingerbread. He'd eaten heartily at Schenectady.

Then Grandfather came in. "I've just talked to Mr. Brown. He says you weren't a truant, Derek; you had no suspicion of the trick he played on you."

"No, sir, I hadn't."

"Brown says he thought it was a fine experience for a lad of twelve. And I guess he's right. A tale for you to tell your children—that you rode on the first train running between the two cities of Albany and Schenectady."

Grandfather took something out of his pocket. "You know what that artist's done? He's made a sketch of the train and cut a silhouette of it out of black paper. He plans to exhibit the silhouette, and here's the original sketch for Derek."

"My lands!" exclaimed Grandmother.

Derek took the paper. Yes, there was the *DeWitt Clinton*, so lifelike that he could almost smell the smoke and hear the shrill whistle. Below the picture Mr. Brown had written *All Aboard!*

Derek glanced at his grandparents. "Would you like me to describe the ride?" he queried timidly.

"Yes, do," said Grandfather, "for next time *I'm* going."

"It was splendid," Derek began. "We went awfully fast. We went almost thirty miles an hour!"

Can't a Machine Do It?

"Cyrus, I need an extra man today. You'll have to help cut wheat in that forty near the workshop."

"All right, Father." Then taking the cradle, the boy went off to the wheat field.

For months Cyrus had watched that forty acres as he went back and forth to school. He had seen the first green shoots pushing up through the soil of that Virginia valley near the Blue Ridge Mountains. He had seen the shoots grow till they were knee-high; then slowly turn from green to gold, the wonderful gold of the wheat. And now at last he was to try his hand at reaping the grain—a grown man's job, not a boy's.

Cyrus McCormick was strong for fifteen, tall and broad-shouldered. But in an hour he found that cutting wheat wasn't so simple as it looked. The perspiration rolled down his face in tiny streams. His back ached with the steady swing, swing of the heavy cradle, as swath after swath was cut. Soon his head ached, too, and the burning sun made him dizzy. But the wheat was ripe, and if it wasn't cut at once, the whole crop would be lost.

As the boy worked on that hot July morning, he thought of all the years that men had planted wheat and harvested it—even in Bible times. Strange, wasn't it, when they'd invented so many things to make work easier, they'd kept on harvesting wheat by hand for five thousand years and more?

Swinging the large cradle was a backbreaking task. As he rested in the short yellow stubble, an idea flashed into his mind—why not make a smaller cradle that would be easy for a boy to handle?

"Try it," said his father when Cyrus presented the same question to him. "Come down to the shop and work side by side with me."

Robert McCormick was a skilled toolmaker, and he had invented many labor-saving devices. While he made sickle blades for a new machine he was working on, Cyrus whittled out a cradle, just the right size and weight for his own use. And as he whittled, his thoughts were busy. "Reaping the way they did in Bible times is drudgery. Can't a machine do it? Father has invented other things that work—the bellows, the clover huller, and a threshing machine. Will this new invention—his reaper—work?"

Cyrus looked around the old cabin that had been made into a blacksmith's shop. It was the place he liked best of all on the big prosperous plantation—a place equipped for real work, with two forges, an anvil, and a carpenter's bench. Here all sorts of things of wood and iron were made for the house, for the sawmill by the brook, and for three flour mills. And it was here that his father's inventions had been worked out.

He remembered the day when, running down to the shop to help his father, he had found him tinkering with a new piece of work—a queer-looking, clumsy machine.

"Father, what are you making now?"

Then Robert McCormick had looked up and answered, "What's this? A reaper, perhaps. And if it works, it won't have the backache. It won't mind the hot sun. It won't have to stop and rest and take a drink of cider every time it walks around the field. Why, my boy," he cried with a merry look in his eyes, "it won't walk around at all! It'll be pulled round the field by a horse. No more drudgery, Cyrus, at harvest time!"

Patient planning and experimenting were finally making Robert McCormick's dream of a reaper come true. Then one summer came the real test. Would it work?

At first the machine seemed to work all right in the field. But on rough, uneven ground the stalks of wheat bent; they twisted and bunched and choked the cutting blades till the machine ran over the wheat without cutting it at all. Where the ground was perfectly level and the grain stood straight and even, the reaper cut the wheat properly, but tossed it all about in a tangled mass that made it unfit for threshing.

"All my plans and hard work gone for nothing!" Robert said to Cyrus, who had been riding the horse that pulled the machine through the field. "No one can ever straighten out that mess. It looks as if the witches had played with it. Well, forty-six other men have tried to make a reaper, and they all failed. Here's another failure. Take the thing back to the workshop, Cyrus. Don't bother to try it any longer."

"Of course it's a failure," his neighbors remarked. "McCormick must be crazy to think he could reap with a machine pulled by a horse. Nothing can take the place of honest toil with the hands."

"Cutting wheat is drudgery—terrible drudgery," Robert McCormick said to his son. "And all it ever gives the farmer is a bare living. But my dream of ending farm drudgery is over. My reaper won't reap. It's not practical. I'm through with it!"

But Cyrus wasn't. "Surely," he thought, "there must be an easier way to cut wheat. Why, even a strong man who doesn't mind the hot sun can do only two acres a day, and a day means twelve to sixteen hours of hard work. A reaper would save all that toil. It would save the wheat, too."

In this valley there was ample time during the spring season to plow the fields and to sow the wheat, but the harvest season was usually short— ten days, sometimes only a week; then the stalks would begin to break and fall; the grain would shatter, and a hard rain might ruin the crop—then there would not be enough wheat to make bread for hungry people.

Cyrus stared at the huge reaper lying near the workshop in disgrace. What was the trouble with it? Could it possibly be made to work?

"Let me take it and tinker a bit with it," the boy suggested to his father.

"Think you can win where I have failed—and forty-six other men besides? I spent years on that reaper, thinking and working, trying this and that. I warn you—don't waste time and money on such a hopeless dream. But if you still want to see what you can do, go ahead, son."

"There *must* be a reaper," Cyrus said doggedly to himself. He began thinking how to make one that would work on uneven ground; that would work if the wheat stood up straight, or if it was matted and tangled, or beaten down by wind and rain. It must do more than *cut*—it must handle the wheat properly after it was cut and not shell out the grains.

And the things Cyrus did to improve the reaper were so easy and simple that he wondered why, in all those centuries of drudgery and wasted grain, no man had thought of them before. He found a way to separate the stalks that were to be cut from those left standing, and also a way to hold the grain while it was being cut. To keep the grain straight and to sweep it toward the cutting knife, he made a huge revolving reel.

He also found a way to prevent the cut stalks of grain from being tossed about in a tangled mass. He added a platform where the grain could fall from the reel and be gathered into sheaves.

Some of these improvements were McCormick's own ideas. Some had been used by other inventors. But no one had ever put all of these ideas together in a single machine.

With his own hands Cyrus made every part of his reaper. The wooden reel, cranks and gears, blades of steel, he hammered or whittled into shape. He worked hard to get the reaper finished in time to try it out that year—1831—before the harvest season was over.

"Won't you leave one end of a field of wheat till I get my reaper done?" Cyrus asked his father.

"Yes. I know what it means to have only a few days for experimenting," said Robert. He was anxious about the reaper. Would it succeed?

At the end of July, Cyrus hitched a sturdy farm horse to his queer, unwieldy machine and clattered out of the barnyard. Up the road and into the field he went, where the ripe golden grain waited in the hot sun, ready for the reaper.

Young McCormick's sisters and brothers looked on, excited and breathless. Father and Mother watched with keen interest.

Around, around went the reel, sweeping the stalks of wheat downward to the knife. Forward and back, and at the same time sideways, shot the cutting blade with its sharp metal teeth. Click, click it sheared off the dry grain. The wheat heaped up on the platform, a shimmering, golden mass, but tidy and even, all ready for one of the men to rake it off into a bundle.

The machine was loose-jointed and crudely made. It creaked and grumbled along. It wasn't handsome at all. But it worked! For a first trial it was a splendid success—a magnificent success!

Cyrus saw the joy on his mother's face, and knew how happy she was to see that his reaper was a real machine, not just a dream.

"Oh, I'm proud," exclaimed his father. "Proud to have you succeed where I failed."

Yes, the new machine was practical, but Cyrus could see that the reel worked poorly. It ought to be larger, so that the very lowest stalks of grain wouldn't escape being cut. He spent a few more days making improvements. Then he gave a public exhibition to show the farmers of the neighborhood his wonderful invention. At a nearby village he cut six acres of oats in one afternoon—a big task for even six men, the astonished owner said.

The next year, when Cyrus was twenty-three, he took his reaper, now drawn by a pair of horses, to a farm near Lexington. He had an audience of a hundred people—some of them college professors. There were farm laborers, too, whose hands were calloused with harvest drudgery that paid them five cents an hour for a long sixteen-hour day.

Young Cyrus started his team. Click, click went the teeth of the sharp steel blade of the reaper, and the ripe wheat stalks fell onto the platform built to catch the grain. The onlookers stood in open-mouthed astonishment.

The field was hilly and rough. The reaper jolted this way and that. It slipped and slid and bounced and floundered about. It cut the wheat stalks unevenly.

"Here! Stop, stop!" yelled the worried farmer. "This won't do, young man. Stop your team, I say. You're rattling the grain out of the heads of wheat. It'll be ruined."

McCormick stopped.

"It's all a humbug, this reaper," jeered one of the laborers.

"Well, boys, give me the old cradle!" called out another laughingly.

The inventor's face was white. His heart sank. Was he to meet only laughter and ridicule? Was his reaper no good under difficult conditions?

"I'll give you a chance in a level field, young fellow," he heard a friendly voice call out. "Come, men, lend a hand here. Pull that rail fence down. Yes, yes, this is my land. Drive right in."

Just what Cyrus wanted—a level field of wheat! Again he spoke to his horses. Again the reaper began to click. Before sunset he had cut several acres of grain. The farmers broke into shouts of praise, trooping after the reaper as it left the field for the highway like a crowd of boys following a circus parade.

It was a queer procession that wound its way into Lexington. The reaper made such a terrible racket that it scared the horses. Cyrus had to hire two strong lads to lead them. Dogs barked, and small boys yelled.

Men stared curiously at the strange contraption and joined the excited throng behind it.

"A right smart curious sort of thing," said one doubtful observer, "but I don't think it will ever come to much."

In the courthouse square, Cyrus McCormick stopped his team in triumph. Everyone turned out to see this new reaper; men, women, and children crowding around to see the reel, to touch cautiously the keen blade of the cutting knife, and to learn what the huge, clumsy object was for.

"This is an astonishing machine," announced one dignified professor from the Lexington Academy, after he had looked it over carefully and heard what it had accomplished that afternoon. "This machine is worth at least one hundred thousand dollars!"

Riding homeward in the twilight, the young inventor's eyes were still filled with awe.

"A hundred thousand dollars!" said Cyrus half aloud. "No, that's a dream as far off as that star over the mountains. Well, whether I make much money or not, I've done something worth while. If farmers have a better way to cut wheat, they'll plant more wheat. People will have more bread. There'll be less hunger in the world."

Newfangled Notions

"Dear me, Nan," cried Mrs. Dana, who was in charge of the needlework booth. "You don't mean you've come to the fair without your quilt?"

Nan nodded, winking back the tears that were rising in her blue eyes. All summer long she had worked piecing the quilt; sewing thousands of tiny, even stitches so that she would have a handsome quilt to exhibit at the County Fair. Then in the excitement of departure, she had left it at home!

"We could get it here by one o'clock," suggested Mrs. Marshall, Nan's mother. "My son Jimmie has taken our horse and buggy back to town, but he's coming back this afternoon, and he could bring it."

"A rule's a rule," maintained Mrs. Dana. "The quilt must be here by half past ten."

From *Father's Big Improvements* by Caroline D. Emerson, published by Frederick A. Stokes Company, Inc.

"If I could get word to Jimmie!" Mrs. Marshall sighed hopelessly.

Suddenly an alert expression came over her friend's face. "That newfangled machine might be of some use," cried Mrs. Dana. "Come with me."

As Nan and her mother hurried after Mrs. Dana, they were too excited to notice the dark clouds that were beginning to fill the sky. They followed their friend to a small building beside the grandstand.

"In here's one of those newfangled affairs that you talk over," explained Mrs. Dana. "They've run a wire down to the Town Hall to show what the thing can do. My husband has been here fussing with it for a week, and I can hardly get him home for meals."

"My husband's been talking about it, too," said Mrs. Marshall. "It's called a telephone."

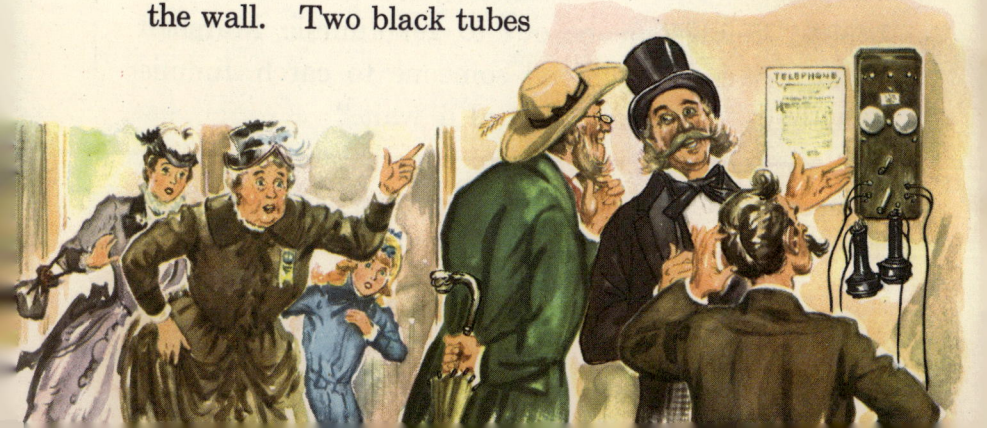

"Sometimes it works, and sometimes it doesn't," said Mrs. Dana, "but if it gets that quilt here in time, it'll be worth all the fuss that's made over it." Inside they saw Mr. Dana standing by a queer box on the wall. Two black tubes were fastened to it with long cords. There was a bell and a handle to ring it by.

"We want to catch Jimmie Marshall as he drives past the Town Hall," panted Mrs. Dana, quite out of breath. "He left here about twenty minutes ago, and he'll just be getting there. Tell him to drive home, get his sister's quilt, and hurry back to the fair immediately."

"I'll try," said Mr. Dana. He rang the bell on the box. Nan watched eagerly. Then Mr. Dana took down one of the black tubes and held it to his ear. He spoke right into the other black tube.

"HELLO!" shouted Mr. Dana so loud that Nan jumped. One could almost have heard him at the Town Hall, without any wire between, she thought.

"HELLO!" shouted Mr. Dana once more. Then he hung up the tube and rang the bell again.

"The man at the other end has probably gone home," said Mrs. Dana.

At last Mr. Dana contrived to get the box to say something to him, but Nan could not hear what it was. Then Mr. Dana began speaking in very clear tones, "Send someone out to get Jimmie Marshall as he drives past. Send someone to catch Jimmie Marshall——Oh, all right, I'll wait."

Nan stood first on one foot and then on the other. It seemed as if that telephone were going to keep them waiting forever. She doubted if it had really said anything to a man away back in town anyway. Such newfangled notions were just silly.

"Looks as though we're going to have a storm," said Mr. Dana as they all stood and waited. The rumbling of thunder seemed very near.

All at once Mr. Dana stood erect and held the black tube close to his ear.

"HELLO!" he bellowed. "Oh, hello, is this Jimmie Marshall?"

Nan's eyes began to gleam. Had the thing really worked? Could they talk with Jimmie when they were on the fairground and he was in the Town Hall? She crept close to Mr. Dana—yes, that really was Jimmy's voice, only very faint and faraway.

"Oh!" gasped Nan with breathless delight.

"Tell him to come back here as fast as he can," cried Mrs. Marshall excitedly, "and to bring——"

"One thing at a time, now, one thing at a time," implored Mr. Dana. Then he shouted to Jimmie, "Your mother says to come back as fast as you can. Do you hear? Come back as fast as you can."

"He must be back here by half past ten," cried Mrs. Marshall.

"Be back by half past ten," roared Mr. Dana.

"And bring Nan's quilt," cried Mrs. Marshall.

"What's that?"

"Quilt. Q-u-i-l-t," repeated Mrs. Marshall. "Tell him to go home and get his sister's quilt."

Mr. Dana turned back to the telephone. "Go home and get your s——"

But just then there came a flash of lightning and then a crash. Mr. Dana dropped the black tube that he held in his hand and jumped halfway across the floor. Nan scurried to her mother and hid her face in Mrs. Marshall's lavender taffeta skirt. The crash of thunder was followed by a deluge of rain. There were shrieks from outside as everyone on the fairground dashed for shelter.

When Mr. Dana gingerly took up the black tube again, not a single word could he get from it. He rang the bell and he shouted until he was hoarse, but no answer came. There was nothing to do but stay beside the useless telephone and endure the suspense until the storm was over. Nan looked ruefully at the box on the wall. It was worse than useless, getting up one's hopes all for nothing!

Mrs. Marshall tried to talk courteously to Mr. and Mrs. Dana. She did not like the storm, and she was worried about Jimmie and disappointed about the quilt. Jimmie was probably driving posthaste to the fairground through all this storm and with no quilt. These complicated modern inventions tried her patience. Her husband was all for them. But she knew they were not to be depended upon.

"In a few years there'll be a telephone in every house," Mr. Dana was saying. "It is one of the most remarkable inventions of the century."

Mrs. Marshall was quite sure there wasn't going to be one in *her* house; not if she could prevent it! There was another clap of thunder, and she wrapped her arm tightly around Nan. If she had her way, someone would invent a machine to do away with thunderstorms.

Above the thunder and rain came the sound of the clock on the grandstand. It struck ten, and Nan counted each stroke with a sinking heart. Her quilt must be at the fairground by half past ten, and, as far as she could see, there was no way short of magic to get it there if Jimmie didn't bring it.

Meanwhile Jimmie had been having excitement, too. On leaving the fairground he had driven into town and on down the main street. The town looked very empty. Stores were closed, and most of the people were out at the fairground.

As Jimmie had neared the Town Hall, he saw a man dash out to the sidewalk and stand there waving his arms wildly.

"Whoa," called Jimmie to Lily as he tightened the reins and slowed her down from a trot to a walk.

"Come inside!" shouted the man. "They want to speak to you down at the fairground."

Speak to me? wondered Jimmie in surprise. At the fairground—from the Town Hall? Why, the fairground was three miles out of town!

Then Jimmie remembered hearing about a new invention to be shown that year at the fair. Jimmie liked new machines and inventions, and he had intended to try the talking box when he went back to the fair that afternoon. This must be it that he was to talk into now!

Jimmie stopped Lily. He jumped out of the buggy and tied Lily to a hitching post. He followed the man to the Town Hall and down into the cellar. On the wall hung a strange-looking box with two shiny black tubes fastened to it.

The man picked up one of them and held it to his ear. "HELLO," he shouted.

Then he put the black tube into Jimmie's hand and pulled him toward the box.

"You listen *here*, and you talk into *that*," he instructed Jimmie.

Jimmie held the black thing against his ear and listened. At first there was only a murmuring and a rumble. Then a voice came.

"Hello," the black tube said. "Oh, hello, is this Jimmie Marshall?"

"Yes," shouted Jimmie in amazement. How did the thing know his name?

For a minute there were vague sounds that Jimmie could not understand. Then the words came clearly again.

"Your mother says to come back as fast as you can. Do you hear?"

"Yes," shouted Jimmie.

"Be back by half past ten," said the voice from the tube.

"It's nearly ten now," thought Jimmie.

The voice went on, "Go home and get your s——" But Jimmie could not make out what he was to get, because suddenly there came a crash as the storm broke about him. It did not sound so loud to Jimmie as it did to Nan and her mother at the fairground. For the lightning had struck the elm tree just outside the fairground gate, and Jimmie was three miles away, but it was loud enough to make him jump.

When he took up the tube again, not a sound could he get out of it. "I don't know what they want me to bring from home," cried Jimmie, "but whatever it is, it's got to be there in half an hour."

"You'd better hurry on home and see if you can discover what they want," suggested the man by the telephone.

Jimmie tore across the sidewalk, with the rain running down the back of his neck. He untied the thoroughly drenched and miserable mare and climbed into the buggy.

"Poor old Lily, there's no dry stable for you yet," said Jimmie sympathetically as the nervous, fidgety animal tried to head toward her stall in the town livery stable. Firmly but gently Jimmie turned Lily away from the livery stable and toward the Marshall house.

There was no one at home. Jimmie had to solve the riddle alone. What was it they wanted? Was it his mother's purse? He ran upstairs and looked in the top bureau drawer. Nothing was there. Was it the lunch basket? He peered out of the window to see if it had been left on the veranda. It was not to be seen. Could it be Nan's quilt? He raced to the parlor. There lay the quilt on a table, wrapped neatly in a sheet!

"That's it," cried Jimmie triumphantly. "That's what Mother wants me to bring out to the fairground by ten-thirty!"

He put on a rubber coat. "Mackintoshes" people called them. Then he wrapped Nan's quilt in his father's mackintosh and hurried out into the storm, carrying it carefully.

Under the hood of the buggy Jimmie kept as dry as possible. The rain beat on him, and it was hard at times to be sure that he was keeping Lily on the road. But there was no time to be lost. Lily was a good horse, and they'd make it yet. The downpour was lessening, and the black cloud was moving away as swiftly as it had come.

Lily looked wild-eyed and frightened. She had never had a day like this before! But into the fairground they came at last. Jimmie hitched Lily as quickly as he could and carried the quilt into the needlework hall.

The clock on the grandstand was just striking the half-hour. The storm was over. The people were coming cautiously from cover.

When Mrs. Marshall saw Jimmie, she scarcely believed her eyes. Nan jumped up and down crying, "Did you bring the quilt? Did you bring the quilt?"

"Yes," Jimmie assured her. "I took it right over to the booth." Then nothing would do but they must all go to see it. There it was, labeled:

PATCHWORK QUILT PIECED BY
NAN MARSHALL—AGE 8 YEARS, 6 MONTHS

Later the judges came by and examined each bit of needlework. At last one of them reached over and put a blue ribbon on Nan's quilt.

Then Nan gave a sigh of happiness. First prize! And the telephone had helped her win it. She decided she liked newfangled notions after all.

The Horseless Carriage

On the first day of the school vacation in the summer of 1894, Terry Randall sat at supper in his home in Kokomo, Indiana. He had eaten his ham and biscuits and had finished up the applesauce, and he was impatient to get out to play a couple of innings of back-yard baseball before dark. But it did not look as if supper would ever be finished, now that Father and the boarder, Mr. Haynes, were arguing about "Progress" again.

Grown-ups continually talked about "Progress." For half a hundred years invention had followed invention. Steam engines crossed land and sea. Gas and oil, the food for machines, had been found.

Electricity shot through wires and carried messages, even under the Atlantic Ocean. Mr. Haynes was full of interesting information about all these discoveries. He knew about machinery, too; how engines worked and what made pistons go up and down in a different direction from that of the wheels they were turning. He knew about electricity, too, and the way it ran along a piece of wire. And about gas light, of course, since that was the reason for his being in town.

He had come to lay a pipe line so that people in Kokomo could cook with natural gas and light the streets and houses with it. In the daytime he rode out into the country, supervising the laying of the pipe line. At night he retired to his room and tinkered on his inventions. Mr. Haynes was a wonderful man. He was always getting "parts" sent in by express, or asking Terry to stop at Mr. Apperson's blacksmith shop for a roll of wire or a piece of iron rod. His room was always littered with unfinished contraptions.

"And they're likely to stay unfinished," Terry's father had been heard to remark. He meant no disrespect to his boarder. He admired him very much. But it stood to reason, Mr. Randall always said, that there were limits to the ingenuity of man. "Even of Americans," he would add proudly, because he was extremely patriotic. Then he would go on to enumerate all the new inventions that had come into use just in the last century—railroads, gas and electric lights, telegraph, talking machines, and telephones. "And that's all," Terry's father would say. "We've gone far enough. There won't be any more changes after today."

But the disapproval of Terry's father had not kept Mr. Haynes from tinkering away in all his spare time. He was trying to make a self-propelling buggy. He had a lot of traveling to do in the country, and his horse always seemed to wear out before the end of the day. "A vehicle that can go without being pulled by a horse is what I really need," he was saying at the supper table.

A horseless carriage! The very idea annoyed Mr. Randall. "It can't be done," he snorted, "and if it could, it would be perfectly useless. What are horses and railroads for? Anyhow, they tried something of the sort in England, and it was so noisy that a man had to walk ahead with a red flag to warn drivers to keep tight hold of their horses."

"That was a *steam* vehicle," Mr. Haynes said mildly. "I'm not planning to use a steam engine," he added. "I thought of it, but a steam engine is too heavy, and I'd have to stop every mile or so to fix the fire and get steam up. I thought some of using electric batteries, too. There was once an electric carriage on the streets of Paris, France.

But it couldn't compete with steam engines. And the inventor died before he could really get it going."

Terry wished that Mr. Haynes wouldn't go into so many details. If supper wasn't over soon, it would be too dark to play.

"I've ordered a gasoline motor from an engine company in Michigan," went on Mr. Haynes. "A one-horsepower gasoline engine."

All at once Terry's mind made a connection with Mr. Haynes' talk and what Mr. Hollins, the stationmaster, had said that morning while Terry was at the depot to watch old No. 703 pull in. He leaned forward and entered into the conversation.

"Mr. Haynes, your engine's come. It's down at the depot. Mr. Hollins said it was so big you'd have to fetch it in a dray!"

When the motor came to the house, there was no place for it. It weighed a hundred eighty pounds, and taking it upstairs was out of the question.

"The kitchen is the biggest room in the house," Terry ventured to suggest timidly.

"I always did want to see how these inventions came about," Terry's mother said. "I'd be glad to have Mr. Haynes put his engine in my kitchen, where I could keep an eye on it." So she made room for the strange contraption in one corner.

Then Mr. Haynes wanted to test the gears and the traction. So he got Terry to fasten his bicycle by a rope to the rear of the buggy and tow it up Maple Street. And when Mr. Apperson came out from the blacksmith shop, they made the test all over again for him to see.

Every time Terry went by Mr. Apperson's for the next few days, he'd see him working on something for Mr. Haynes' machine. When Terry went to the depot to meet the trains, people would ask him, "How's the invention?" Everybody in town was interested; everybody, that is, except Terry's father, who was pretty well occupied working on his speech for the Fourth of July celebration. Mr. Randall had an ancestor who had signed the Declaration of Independence, and that made it seem proper for him to read the Declaration at public gatherings.

The night before the Fourth, Mr. Haynes pulled his buggy to the back yard outside the kitchen door, and Mr. Apperson came to help him. They lifted the motor into a frame they'd made and fastened the gears and levers next to the hand brake, while Terry stood around and watched. They all saw Mr. Hollins come to the front door and speak to Mr. Randall. But they did not think about his being a deputy constable, as well as station agent, until the next day when everyone was ready for the barbecue.

Mr. Haynes had got all dressed up in his striped pants and a stiff straw hat with a brown and purple hatband. Terry followed him out to the yard where the buggy was standing. He saw Mr. Hollins step up and pull out his constable's badge and heard him say, "You can't take that contraption on the streets of Kokomo!"

"The streets are free, aren't they?" Mr. Haynes retorted.

"Sure, they're free. What's that got to do with it?"

"Go listen to the Declaration of Independence, and you'll see what it has to do with it. *All men are created equal with certain inalienable rights. And among these are life, liberty, and the pursuit of happiness.* Liberty's made up of all sorts of little things, Mr. Hollins. And the pursuit of happiness is more important than people let on for it to be. America's a big country. How are we going to get about it with an old-fashioned animal like a horse that gets worn out before the day is gone?"

"There's the railroad," Mr. Hollins said, forgetting that some old fogies had tried to stop the railroad, too, when it first began.

"The railroad is fine for where it goes. One road west; one east; another south to Indianapolis, and one north to Fort Wayne. But what about going somewhere the railroad doesn't go?"

Mr. Hollins looked very uncomfortable as he wiped beads of perspiration off his forehead. "I tell you what," he said; "I can't let you start to drive a horseless vehicle on the streets of Kokomo, because there've been objections, but you could pull the buggy out of town where I have no authority. Then if you happened to come back again, I don't see how I could stop you—not if the engine does what you say it will. I don't see how anything would be swift enough to stop you at all."

"I could hitch the horse to the buggy. But how would I get the horse home?" Mr. Haynes asked.

"How about the Randall boy? Couldn't he go and bring the horse back?" queried Mr. Hollins.

That was how it happened that Terry Randall set out with Mr. Haynes for the crossroads three miles out in the country. Away they went in a buggy with a gasoline engine fastened under it, all ready to run by itself when given the chance!

At the crossroads Mr. Haynes did not talk; neither did Terry. They unhitched the Randalls' horse and buckled on his saddle. Next they pulled the shafts off the high-wheeled buggy. Then they poured a can of gasoline into the tank underneath, and there the thing was, waiting to go traveling. Terry felt kind of queer. The horseless carriage looked so small and lonesome with the high cornfields closing it in.

Mr. Haynes must have thought the same thing, because he said, "Maybe she won't work. Maybe it's not possible—but anyhow——"

He swallowed hard and did not finish his sentence. He jumped into the buggy and set the levers for starting. Then he climbed down and pulled out the crank handle, fitted it into the part of the engine that was set between the iron wheels, and gave a quick twirl.

"I'd take you along," he said to Terry, "but the ride might be dangerous."

It seemed at the moment that indeed it might be. There came a sputter and a cough and a great chugging like a railroad train. A trail of smoke came out at the back of the vehicle. Then the noise stopped, and the little buggy stood helpless once more in the road between the green cornfields.

Mr. Haynes twirled the crank again. There came another sputter and chug. This time he jumped into the seat, grabbed the steering stick, and fed gas to the motor before it could stop again.

"Better hold the horse," he called to Terry as the wheels began turning, and the buggy lurched forward. "Come down to the barbecue. I'll *try* to stop there." The rest of Mr. Haynes' words were completely lost in the sudden tumult. Down the road in a column of dust went the amazing vehicle, with nothing to pull it except some machinery that was fastened with wire under the seat and hitched somehow to the wheels.

Terry rode the horse at a gallop, but he did not catch sight of Mr. Haynes again until he arrived at the picnic grounds, out in the field back of the courthouse. There in the center of an awe-struck crowd was the horseless buggy, dust-covered and smoky, but looking as if it knew that it had done something pretty fine. "Buggymobile, that's what you ought to call it," somebody said to the inventor. "I'll be doggoned if it didn't tear up the street. It must have been going *ten miles an hour!*"

Then Terry's teacher, who was always spouting poetry, remarked, "When Mr. Haynes rode up, I just said to myself, ' 'Tis well to borrow from the good and great. 'Tis wise to learn; 'tis God-like to create.' "

"The engine stayed in my kitchen," said someone, and Terry saw his mother, very stylish in her best starched white shirtwaist dress. She spoke in a low voice, but Terry could see she took pride in her boarder's accomplishment. Terry looked around for his father, wondering what he would say.

Mr. Randall was still on the speaker's stand, but he was nodding his head the way he always did when something pleased him.

Mr. Haynes waved to Terry's father. "If it hadn't been for the Randalls, I couldn't have built it," he said. "And I'd be honored if Mr. Randall would take a short ride around the town with me.

And there'd be room for Terry. I don't think there is any danger now, though of course it is still too risky for the ladies."

Terry's father folded up his speech. Nobody even remembered that he hadn't finished it. He put it in his pocket carefully. Maybe somebody would remember after the barbecue and ask him to complete the reading of it. He had only gotten as far in the Declaration as "preservation of life, liberty, and the pursuit of happiness." He climbed into the buggy and clutched the sides firmly. Terry squeezed close to him and sat on the edge of the seat to leave room for Mr. Haynes.

The crank was turned. The spark caught, and the explosion sounded reassuringly.

Mr. Haynes leaped nimbly into the driver's seat and caught hold of the steering stick. They started down the main street, with a shouting, cheering crowd following along behind.

Near the railroad station they met Mr. Hollins ambling toward them. He had pinned his constable's badge on his coat, and you could see that he meant to take some action, however reluctantly. He was just about to step into the road and halt the buggy when he saw Terry's father waving him out of the way with a gesture of authority.

"It's all right, Hollins!" Mr. Randall called. "I've changed my mind about this gas vehicle. If they're going to be invented, Kokomo might as well get the credit!"

After they had gone on a little farther, he spoke again, rather slowly and thoughtfully. And if Terry hadn't been squeezed in so close to him, it is doubtful if he could have heard his father's words.

"I guess we have to get used to the idea," he said, "that America is always going to be thinking up something new."

Man-made Wonders of Today

Coast Guard to the Rescue

Jim Brewster felt a sharp thrill race along his spine. Here he was droning aloft 1000 feet over the world's busiest harbor, co-pilot of a Coast Guard patrol plane! He looked down at the vast reach of the Atlantic far below. On the starboard side, on the water, he could see the perfectly outlined shadow of his plane racing along slightly ahead of the plane itself. He sighed contentedly.

The pilot, Lieutenant Curt Sprong, circled over docks where ships were taking on cargoes. Then, heading north, he flew up the Hudson River above the towering skyline of New York. Here there were many things to observe: ferries shuttling back and forth, toylike tugboats chugging importantly about their business, fuel barges and other small harbor

Adapted from *Air Patrol* by Henry B. Lent. By permission of The Macmillan Company, publishers.

craft—all weaving in and out in a complex traffic pattern. Not a single ship nor a single small powerboat escaped the sharp eyes of the two officers in the Coast Guard plane. They were carrying only a skeleton crew—a mechanic and a radioman—for this was an ordinary patrol flight.

Just as the pilot was about to ask the radioman to report that they were coming in, a radio message came from the Coast Guard station on Long Island.

"Two boys in a catboat somewhere off Draper Cove," the message said. "We are requested to find out if they need assistance."

While the radioman acknowledged the report, Curt wheeled the PH-3 around toward the Cove, which he readily found on the map. Climbing to five hundred feet, he swung the ship onto a course over the south shore of Long Island.

"Looks plenty rough down there," Jim said to his fellow flight officer.

"About three feet from crest to crest, I'd say," the pilot judged. "Keep your eye peeled for the boys. Wonder how they happened to get so far out on a day like this."

Both men kept a close watch on the bays and inlets that unfolded below them as they sped on.

"See anything?" Curt asked.

"No—not yet. Wait—now I do!" Jim exclaimed. "Looks like a small sailboat turned bottom up."

Curt brought the plane down to within a hundred feet of the water and circled around the capsized boat to come into the wind. Now he could clearly see the two boys clinging desperately to the boat. They seemed completely exhausted.

"Look! There's a boat trying to reach them," Jim said.

Two men in a surfboat were doing their best to work their way out to the boys, who were about a hundred feet offshore. But each time the rescuers headed into the breakers, the waves would catch their boat and hurl it back toward the beach, where an anxious crowd had gathered. As Jim watched, the rescue boat, too, almost capsized.

Ordering the crew to prepare for a rough-water landing, Curt put the plane into a glide. With the stick hard back and the flaps down, he let the ship down onto the rough sea. The plane smacked the first wave hard, and then bounced to the next one. But the severe shock of the second contact was lessened by the way the pilot worked the throttles during the split second that the plane was in the air between waves.

As Curt carefully worked the seaplane toward the overturned boat, Jim climbed onto the hull. In his hand he held a coiled line and a life preserver ready to toss to the boys.

"Hang on, boys!" Curt called out.

The victims were apparently too frightened or too weak to reply. Each wave that lashed over the boat threatened to break their hold.

"Grab this line when I throw it," Jim shouted above the sound of wind and waves.

As soon as he was certain that the older boy had understood his order, Jim heaved the life preserver through the air toward him. It shot over the boat, which was now broadside to the plane, and the line slapped down lightly beside the larger boy. The youngster relaxed his grip on the boat just long enough to grab the life preserver and slip his companion's arms through it.

Jim pulled in the slack. "All right now," he shouted. "Make a try for it. I'll help you."

The smaller boy slipped into the water, clinging to the life preserver with his last ounce of strength. Half swimming, he was pulled steadily toward the plane and was soon alongside. Jim reached down, grabbed him under the arms, and pulled him aboard. The youngster was limp as Jim lifted him up to the mechanic.

Once more Jim coiled the line. By this time the plane had drifted farther from the capsized boat.

"Think you can make it?" Curt called down from the pilot's compartment as Jim tossed the life preserver again. The line whistled through the air, but missed the boat by inches. To make matters worse, the boy stretched out his arm to grasp it and lost his hold on the boat. For a moment Jim thought he would have to go in for him. But the plucky lad swam to the life preserver, hooked his arm through it, and Jim soon had him alongside.

Both boys lost consciousness when they reached the safety of the plane's cabin, but they soon came around with the application of first-aid measures. Jim helped make them as comfortable and secure as possible for the take-off. "How do you feel, old-timer?" he asked the smaller boy.

The youngster smiled weakly.

"I—I—guess I'm all right now," he answered.

Jim turned to the other boy.

"You saved your chum's life," he said.

"Aw, shucks," the boy replied. "He's littler than me. He couldn't've hung on much longer. I couldn't either, I guess," he added. "Thanks, sir, for what you did."

Jim, himself almost as wet as the two boys who had been in the water, went forward for the take-off. Curt gunned his engines and lifted the ship into the air for the return flight. Calling the radioman, he directed him to notify the station to tell the boys' families that both boys were safe and making for port. Then he put the big ship on the home course, the morning's work finished.

Smoke Jumper

"Smoke on Billy Goat Mountain!" came the radio report at the landing field maintained by the Chelan National Forest Service. Before the warning ended, Pilot Benson had started out to warm up his motor. Rex Boyd had hustled into his smoke jumper's suit, zipped it up the front, and belted it closely. The trousers reached high above his waistline and fitted snugly over his jacket. They zipped from waist band to ankles and were padded with thick felt material, like a football suit.

Inside the pocket of one trouser leg was the rope Rex might need to lower himself to the ground if he should land in a treetop.

He adjusted the harness of the folded parachute. Then last of all, Rex adjusted his helmet, which had a mask of heavy steel wire mesh that hinged over his face.

"Ready?" called Pilot Benson, and Rex waddled over to the waiting plane. He climbed aboard, and soon they were soaring high over the dark, wooded slopes, skimming low over the ridges.

The tall column of smoke was in a small clearing in the very heart of the wilderness. Pilot Benson circled the spot, then flew across it, letting go a small burlap test 'chute with a ten-pound bag of sand attached.

As the 'chute drifted down, Rex watched intently, noting and carefully estimating the wind drift.

Pilot Benson watched no less carefully, for he must signal Rex when to jump. Approaching the spot, the pilot made his correction for wind and location and gave the signal.

Then firmly gripping the parachute rip cord, Rex descended the two steps let down from the plane and leaped into space. "One—two—three," he counted slowly and pulled the cord. His body jerked as the 'chute billowed out. After the opening shock, the descent was pleasant. The green earth rushed up to meet him.

At last he reached the treetops and came to rest, securely caught high in a tall pine. Rex quickly rid himself of the parachute lines, made the rope from his pocket fast to the nearest limb, and descended to the ground. Snatching off his helmet, he looked up toward the plane circling overhead. He was watching for the burlap parachute that contained his fire-fighting pack of tools, lamp, emergency food rations, first-aid kit, and water canteen. Down it came and landed a short distance away.

With one practiced motion Rex unzipped his jacket, deposited on the ground the small two-way radio set he carried under it, and crashed through the brush to get his tools. Seizing ax and spade, he hastened to the now blazing fire.

A stump was burning vigorously, and the underbrush was spreading the blaze. Rex bent to his job, shoveling dirt on the flames. As they were checked, he began hacking brush from the fire's edge.

Meanwhile his work was being watched by the fire guard who had reported the first wisp of smoke. Miles away in his lookout on the mountain top, the guard continued to sweep the landscape with his telescope. He had seen the descent of the smoke jumper. Now he watched the tall column of smoke die down to a lazy cloud and then disappear. "Out in less than three hours!" he exclaimed. "Talk about modern miracles!"

In the fire-blackened clearing the smoke jumper was leaning against a tree, exhausted but happy, eating ravenously the hardtack from his ration kit. He had three burns on his arm, and his face was smudged, but the fire was out. Only the whisper of a light wind broke the profound stillness.

There would be bears in this forest, all right, and mountain lions, too. But he was too tired to make his way back to the Ranger Station tonight. He must clear away more underbrush and build a campfire to sleep beside. He looked up to the towering pine where his parachute hung, still caught in the treetop. He would have to leave it there. A telephone man or a ranger equipped with climbing spikes would come and extricate it later.

Rex had done a good job. If that fire had had to wait for a ground crew to come from the nearest Ranger Station, acres and acres of magnificent and valuable Douglas firs would have been burned. Even with pack and saddle horses it would have taken eight or ten hours for firefighters to arrive. The smoke jumper would sleep well that night—in the heart of the forest he had saved.

Miracle of the Air

The January afternoon was bitter cold, and a frosty haze hung over the mining village of McClary in the Yukon region. But within the radio station of the Midcontinent-Alaska Airlines there was warmth and cheer—much cheer—a birthday party for Jenny Ivorsen was in progress.

Every miner wintering on Jewelry Creek had come to the celebration, a score of bearded men in overalls and woolen shirts, their fur parkas piled by the door. At one end of the long room a stove roared and crackled, eating spruce chunks hungrily.

Sourdough Grant's regular job was to service the Midcontinent planes, but tonight he had volunteered as master of ceremonies, since Jenny's father was not at home. Gus Ivorsen was out looking after his trap lines and could not afford to leave until he had the pelt of every animal caught in his traps. Each pelt meant money to pay for the farm he and Jenny were planning to buy.

Tearing the wrappings from a box, Sourdough lifted out a phonograph and a flat package of records with a card attached, which he handed to Jenny. "Read what it says, Jen. Loud, so we all can hear."

The little girl stood up, her thin face flushed happily, and read in a shrill, piping voice:

> You'll have a farm and very soon,
> Like old MacDonald in this tune,
> And have a hundred things to pet,
> But please do not old friends forget.
>   Johnny Caruthers

The miners applauded noisily, and Jenny said, "I love Johnny." She pointed to the phonograph, her eyes sparkling. "What is it?"

"For Pete's sake!" muttered Sourdough. "She's never heard of a talking machine! Hitch up the farm record, Akers—no use waiting for Johnny to bring in his freight plane. He might be delayed a week. He'd never shove off in bad weather in that old crate."

Akers, the radio operator, inserted a needle and began cranking the motor. Suddenly he reached over, switched his two-way radio to SEND, and said to Jenny, "Maybe your pop will be tuned in on that short-wave portable I made for him and hear this record."

Jen wriggled ecstatically as Akers snapped on the transmitter switch and started the record. The needle made scratchy noises, and a voice began:

> Old MacDonald had a farm,
> Ee-i-ee-i-oh!
> And on that farm he had a duck,
> Ee-i—ee-i—oh!

The song went on, listing all of old MacDonald's pets. When the part with a barking dog was reached, Sourdough exclaimed, "Sure sounds like Jen's old dog Nicky!"

And Jen said, "Please, Mr. Akers, see if my dad is listening."

Akers picked up the transmitter mike and called, "McClary to Ivorsen. Come on in, Gus."

Faint sounds issued from the radio and became a voice; but not Ivorsen's. "Calling McClary," it said faintly. "Caruthers calling McClary. Cracked up . . . on north fork of Buckstone. Slight . . . injury. Send . . . help."

"Why, it's Johnny Caruthers!" Tex Jensen said.

Sourdough sprang up and shut off the phonograph. "That boy's hurt bad, or he'd never call for help. Get the location, Akers—where he crashed."

Quickly Akers flipped over the transmitter switch. "Listen, Johnny. Give us a better location. Tell how bad you're hurt." He switched to RECEIVE, and Caruthers' voice answered, "Shoulder—out——"

Suddenly the power hum stopped. Akers twisted the dials, but failed to establish contact with Johnny. Then he said, dismayed, "His radio's failed. And he didn't give us his exact location. He only said the north fork of the Buckstone."

Tex muttered, "Two days' trip by dog sled from here to there, and two days is a long time when a man's hurt bad and there's a deep cold setting in."

The room grew still. Suddenly Jenny spoke up. "Daddy always makes Fry-pan Creek on Friday night. That's not so far from Buckstone, is it?"

Tex Jensen slapped his knee. "Jen, you're smart! Akers, try to get Gus again."

Once more the radioman bent low over the transmitter. "McClary to Ivorsen. McClary to Ivorsen. Answer, Gus." He tried a dozen times, but the calls remained unanswered.

Sourdough bit his lips. "Tex, starving wolves are drifting down from the North. And Johnny's lying out there—helpless, maybe!"

Tex said, "I'm hitting trail tonight. Which one of you wants to take care of Jen while I'm away?"

"Reckon that'll be Akers' job," answered a huge black-bearded miner. "The rest of us will go. The more that start, the more chance that some of us'll make it in time."

While the men slipped on parkas and filed out of the room, Jen said again, gulping back a sob, "We'll get my daddy on the radio, Mr. Tex. Johnny helped him once—and Nicky, too. They'll help Johnny now."

"If they can, they will," muttered Tex, his face bleak as he picked up his snowshoes.

Johnny Caruthers himself, in the cockpit of his wrecked plane on the ice-covered Buckstone River, was not worried. He was sure that Akers had picked up his call all right before the radio went dead and would organize a rescue party.

He had to carry on until the party reached him. That meant building a fire to keep warm. It was cold in the plane with the cabin door torn from its hinges. He pushed himself up from the seat, though the severity of the pain in his right shoulder set everything about him whirling.

Johnny snapped on his flashlight and crept back into the cabin. He dragged out sleeping bag, skillet, and coffee pot and pushed them over the doorsill into the snow. Then he found the pail of rations—flour, bacon, tea, and sugar. But his efforts sent hot, fierce pain twitching through his arm, giving him a queer, sick feeling. He stumbled dizzily to the plane and clung to it until the trees on the bank stopped whirling. His face was numb with cold; he'd better get a fire started.

Johnny took out a can of motor oil and a newspaper to kindle a fire. Then painfully he began his first trip across the snow that blanketed the river ice. The bank was farther away than he had thought. As he passed the tail of the plane, something wrapped itself around one ankle. He kicked at it and found it was a wire—his radio antenna. He unwrapped it and tossed it aside.

Pain had clogged Johnny's brain or he would not have done that. He would have realized that the wire's making ground contact was what had killed his radio. But he plodded on, heedlessly, and finally reached the shelter of an alder thicket. He made three more trips, every step sheer torture, but at last his supplies were on the bank.

He twisted the newspaper into a knot, saturated it with oil, and got his fire started. He gathered twigs, moss, and bits of brush in the alder thickets to keep his fire going. Then he pried the lid off the ration pail. There was a package of soup cubes wrapped in tin foil, and he ate three of them raw. They tasted good.

Tea and bacon lifted Johnny's spirits higher. But presently his shoulder began to throb wickedly again, and he grew keenly aware of the ghostly sweep of the Buckstone and the still, cold silence.

The best thing was to sleep. He managed to roll a fallen cedar into the embers and crawled exhausted into his sleeping bag. As he pulled the flap around his ears the distant hoot of an owl reached him—at least he thought it was an owl. Then the sound came again, and this time it sent a queer ripple down his spine. That was the baying of a wolf. Could it be a white wolf?

Johnny had heard stories of these white wolves. Sourdough had seen them in the barren plains of the North and said that they were yellow-white, with fangs as long as his middle finger. They stood waist-high to a man and weighed two hundred pounds. They wouldn't attack you if you were on your feet, Sourdough claimed, but they'd been known to stalk a lost trapper for days until he fell from weakness.

Johnny shivered and decided he'd better think of other things. He glanced at the plane, and suddenly his brain cleared. That tangled wire was his grounded aerial! Why not fix it, call McClary, and ask about the rescue party? It would boost his courage to hear a human voice in that solitude.

He searched in the snow, found the radio antenna, and with painful effort tied the ends to a willow branch. Clear of the ground, it would work.

But even that slight activity was a nightmare of fiery pain. Johnny's lips were white as he crawled into the control cabin and eased down to the bucket seat. He tested the transmitter circuit and found it in working order. He switched the key on the instrument panel to SEND and began calling in a steady voice, "Caruthers to McClary. Caruthers to McClary. Come on in."

Akers' voice came in through the earphones, "McClary to Caruthers. How're you making it?"

Forcing a jovial tone, Johnny answered, "Making it fine. Did Tex get off? How many with him?"

"Everybody's with him," Akers chuckled. "Jen and I are the only ones in camp."

He paused, and Jen's voice said, "Hello! Are you all right? Johnny—want to hear Nicky?"

Johnny switched to SEND again. "What's Nicky doing in the radio hut? I thought he was with your father on the trap lines."

Jen laughed. "He is. This is just your record about old Mr. MacDonald. He had a farm, you know, and a dog that barked like Nicky. Listen."

Jen's voice seemed deafening. The intense quiet of the atmosphere seemed to give double volume to the radio. Johnny removed the earphones and held them in his hand as a voice began singing:

> Old MacDonald had a farm,
> Ee-i-ee-i-oh!
> And on the farm he had a—

The volume kept increasing, and Johnny moved the dial to hold it down. He looked up, and a trickle of cold ran through his body. On the bank a tawny white wolf was gazing steadily at him from beside the campfire.

Brush crackled, and a second wolf moved from the thicket like a silver ghost. Farther down the bank another emerged. White Siberians—famine-driven from the Arctic Barrens. Slowly they crept forward across the ice. Johnny watched them with a sense of unreality as though he were seeing a movie. . . . Wolves didn't attack people . . . *unless they were helpless.* But perhaps this white Siberian sensed that he was helpless.

Jen's voice burst out again, "Johnny, did you hear the record? It *is* like Nicky. Daddy said so. He talked to us at midnight from Fry-pan Creek. I played the record for him, but he couldn't listen to all of it. He said you might be hurt bad, and he must start for the Buckstone right away. And he's seen wolves. You aren't hurt bad, are you, Johnny? And there aren't any wolves near you, are there?"

The booming of Jen's voice halted the wolves, but as she stopped, they started forward again. Then the wary, starved beasts paused once more as Jen's voice cried, "Why don't you answer, Johnny? Can't you hear? Please answer—there aren't any wolves, are there?"

Johnny Caruthers laughed—a queer, muddled laugh, for the pain in his shoulder made him light-headed. It seemed funny to be looking at wolves and listening to Jen. Her voice sounded clear and close, when really she was far away.

Jen's voice broke in, "We heard you laughing, Johnny. I'm glad you're all right. Mr. Akers is going to play the Nicky record again. Listen hard, Johnny—the dog *is* just like Nicky."

The wolves halted as the music began, and crouched beside the edge of the wing tip, sniffing at it. Soon they would see that the cabin door was gone and then . . . .

Through the earphones poured the loud and tuneful story of old MacDonald's dog:

> With a bow-wow here, and a bow-wow there,
> Here a bow, there a bow,
> Everywhere a bow-wow—

The wolves stiffened and gave a snarl of fear and hate. Johnny stared at the beasts—and a thought stirred in his mind. He switched on the transmitter and, with a shaky laugh, said to his unseen friends, "The wolves *are* here. Nothing to worry about—but keep that Nicky verse coming!"

There was a discord of sound as the phonograph needle shifted. Johnny turned the amplifier to full strength as the barking chorus started again. The nearest wolf, hair bristling, began to retreat. The others followed, nervous and wary. Again came the scratch of the shifted needle, and Johnny held the earphones to the open window. Once more the tune poured forth with a volume that made the barks seem to come from a real dog. The wolves edged away from this noisy but unseen enemy and gained cover in the alder thickets. There they waited guardedly. Johnny glanced at his watch—nearly two hours yet before Ivorsen could get to the Buckstone. The pain in his shoulder was pretty bad. When the music stopped, he ordered hoarsely, "Keep playing, Jen!"

The bark of old MacDonald's dog began once more. Again and again the barking chorus of the phonograph record was repeated, while the hands of the watch moved slowly on.

An hour passed; then a quarter hour. In the shadow of the alder thickets the white wolves waited, turning nervously at times, lest their unseen enemy charge them unawares.

At last Akers' voice broke through the loud song. "Build a fire, Caruthers. Wolves are afraid of fire. Your radio battery won't hold up much longer."

Johnny said, "Tell ... Jen ... to ... keep playing."

Five minutes later the radio began losing volume. Johnny saw that the ammeter needle was dropping fast. The battery was almost drained; soon this miracle of the air would fail him.

The white leader began moving out from the trees. Crouching, it crept forward. Johnny yelled. The wolf bared its teeth, gave a menacing snarl, and came on. The two others, gaining courage, trailed the leader, closing in on the plane.

Johnny struggled to his feet. Fever gripped him strongly now. Everything seemed badly out of focus, with the trees wavy and blurred, and the figures of the wolves distorted and magnified. The sound in the phones kept fading, fading. . . .

Johnny thought dizzily, "It's the end for me." But he picked up a wrench and staggered to the door. The white leader, passing around the wing, stopped and gazed at him with cold cunning.

"Come on," said Johnny, "I'll . . . ." His words faded to meaningless babbling as dizziness rushed over him.

Suddenly the radio started again; as if the battery had flared up just before the current died out. The barking of the dog came clearly once more. But the white wolf was no longer afraid. The great beast flattened, ready for the spring.

Johnny waited, gripping the iron wrench, trying to fight off his faintness. But the trees and the moonlit path of the river were spinning now. They began slipping away. Strangely he could still hear that dog . . . in . . . the . . . phonograph. . . . It was . . . real. Like . . . Nicky. Then it faded out, and he knew nothing more. . . .

Meanwhile in the radio shack on Jewelry Creek the phonograph played on. A dozen times Jen shifted the needle; then it broke, and she cried, "Fix it, Mr. Akers—we've got to make it bark!"

Then she stopped. A voice was coming from the radio, sharp and excited.

"Calling McClary. Ivorsen calling McClary—Akers, you there? I made it. Found Caruthers in his ship. A dislocated shoulder—he'd passed out. But I brought him round, and he's going to be okay. Say, tell Jen our luck's turned. I shot a white wolf just as I reached the plane. Understand me? A genuine white Siberian! They're scarce—worth five hundred dollars or more. With the spring break-up we'll get that place in the country she's been wanting. Tell her *Happy Birthday!*"

The Night Express

It was just past midnight when the Chicago express pulled out of Galesburg, Illinois, with Potts at the engine throttle. There was a full moon, making the tranquil countryside almost as bright as day; the September air was warm and sweet with the smell of the woods. Harrison, the fireman, was adjusting the stoker that fed coal into the roaring firebox.

Potts, with his left hand resting carelessly on the throttle lever, leaned out of the cab window and wished that every night run might be made on a night like this one. Under him quivered the great steel giant that he had grown to love, and behind him trailed the long, dark, voiceless train.

There were eleven cars in all, four baggage cars, three day coaches, three Pullmans, and a mail car.

Packed away inside of them were two hundred fifty persons or more, bound eastward from Burlington, Omaha, Denver, and California. They dozed or slept, secure in their faith that the steady but unknown hand that guided the engine would bring them safely into Chicago.

At the blinking of the Altona semaphore, Potts drew down on the whistle lever, and the engine gave a prolonged cheer for the little town it intended to pass with no other notice. As the train slowed down to schedule speed, a few straggling buildings came up suddenly into the moonlight, stood for a moment in plain view, and then darted back again into the darkness. Altona was passed with a clear track and a long upgrade ahead. A mile to the eastward blinked a semaphore, green and safe, and to its left, close down to the track, there were three other lights, a large one and two small ones.

"Extra freight," muttered Potts to himself as he saw the lights of the stranger slowly brighten. There was no need of further reducing his speed. It was a double track all the way, and the express must make time. The two trains would slip by each other with the usual roar of passing greeting.

An ordinary engineer might have rested on his arm pad and left the throttle wide open; but Potts leaned suddenly farther out, peering up the track with a wrinkled frown. Behind the headlight of the freight he saw the dark, hulking boxcars half-hidden in smoke from the engine stack. Behind them a long chain of tank cars, filled with gasoline, naphtha, and kerosene, was dimly outlined in the moonlit distance. To the engineer they looked, as they moved, like a continuous black tube.

"Say, that's a long train," he exclaimed.

Then, as his quick eye traveled again from the yellow headlight back to the green lantern on the faraway caboose, he saw with a sudden sinking of his heart that the train was *much too long*. He knew that somewhere in the middle of it a coupling had broken, and that the front end with the engine was roaring down the grade with the rear end pursuing it.

The impossible had happened! The freight's air brakes, which apply automatically when a coupling is broken, had failed. Sooner or later, unless the freight crew manned the hand brakes, the two parts of the freight would collide.

In the face of sudden danger an engineer's first impulse is to stop his train. Potts sprang back to his place. He jammed the throttle forward and drew back the reverse lever. Then his hand closed on the brass handle that controlled the air brake. There was a deafening hiss and crackle, and the needle on the air-pressure indicator dropped from 90 to 85 to 80 pounds in two seconds. The wheels underneath whipped up a bright fountain of sparks, and the sleepers in their berths turned over and grumbled at being disturbed.

All these events had taken place well within the time of a long breath. Now there were three biting shrieks of the whistle—Potts' cry of warning to the freight engineer that his train was broken. Harrison, the fireman, who well knew the meaning of the signal, sprang to his window on the left.

"The break is among the tank cars," he shouted as he watched the approaching freight.

The cab was dark, except for the shaded light at the air-pressure indicator, but Harrison saw Potts nod grimly, and again the three warning whistles cut the air. Potts was doing his best to warn the crew of the freight, but the tank train continued to advance at the same rate of speed. Its engineer had evidently failed to hear the signal, or else he would be speeding up in order to escape a collision that could only mean a disaster such as would rival an exploding powder mill.

Suddenly Harrison drew in his head, his face showing ghostly pale through the smudges of smoke.

"She's slowing up to take water," he exclaimed.

For a second Potts was undecided. Very soon he would be alongside the broken freight. The stopping of its detached head end would hasten the collision of the tank cars. The passenger train had only partly slacked its terrific speed. If he waited to stop and back, and there was a collision, what would become of his train as it passed on the other track? In a flash of imagination he could already see the fiery burst of the explosion, the heaps of crushed cars, tangled and twisted with burning oil spluttering over them; and he seemed to hear the agonized cries of the passengers pinned to their death under the wrecked sleeping cars.

But in a moment the horror of his terrible vision passed. Potts weighed two hundred twenty pounds. He stood six feet one in his stockings, and there was undeniable courage in every inch of him. Besides, he knew the huge, breathing machine under him and had confidence in her. He shut off the air brake.

"Coal her up!" he shouted to Harrison.

"But you can't run by—there isn't time——"

"Coal her up!" roared Potts' voice again, and the engineer's huge height loomed up in his place at the right of the cab. His hair was loose, and his face begrimed. He knew the risk of attempting to drive past the danger point. He knew this method might cost him his life, but his hand never wavered.

Open came the throttle, the whistle screeched, and the engine leaped forward as if it appreciated the need of extra effort. Again the passengers in the Pullman cars grumbled at being shaken up.

The fireman had the mechanical stoker grinding fuel into the firebox at its greatest capacity, and the flames glowed fiercely. All this happened within the space of a dozen seconds, for at such a time an engineer must act as quickly as he thinks. The loss of one second may cost a hundred lives.

As the engine of the freight came nearer, Potts caught a glimpse of its fireman leaning out the window, and knew that he and the engineer were unaware of their train's separation. The detached end of the freight, as Potts saw it now, was well down the grade, rushing straight for the head end at terrific speed. The roar and jar of its wheels could be heard above the sound of his own train. Fifty thousand gallons of inflammable oil soon to collide with another fifty thousand gallons—and then——

Potts put on sand. The engine leaped forward, its wheels biting the track with a firmer grip at every second of their progress. The throttle was wide open. From the stack belched a fierce fountain of sparks, and the bell jangled continuously.

"She'll do it; she'll do it; she'll do it," said Potts to the beating rhythm of the piston rod.

The engineer knew the creature he was driving. He heard her pant with the exertion; he saw the flames belching from her nostrils; he heard her clamoring hoofs; he heard the "squeak, squeak" of a spot where the harness was wearing.

The first half of the freight had now thundered past; there was the long flash of open space; then came the tank cars of the loose end of the train. There was a flash of green light, and Potts knew that his engine was clear of the caboose. But would he pull past far enough to save the last Pullman on his train?

All this time the passengers slept quietly. The Pullman conductor was checking his tickets, and the brakeman was joking with the newsboy. No one knew of the danger save the two quiet, tense men in the engine cab. And in the seconds which elapsed after Potts first scented danger, they lived a year.

Then the split freight came together. High in the air a great splash of fire flowed bright against the black sky as tank car after tank car exploded, hissing with flame.

The explosions shook the earth, blew great holes in the roadbed, tore away the rails, hurled the sleepers in the express from their berths, jarred out the lights, and swayed the fifty-ton Pullmans as if they had been cardboard.

Potts, dripping with perspiration, sank weakly to his seat. His train came to a standstill, the engine breathing as if exhausted with its race.

The conductor came on the run, pale of face, and held up his lantern as Potts jumped from the cab.

"Whew, that was a narrow escape!" he said. "We're lucky."

Potts smiled at the man's excitement. He laid his hand caressingly on one of the steel driving rods of the engine as though he feared it had been strained in the desperate race.

"We're behind two minutes, now," he said calmly, as if being on time was the one thing of importance in the whole world.

A mile back the tank train was blowing up, car after car, like a bunch of giant firecrackers, and the panic-stricken engineer was escaping up the track with the detached head end.

In all, thirteen tanks of oil were exploded, and two buildings were burned, but the Chicago express and its passengers were safe.

A Fireman's Bag of Tricks

Old Terry Donohue, captain of Brunswick Engine Company Two, knew how to fight fire. Just give him enough sections of good hose in the box and a stout pumper to feed him pressure, and he would wash the life out of any ordinary blaze before it could get its second wind. He had no use for the modern methods of Stan Parker, lieutenant in the newly organized Rescue Squad.

"Fads and frills," Terry boomed at Stan. "The department's gone hog-wild with newfangled ideas. Water! That's what it takes. Water! Just show me a blaze you can't black out with water."

Lieutenant Parker had recently come back from Chicago, where he had taken a course in modern fire fighting, but he knew better than to argue with the impetuous Donohue. Stan was young, but he had a genuine respect for the old-timers.

"Oh, you're just old-fashioned, Terry," Captain Hastings of the truck company said, without looking up from the sport page of his newspaper.

"Old-fashioned, my eye! They'll be fighting fire with water long after my time."

Stan Parker grinned mischievously at the stubborn old-timer. "You're right, Donohue. Two parts of hydrogen to one part of oxygen make an efficient fire-fighting material."

"Harumph!" old Donohue spluttered. "You and your chemicals. All I know is—water's water. *It* puts out fire; not that stuff in your toy wagon."

The two men met again one day in the room where the Rescue Squad wagon stood. Captain Donohue leaned against the wall, feet apart, surveying the wagon with scorn.

"What in thunder are all those things in there, Stan?"

"Why are you interested?" asked Stan with a grin. "Are you planning to take up scientific fire fighting, Captain?"

"I'll roast, first," snorted the stubborn old fireman. "Just curious, that's all. I don't have much confidence in your bag of tricks."

"Since you ask me," Stan returned, "I'll tell you what's in that bag of tricks, as you call it. We're equipped with a pulmotor for drowning cases. Steam hose for fighting fire in ships. Equipment for handling live wires. Jacks for lifting wrecked streetcars and trucks. Implements for extricating persons from jammed automobiles. Drills, asbestos screens, sledges, electric torches, gas masks——"

"Stop! Stop!" Donohue roared. "I can't stand this. They're not fire-fighting equipment; they're burglar's tools."

"I forgot to mention explosives," Stan continued wickedly. "Sometimes we fight fire with dynamite."

149

"DY-NEE-MITE!" Donohue boomed. "In my station house? I'm going to object. I'm going to see the chief of the department. Dy-nee-mite!"

After that when Engine Company Two rolled out, old Terry would shout at Mack, the driver of the pumper, "Keep out of the way of that devil wagon! It has dy-nee-mite aboard."

But all that was before the Northwest Chemical factory burned.

The call came late one afternoon. It was a short run to the factory, but already a queer smoke—ash-gray, and evil-looking—was pouring out through the cracks of the big warehouse.

Old Donohue took one look at the gray smoke and scratched his grizzled head. Gray smoke, and the fire just under way? That wasn't according to rule. Something was wrong here.

But Donohue didn't hesitate. If there was a fire, he knew how to mop it up. Throw water. That's what you did. Throw water!

Engine Number Two laid a line from the warehouse door to a nearby hydrant. Couplings were twirled and the pumper started up. Donohue and a fireman cracked the warehouse lock and pushed back the heavy doors on rollers. A dense fog rolled out of the shed. A fog with a stifling odor.

Donohue stared into the smoking building. "Water! Charge line!" he bellowed.

The nozzle valve clicked, and a two-hundred-pound pump pressure sent water exploding from the nozzle. With a boom the stream went crashing into the interior of the building.

In thirty years Donohue had never seen water stir up such bedlam. As the stream landed inside, a roaring, growling, hissing sound issued from the huge warehouse.

"Stop! Stop!" someone was shouting. "Stop that stream of water."

Donohue whirled to see who was giving the order and found himself face to face with Stan Parker.

"Who's running this outfit?" Donohue yelled.

"Stop it, I say," ordered Stan. "That's calcium oxide."

"That's *what?*"

"Calcium oxide. Quicklime. You're turning it into calcium hydrate."

"Huh?" Donohue grunted. "I'm putting a fire out, that's what I'm doing. Keep away with your bag of tricks."

"You're *making* a fire. Calcium oxide and water *make* fire."

"You're crazy. Where's the flame?"

"It has no flame. Turn that water off."

"I'll do nothing of the kind."

Stan Parker whirled to the firemen holding the hose. "Shut that valve. We're fighting this with shovels and chemicals."

The men hesitated, looking at Donohue.

"Okay," Donohue muttered, "but the chief of the department will hear of this!"

Stan Parker's Rescue Squad quickly laid down the chemical hose line. Then his men, armed with shovels, groped their way into the building.

The city fire chief arrived, and Donohue strode up to him. "I was fighting this fire, and that young puppy started giving me orders."

The chief brushed Donohue aside. "Parker knows chemicals. The Rescue Squads have charge here."

Donohue stared, his mouth wide open.

Stan Parker followed his men into the smoke-filled building just as another Rescue Squad wagon from headquarters arrived.

"Fighting a fire with shovels!" Old Donohue grumbled. "Of all the crazy ideas!" Nevertheless, the old firefighter hung on the outskirts and watched the younger men match their new methods against a fire that had him stumped.

They were getting it mopped up, all right, and doing a good job of it, too. Already the smoke was clearing out of the big shed. Stan was out on a steel beam, shooting a spray of sodium bicarbonate and sulphuric acid into the bubbling, foaming mass of lime.

"How'd the fire start?" Donohue asked the chief.

"Water backed up in an overtaxed storm drain and overflowed into the lime," was the reply.

Donohue rubbed the back of his neck in awe. It was a new experience for him. Water *starting* fire!

He glanced up at Stan Parker, clinging to that perilous beam. A reluctant gleam of admiration twinkled in the old captain's eyes. "Brains," he muttered to himself. "Stan's got 'em. Guess I'm getting old and a little out of date."

A startled cry rang on the air. Eyes flicked to Stan Parker. Stan had slipped from that overhead beam—was falling—falling—falling straight into that bubbling mess of burning lime.

Terry Donohue saw Stan Parker hurtle through the air like a high diver. He struck the oozing, fiery puddle feet first. He sank to his knees and stood there swaying dizzily.

Donohue saw the look of terror on Stan's face— heard the agonized cry on his lips.

"Get him!" someone shouted. "Get him!"

The men hesitated. They dared not wade into that steaming caldron. The lime would eat through their boots before they could reach Stan. For a horrifying instant everyone seemed paralyzed.

Then Terry Donohue sprang to action. He whirled and raced out of the building.

There at the curb stood the Rescue Squad wagon, Stan Parker's bag of tricks.

For all his fifty-nine years, Donohue sprinted.

"Asbestos screens!" he shouted. "Bring 'em all."

Men jumped at his command. They pulled out huge sheets of asbestos. Donohue gathered as many as he could carry and rushed back to the shed.

Men were running frantically—throwing life lines at Stan, who was too weak to clutch them.

Donohue flipped a sheet of asbestos on the burning lime, walked across it, and spread another sheet. Another—then another. He walked on his fireproof bridge to the trapped fireman—reached out and caught Stan by the shoulders.

Stan collapsed in the captain's arms. But the veteran picked the younger man up and started back along the bridge of asbestos sheets. Lime was creeping over the edges, sucking around his ankles. He ran through the foam until he reached a raised cement platform where strong hands relieved him of his burden.

They carried the unconscious man to a fire-department ambulance.

"Lime burns!" the fire chief shouted to the driver. "Emergency case! Get him to the hospital as fast as you can."

With a wail that screamed for the right of way, the ambulance shot into the street, swerved around a corner, and raced for the hospital.

It was three days before the doctors would give Stan a fighting chance, but a fighting chance was all the sturdy lieutenant needed. On the fifth day, when Stan was allowed to have visitors, old Terry Donohue walked hesitatingly behind a nurse to Stan Parker's room.

Stan smiled weakly from the white pillowcase.

"Well, Terry—you old firedog, you. Tell the boys to get me some new clothes. The doc says I'll be back in a month or two."

"Stan—" Donohue paused, embarrassment in his tone. "I want to apologize. I always said there was only one way to fight fire. But I was wrong. There're two ways. Water and asbestos. Don't know how I came to forget asbestos."

Fun and Fancy

The Caliph's Clock

The Caliph Keeps Up with the Times

It was morning in the city of Chunder-abad-dad. The Caliph sat upon his divan moodily stroking his beard. Suddenly he called impatiently, "Selim! Are you never going to eat breakfast?"

As he spoke he cracked and emptied into his cup the last of the soft-boiled eggs.

The Grand Vizir laid down the morning paper he had been reading. "Oh," said he, "how could I know it was breakfast time? You didn't ring a bell."

"You could look at the hourglass."

"It leaks," replied the Vizir. "Somebody cracked it—not I."

"Why did you not observe the sundial?" said the Caliph stiffly.

"There is a dark cloud over the sun. Why don't you have a sundial that works in cloudy weather?"

"Cloudy weather?" exclaimed the Caliph. "This is not cloudy weather!"

"It is for me," said the Grand Vizir ruefully, and subsided into gloom.

As the Caliph of Chunder-abad-dad finished eating, a wandering Yankee peddler knocked at the palace door. The Grand Vizir immediately arose as the peddler entered.

He wore a pinch-backed coat, a bright green hat, had long elastic legs, white spatterdashes, and an air of boastful superiority. He very briskly said that he had clocks to sell.

"Clocks?" said the Caliph, curious, as he arose from his cushions. "Clocks? Let's see them."

The peddler produced a timepiece. He slipped his hand inside the clock and twisted something which made the insides cluck like a hen. The clock began to go faster. The peddler smiled.

"This," said he, "is a wonderful clock for communities that wish to keep up with the times."

"Will it inspire the idle people to employ their wasted hours?"

"Adopt our daylight-saving plan, and there will be no wasted hours."

"A daylight-saving plan?" exclaimed the Caliph. "And will this clock save daylight?"

"Sire," replied the peddler, "this clock will save daylight as a stingy man saves pennies. Our daylight-saving attachment sells at ten *dinars*. We can make it six *dinars* to you. Shall I say Sold?"

The Caliph hesitated.

The peddler waved his hands. "This unparalleled timepiece runs forty days and forty nights with but a single winding," said he. "It also has a musical attachment which plays twelve perfectly ripping tunes. The cuckoo *cucks* on the hour and *koos* on the half-hour.

"With every daylight-saving device we give a thousand circulars praising the merits of daylight saving as conducted by our clock."

"I want it," said the Caliph.

"To install the daylight-saving device is marvelously easy," said the peddler. "Just set your sundials by the clock, go to bed, and forget it. When you wake in the morning, you'll be surprised to see what time it is."

"I often am!" said the Grand Vizir.

"I must have it," said the Caliph and forthwith purchased the clock from the peddler for the price that he had asked.

"We shall begin at once to save daylight!" said the Caliph. "We shall now keep up with the times. Go! Set all the sundials in the town to keep time with my clock."

Then he caused the clock to be set upon a marble column in the middle of the courtyard and published a proclamation throughout the city, saying:

"I am the Caliph of Chunder-abad-dad, and I have established a Clock. The time of it is *my* time; the hours of it are the *right* time; its hours are those of the Faithful. Henceforth there shall be no other time in the imperial city of Chunder-abad dad."

"Now, wind it up!" he said.

The official clock-winder inserted the key and wound the Caliph's clock. It started with a double chime and such a strange and threatening whirr in its insides that the clock-winder ducked.

The pendulum began to vibrate with an alert, sharp sound, with a clattering of the levers and a brisk, hurrying ting-a-ling of an impetuous silvery bell. The minute hand started its steady round. The hour hand began its revolution. The second hand danced and capered. The fateful clock was going.

"Henceforth," said the Caliph, "there shall be no other time in the city of Chunder-abad-dad!"

Watchmen went about the streets everywhere, crying, "Set your sundials! Set your sundials by the Caliph's clock! Who wastes his hours throws away the golden gift of Allah! Set your sundials."

Confusion Reigns in Chunder-abad-dad

The Caliph and the Vizir sat for hours, watching the pendulum swing.

"Plague take the thing!" muttered the Vizir. "It has an evil look and sounds like a guinea hen in the rain!" The clock was running with a threatening whirr which never ceased nor altered, but seemed hourly to go faster and faster.

"How fast the time flies!" he said nervously.

"Yes," replied the Caliph, "the days are so long at this season that time has to fly fast to get through."

"And the morning is oddly short, Sire. See, it is already half past ten!"

"Oh, that is the daylight-saving device," said the Caliph carelessly. "It is saving part of the day. By thus using less in the morning, we shall have more in the afternoon. It is indeed clever."

The day passed, and evening came gently up the east.

The Caliph sat by his window. There was a bewildered look on his face. He held an almanac in his hand, and he had one eye on the clock.

"Selim," he said uneasily, peering out the window. "It is high time it should be dusk. Sunset was due at ten minutes past six by the almanac. It is more than an hour behind time. I wish you would go out and attend to it."

"But, Your Highness," said the Vizir, "it cannot be sunset until the sun *sets*."

"What?" cried the Caliph. "Must I wait for the sun? Am I not the Caliph? Is it not mine to say what the hours shall be in Chunder-abad-dad?"

"Surely!" replied the Vizir. "But, Your Highness, does not the sun *set* at sunset? And is it not sunset when the sun *sets?* How can it then be sunset until the sun *does* set? We have but one sun, and only when it *sets* is it sunset!"

The Caliph looked dazed. "Now by the prophet's beard, Selim!" he said. "You can say less in more words than anyone I have ever heard. Let the sun set when it will. I will attend to the sunset. When my clock says, 'This is sunset,' it *shall* be sunset. This clock is *my* clock. Its hours are the *right* hours. There shall be no other time whatsoever in the city of Chunder-abad-dad!"

He tossed the hourglass out of the window. It fell with a crash in the street. "Go!" he said.

"Send all the people to bed. It is high time they retired."

Being well acquainted with the Caliph, everybody made haste to go to bed.

Sometime in the night the Vizir woke, and being very thirsty, went out to the hydrant in the courtyard to get himself a drink. In the hush that was over the city he could hear the splash of fountains, and in the palace courtyard the Caliph's clock was running with a strange, uneasy sound.

It had been running fast at sunset. It was running faster now. It sounded as if it were running a race with itself and were gaining on every round. He could hear it catch step and break again at every dozen tick-tocks.

It struck twice as he stood in the courtyard.

It struck thrice as he crept into bed.

It struck four times as he fell asleep.

And while all the world was as black as your hat, he heard the Caliph cry, "Breakfast!"

It was intensely dark; the chill of night was in the air, and the stars were still in the sky. The nightingale was still singing.

"Breakfast!" gasped the Vizir as he sat up in his bed. "Why, we have just had supper!"

"The clock says it is breakfast time!" said the Caliph. "Come promptly, or I'll know the reason why."

"I can't eat a mouthful!" protested the Vizir.

"You'd better!" growled the Caliph. "If you slight the buckwheat cakes, we'll have an account to settle."

The Vizir ate a large breakfast.

As he finished his oatmeal, the clock struck nine. As he ate his buckwheats, the clock struck ten. As he drank his coffee, it struck again.

"Go!" cried the Caliph. "Drive the beasts out to pasture before the morning is spent!"

The Vizir looked at the Caliph's eye. It was red as a ruby-stone. He hurried to the stables, awoke the sheep, aroused the goats, and drove the cows to pasture. He ran back through the darkness, tottering up the palace steps just as the sun rose.

The Caliph was eating gloomily. "Are you aware that it is now dinner time?"

"Dinner time?" stammered the Vizir.

"It is twelve o'clock," cried the Caliph. "It is high noon by the clock."

"But it is not high noon by the noon-mark on the stones in the palace yard; the sun is this minute rising!" replied the Vizir hastily.

"Don't argue with me," said the Caliph.

"I was not arguing with you. I was just stating a fact; stating a fact is not an argument."

"Then why do you always cross me? When the clock strikes twelve, and I say it is twelve, why do you contradict me? See, the clock says it is twilight! You'd better go put up the stock."

The Vizir chased the cows home from the oasis, shut up the herds, folded the flocks, hustled the fowls into the henhouse, shook down straw for the camels and donkeys, gave the elephants hay, and came sheepishly back to the palace.

"Someone is wasting a deal of daylight," he said to nobody in particular as he eyed the rising day.

"Wasting daylight?" cried the Caliph. "How can one be wasting daylight who is not using it? One cannot waste what he does not use. Nobody is wasting daylight. We are saving quantities. Day by day we are saving time. Hour by hour we are gaining upon the sun. Soon we shall have whole days to dispose of!"

And the clock went scuttling along.

Meantime in Chunder-abad-dad things were going very badly. The astonished populace rose in haste and chased the hours with flying feet. They chased them all day. Nobody knew just what time it was; and, apparently, when they did, it wasn't, which was confusing.

The sun said it still was Tuesday noon when the clock said breakfast time the next Sunday morning. Before twilight that day the Caliph and the Grand Vizir had eaten two luncheons, two dinners, two breakfasts, a bedtime snack, and were preparing for breakfast once more. Thus in extraordinary medley, time sped by in Chunder-abad-dad.

Days and nights ran round like water beetles.

Meals followed one another like drops of spattering rain; hours fled by like the flying balls shot from a Roman candle.

Every hour it became more difficult to keep up with the Caliph's clock.

Worn out with perpetual hurry, the Caliph and all the people fell into a deep sleep. But the Grand Vizir in his anxiety lay restless as a cat.

A Miracle Comes to Pass

The road from Samarcand ran down to Chunder-abad-dad like a wide ribbon wandering through the dusty plain. Down the road came a merchant with merchandise for the bazaars. When he came to the city, its walls were deserted. He listened; but all he heard was a sound like a simoom in the distance; it was Chunder-abad-dad's people snoring together.

He pounded on the town gates and shouted, but there came no reply. Opening the postern gate he rode in through the deserted streets.

Over the minarets the noonday sun streamed in a flood of light; yet all was still. Not a person was to be seen; not so much as a dog stirred in an alley. Cold fear crept over the merchant. "In the name of King Solomon's ant!" he cried. "Have I come to a city of the dead?"

The square before the palace lay empty in the sunshine. There was not even a beggar asleep by the gate. But he could hear the fountains babble.

"In the name of Sheba's mule!" he cried. "Is anyone living here?"

He heard a shutter open high up in the wall. He shaded his eyes and squinted up through the sunshine. He saw the head of the Vizir protruding through a crevice.

"Hush!" said the Grand Vizir.

"What in the name of——"

"Hush! Hush, if you love your life!"

The merchant stared in amazement. "What has touched your wits?" he gasped.

"On your honor, tell me, what time is it?" asked the Grand Vizir. "When I ask what time, I mean what hour by Allah's time."

"High noon," said the stranger, marveling much.

"Are you deceiving me, friend?" cried the Vizir.

"Brother, if you cannot take my word for it, just look at the sun. My mule stands with his four feet on his shadow but once in the day."

"What is the day of the week?"

"Friday."

"Friday?" whispered the Vizir, his eyes popping. "See my gray hairs. I am an old man. Do not fool me. Will you take an oath it is Friday?"

The puzzled merchant drew from his saddlebags the *Samarcand Gazette* and showed it to the Vizir.

"You may see the date for yourself."

"*Bismillah!*" gasped the Vizir hoarsely. "Friend, in the imbecile city of Chunder-abad-dad it is forty-two minutes past twelve o'clock come next Sunday fortnight! We are now two weeks ahead of the sun. I knew there was something wrong with that clock, or it wouldn't have kept a cuckoo!"

"Clock?" said the merchant.

"Clock," said the Vizir.

"Show me the thing," said the merchant.

With finger on lip, in tiptoed silence, the Grand Vizir led the merchant through the corridor into the court.

The Caliph's clock stood there upon the top of its marble column.

"There," said the Vizir bitterly, "is the machine which has made this city mad!"

At that moment the clock, which by traveling at breakneck speed had accomplished six weeks' journey in four weeks' time, ran down.

The overtaxed mainspring relaxed with a whine. Something popped inside!——BING! it went——z-z-z-z-z-z-z-z-ee-ee——SPANG——CHUCK!

With a tremendous whirr-r-r, suddenly ended, the clock hands flew wildly round, once, twice, thrice; gave one feeble wave, trembled, and stood still. The hands were just at twelve.

The official clock had stopped!

The two men stood aghast.

From his bedroom across the corridor came the Caliph's voice, "Selim! Selim!"

"Allah save you," gasped the merchant.

"Selim! Selim!" came the stern voice. "Answer me instantly. What are you doing? Have you dared to lay hands upon my royal clock?"

The Grand Vizir clung to a pillar. His legs refused to support him. "Al—Al—Allah!" was all that he could say.

But the merchant of Samarcand was equal to the emergency. "A miracle," he roared, and fell on his knees.

"Kneel!" he gasped to the Vizir. "Kneel, if you value your neck! And shout 'A miracle!'"

"A miracle! A miracle!" shouted the Vizir as he dropped to his knees. "But I don't know what it is."

"Bellow," whispered the merchant. "Louder and louder." And they bellowed lustily together.

The Caliph appeared in his doorway. There was unappeasable wrath in his eyes. He stood a second speechless, candle in hand, staring at the spectacle before him.

"A miracle!" bellowed the Grand Vizir.

"A miracle!" shouted the merchant.

"Where?" said the Caliph stormily. "And what is this miracle?"

"That a clock should cease running with its hands uplifted forever in praise at the hour of prayer!" cried the merchant.

"Cease running? My clock?" cried the Caliph. He threw a glance at the Vizir which made Selim's heart stop beating.

"Great is the Caliph! Our Caliph is mighty!" cried the merchant ecstatically.

"In his hands he holds the hours as one gathers loose sand in a bowl. He commands the darkness to pass, and it passeth. He says the day comes, and it cometh. He gathers the daylight into a bag and presents the superfluous time to his people. *Allah hu akbar!* Our Caliph is mighty!"

The Caliph now began to feel as if he had done something out of the ordinary; as, indeed, he had. He assumed a few airs; he swaggered and began to twist his mustache.

"Behold!" said the merchant. "While the mighty slept, Time came to a stop; the wheels of the Hours stood still. While the Caliph slept, the calendar caught up with the clock. Hail to the Controller of Calendars. The sun, moon, and stars are his servants; the seasons are his toys!"

The Caliph smiled modestly. He loved to hear mild praise of himself.

"Behold," continued the merchant. "He hath laid up fourteen days in his treasury as a miser would lay up his pence. Through his wonderful genius the city of Chunder-abad-dad is a whole fortnight ahead of the sun! Great minds are always ahead of their time!

"And now," said the merchant, and waved at the clock. "This crafty machine confesses the truth: There is no time but Allah's."

"This is a very wise man," thought the Caliph. "A very wise man, indeed." And he drew himself up pompously to the utmost of his height.

"Now," said the Caliph, "I have had enough of trying to keep up with the times; I shall never hurry again."

Then the Caliph sent forth a royal proclamation, saying:

"In the name of the Prophet! I, Sulieman the Magnificent, Caliph of Chunder-abad-dad, have now saved two weeks, which otherwise would have been wasted in sheer frivolity, and return them as a gift to my people that they may live them over; that those who did ill may do well; that those who did well may do better."

And if you ever should come to Chunder-abad-dad, you will find a city where everyone is idle and happy, doing just as he pleases; where no one ever hurries, yet the world goes very well.

Rhyming Ink

Once there was a man called Simon Smug; his wife was called Sarah, and they kept a shop.

Every morning at eight o'clock precisely, Simon unbolted the shop door and took down the shutters. Then he stood behind the counter and weighed out sugar and currants and wrapped up parcels and made out bills and said, "What next can I get for you, ma'am?" and "Dreadful weather for the time of year!" to all the customers. And every evening as the clock struck seven, Simon put up the shutters again and fastened the door.

"Now I'm going to enjoy myself!" he would say, rubbing his hands with enthusiasm.

Sometimes he enjoyed himself by sitting with his feet inside the fender reading the paper to Sarah; sometimes he enjoyed himself pottering about the back yard and painting the water barrel or sowing Virginian Stock seed in the rockery; and sometimes he enjoyed himself by falling asleep in his chair.

And then one day he decided to become a poet.

"You'd be surprised at the thoughts that come into my head, Sarah," said he. "I'm going to put them into poetry and become famous."

He got out a very large sheet of paper and a very large pen and a very large pot of ink and sat down at the kitchen table. Sarah looked at him proudly.

"Just fancy me a poet's wife!" she thought, and held her head two inches higher than usual.

Simon began to write as fast as he could. "Just listen to this and tell me if you ever heard so fine a beginning to a poem," cried he.

Some poets praise the hairy lion;
I praise the hippopotamus,

"And what comes next?" inquired Mrs. Smug.

"I don't know yet," said Simon. "I haven't had the time to find a rhyme."

He sat at the table and thought and thought and thought. He bit the end of his pen to shreds; he found a box of nibs and tried them all; he rumpled his hair and inked his face and made scribbles and patterns all round the edge of the paper; but it was no use.

"I don't believe there's a rhyme to hippopotamus in any language under the sun!" he groaned.

"Why not start with something easier?" suggested Mrs. Smug.

So Simon began again; he began a dozen poems at least, but he could not finish one.

"Is anything wrong, my dear?" asked Sarah.

"Wrong!" echoed Simon. "I should think there is! There's not a single rhyme to any word I've used. I can no more make poetry without rhymes than you can make pancakes without eggs! I'll never be a poet at this rate."

It was the same every time he sat down to write; his verses never got beyond the first two lines, and all for want of rhymes. He grew quite thin and ill-tempered with worry; he lost his appetite; he lost his sleep; he was impatient with the customers and made mistakes in their orders; and wherever he was and whatever he was doing, he was muttering scraps of poetry to himself and trying to find the words he wanted.

"Things can't go on like this," said Mrs. Smug, but she had not the least idea how to stop them.

Then she saw the advertisement for Rhyming Ink:

Important to Poets!

Here is the Most Wonderful Invention of the Age. Just dip your pen in Rhyming Ink (only ten shillings a bottle) and you cannot help writing poetry. If our Ink fails to find a Rhyme to any word in the dictionary, your money will be refunded.

"Now if that isn't exactly what Simon wants!" she cried and sent for some rhyming ink immediately. She did not tell Simon anything about it, of course, for she felt sure he would not feel like a real poet if he knew his rhymes came out of a bottle instead of out of his head.

When the ink arrived she washed the old inkpot that Simon always used and filled it to the brim. "Now perhaps we'll have a little peace," she said

Presently Simon came in, gave a great sigh, and sat down at the kitchen table to write poetry, just as usual. He sighed again as he spread out a clean sheet of paper; he sighed as he chose a clean nib for his pen; he sighed as he opened the inkpot, for he supposed that everything would happen as it had always done before and that in five minutes he would be rumpling his hair and rolling his eyes in his struggle to find a rhyme. And he had thought of such a beautiful beginning for a poem!

I would that in the summer sun
I flitted as a butterfly!

He wrote that much quite quickly, but that was not surprising because he always wrote the first two lines without any trouble; the surprising thing was that the pen went on and finished the verse!

But then before the day was run
Perhaps I'd in the gutter lie!

"I've done it!" shouted Simon Smug. "I've done it! I've written a poem!"

"There, now, just fancy that!" said Sarah.

"But I don't suppose I'll ever be able to write another," he added gloomily.

"I should try if I were you," said Sarah.

"I might as well," said Simon. "I'll see if I can finish the hippopotamus one."

He dipped his pen in the ink and began to write

Some poets praise the hairy lion;
I praise the hippopotamus

And once again the pen went gliding on:

He's got a mouth with teeth like iron—
If he should nip, oh! what a fuss!

"I've done it again!" he exclaimed. "I can write poetry as easily as signing my name!"

He scrawled *Simon Smug* across the paper, by way of illustration, and then gave a gasp, for under his name he had written *Oh, what a mug!*

"I've made a poem even of that," he said in astonishment, "only it's not a very good one. I'm a poet at last! I shall sit and write poetry all day long and never serve in the shop any more."

"You don't mean it, do you?" asked Mrs. Smug.

"Of course I do," said Simon. "Fancy wasting my time weighing out rice and tea and things like that when I've found out how clever I am. If anyone attends to the shop it must be you, my dear, for I'm far too busy to do anything about it."

At first Mrs. Smug made the best of things, but it was inconvenient to have to keep dropping her dishcloth or potato peeler to wait on customers.

It was really very pleasant not to have Simon moaning and groaning over his rhymes, but after a few days she wished she had never bought the rhyming ink.

The kitchen table was smothered in papers; poems fluttered to the ground with every opening of the door; they got into the washtub and the gravy and the flour and the coal scuttle; and if, perchance, Sarah had a moment in which to sit down and rest, Simon would begin to read his favorite pieces to her. And what with the worry of so much poetry in the kitchen and the worry of so little help in the shop, she began to feel quite worn out.

The trouble really came to a head when she used the rhyming ink herself. She would never have done it if she had had time to think, but the shop was so full of customers that she was quite flurried, and when she lost her pencil she carried off the inkpot from under Simon's nose.

"But I can't write without ink!" protested Simon.

"Then you can spend the time tidying the kitchen," said Sarah over her shoulder. "It's disgraceful!"

She deftly wrote receipts and bills and orders, and then she took the ink back to her husband. But never once did she remember that the ink was not of the ordinary kind—until the customers returned, red-faced and angry.

"What do you mean by putting down *white mice* on my bill?" cried one. "I ordered a pound of rice and you have charged for three white mice as well."

"And I ordered a pot of jam," said another, "and you've written underneath *To boil with ham!*"

"Just look at this receipt!" cried a third. "I never saw a bill receipted like this in my life!"

Received with thanks,
Dear Mrs. Banks,
One pound and four—
You owe me more—
A kiss and hug
From Sarah Smug!

"It's that rhyming ink!" cried poor Sarah. And she rushed into the kitchen.

"I've written another poem since you brought me the ink again," said Simon. "It begins, 'Behold the wriggling caterpillar——'"

"I don't care how it begins!" cried Mrs. Smug, and she seized the bottle and emptied the ink out of the window all over the rockery. "You just clear all those papers off the table and look after the shop as you used to do. I've had more than enough poetry, and that's the end of it!"

To tell the truth, Simon had had more than enough poetry, too, and was quite glad to be back behind the counter, but Sarah was wrong when she thought that emptying the bottle out of the window was the end of the matter. The Virginian Stocks began to behave in a most extraordinary way; instead of being miserable and straggling, they grew and budded and blossomed just as though ink were their favorite fertilizer.

"What a charming back yard you have," exclaimed all Simon's visitors. "Your rockery is as pretty as a poem!"

Which just shows what rhyming ink can do—at least the kind at ten shillings a bottle.

The Story of Dr. Dolittle

Once upon a time, many years ago—when our grandfathers were little children—there was a doctor; and his name was Dolittle—John Dolittle, M.D. "M.D." means that he was a proper doctor and knew a whole lot.

He lived in a little town called Puddleby-on-the-Marsh. All the folks, young and old, knew him well by sight. And whenever he walked down the street in his high hat everyone would say, "There goes the Doctor! He's a clever man." And the dogs and the children would all run up and follow behind him; and even the crows that lived in the church tower would caw and nod their heads.

The house he lived in, on the edge of the town, was quite small; but his garden was very large and had a wide lawn and stone seats and weeping willows hanging over. His sister, Sarah Dolittle, was housekeeper for him; but the Doctor looked after the garden himself. He was very fond of animals and kept many kinds of pets. Besides goldfish in the pond at the bottom of his garden, he had rabbits in

From *The Story of Dr. Dolittle* by Hugh Lofting, published by Frederick A. Stokes Company, Inc.

the pantry, white mice in his piano, a squirrel in the linen closet, a hedgehog in the cellar. He had a cow with a calf, too, an old lame horse—twenty-five years of age—and chickens and pigeons and two lambs and many other animals. But his favorite pets were Dab-Dab the duck, Jip the dog, Gub-Gub the pig, Polynesia the parrot, and the owl, Too-Too.

His sister used to grumble about all these animals and said they made the house untidy. And one day when an old lady with rheumatism came to see the Doctor, she sat on the hedgehog, who was sleeping on the sofa, and never came to see him any more, but drove every Saturday all the way to Oxenthorpe, another town ten miles off, to see a different doctor.

Then his sister, Sarah Dolittle, came to him and said, "John, how can you expect sick people to come and see you when you keep all these animals in the house? It's a fine doctor would have his parlor full of hedgehogs and mice! That's the fourth personage these animals have driven away. Squire Jenkins and the parson say they wouldn't come near your house again—no matter how sick they are. We are getting poorer every day. If you go on like this, none of the best people will have you for a doctor."

"But I like animals better than the best people," said the Doctor.

"You are ridiculous," said his sister, and walked out of the room.

So, as time went on, the Doctor got more and more animals; and the people who came to see him got less and less. Till at last he had no one left—except the Cat's-meat-Man, who didn't mind any kind of animals. But the Cat's-meat-Man wasn't very rich, and he only got sick once a year—at Christmas time, when he used to give the Doctor sixpence for a bottle of medicine. Sixpence a year wasn't enough to live on—even in those days, long ago; and if the Doctor hadn't had some money saved up in his moneybox, no one knows what would have happened.

And he kept on getting still more pets; and of course it cost a lot to feed them. And the money he had saved up grew littler and littler.

Then he sold his piano and let the mice live in a bureau drawer. But the money he got for that, too, began to go, so he sold the brown suit he wore on Sundays and went on becoming poorer and poorer.

And now, when he walked down the street in his high hat, people would say to one another, "There goes John Dolittle, M.D. There was a time when he was the best known doctor in the West Country. Look at him now. He hasn't any money, and his stockings are full of holes!" But the dogs and the cats and the children still ran up and followed him through the town the same as when he was rich.

It happened one day that the Doctor was sitting in his kitchen talking with the Cat's-meat-Man, who had come to see him with a stomach ache. "Why don't you give up being a people's doctor and be an animal doctor?" asked the Cat's-meat-Man.

The parrot, Polynesia, was sitting in the window looking out at the rain and singing a sailor song to herself. She stopped singing and started to listen.

"You see, Doctor," the Cat's-meat-Man went on, "you know all about animals—much more than what these here vets do. That book you wrote—about cats—why, it's wonderful! I can't read or write myself—or maybe *I'd* write some books. But my wife, Theodosia, she's a scholar, she is. And she read your book to me. Well, it's wonderful—that's all can be said—wonderful. You might have been a cat yourself. You know the way they think. And listen: you can make a lot of money doctoring animals. Do you know that? You see, I'd send all the old women who had sick cats or dogs to you. And if they didn't get sick fast enough, I could put something in the meat I sell 'em to make 'em sick, see?"

"Oh, no," said the Doctor quickly. "You mustn't do that. That wouldn't be right."

"Oh, I didn't mean real sick," answered the Cat's-meat-Man. "Just a little something to make them droopy-like was what I had reference to. But as you say, maybe it ain't quite fair on the animals. But they'll get sick anyway, because the old women always give 'em too much to eat. And look, all the

186

farmers round about who had lame horses and weak lambs—they'd come. Be an animal doctor."

When the Cat's-meat-Man had gone, the parrot flew off the window onto the Doctor's table and said, "That man's got sense. That's what you ought to do. Be an animal doctor. Give the silly people up—if they haven't brains enough to see you're the best doctor in the world. Take care of animals instead—*they'll* soon find it out. Be an animal doctor."

"Oh, there are plenty of animal doctors," said John Dolittle, putting the flower pots outside on the window sill to get the rain.

"Yes, there *are* plenty," said Polynesia, "but none of them are any good at all. Now listen, Doctor, and I'll tell you something. Did you know that animals can talk?"

"I knew that parrots can talk," said the Doctor.

"Oh, parrots can talk in two languages—people's language and bird language," said Polynesia proudly. "If I say, 'Polly wants a cracker,' you understand me. But hear this: *Ka-Ka oi-ee, fee-fee?*"

"Good gracious!" cried the Doctor. "What does that mean?"

"That means, 'Is the porridge hot yet?'—in bird language."

"My! You don't say so!" said the Doctor. "You never talked that way to me before."

"What would have been the good?" said Polynesia,

dusting some cracker crumbs off her left wing. "You wouldn't have understood me if I had."

"Tell me some more," said the Doctor, all excited; and he rushed over to the dresser drawer and came back with the butcher's book and a pencil. "Now don't go too fast—and I'll write it down. This is interesting—very interesting—something quite new. Give me the birds' A B C first—slowly now."

So that was the way the Doctor came to know that animals had a language of their own and could talk to one another. And all that afternoon, while it was raining, Polynesia sat on the kitchen table giving him bird words to put down in the book. At teatime, when the dog, Jip, came in, the parrot said to the Doctor, "See; *he's* talking to you."

"Looks to me as though he were scratching his ear," said the Doctor.

"But animals don't always speak with their mouths," said the parrot in a high voice, raising her eyebrows. "They talk with their ears, with their feet, with their tails—with everything. Sometimes they don't *want* to make a noise. Do you see now the way he's twitching up one side of his nose?"

"What's that mean?" asked the Doctor.

"That means, 'Can't you see that it has stopped raining?'" Polynesia answered. "He is asking you a question. Dogs nearly always use their noses for asking questions."

After a while, with the parrot's help, the Doctor got to learn the language of the animals so well that he could talk to them himself and understand everything they said. Then he gave up being a people's doctor altogether. As soon as the Cat's-meat-Man had told everyone that John Dolittle was going to become an animal doctor, old ladies began to bring him their pet pugs and poodles who had eaten too much cake; and farmers came many miles to show him sick cows and sheep. One day a plow horse was brought to him; and the poor thing was terribly glad to find a man who could talk in horse language.

"You know, Doctor," said the horse, "that vet over the hill knows nothing at all. He has been treating me six weeks now—for spavins. What I need is spectacles. I am going blind in one eye. There's no reason why horses shouldn't wear glasses, the same as people. But that stupid man over the hill never even looked at my eyes. He kept on giving me pills. I tried to tell him, but he couldn't understand a word of horse language. What I need is spectacles."

"Of course, of course," said the Doctor. "I'll get you some at once."

"I would like a pair like yours," said the horse, "only green. They'll keep the sun out of my eyes while I'm plowing the fifty-acre field."

"Certainly," said the Doctor. "Green ones you shall have."

"You know, the trouble is, sir," said the horse as the Doctor opened the front door to let him out; "the trouble is that *anybody* thinks he can doctor animals—just because the animals don't complain. As a matter of fact it takes a much cleverer man to be a really good animal doctor than it does to be a good people's doctor. My farmer's boy thinks he knows all about horses. I wish you could see him— his face is so fat he looks as though he had no eyes— and he has got as much brain as a potato bug. He tried to put a mustard plaster on me last week."

"Where did he put it?" asked the Doctor.

"Oh, he didn't put it anywhere—on me," said the horse. "He only tried to. I kicked him into the duck pond."

"Well, well!" said the Doctor.

"I'm a pretty quiet creature as a rule," said the horse—"very patient with people—don't make much fuss. But it was bad enough to have that vet giving me the wrong medicine. And when that red-faced booby started to monkey with me, I just couldn't bear it any more."

"Did you hurt the boy much?" asked the Doctor.

"Oh, no," said the horse. "I kicked him in the right place. The vet's looking after him now. When will my glasses be ready?"

"I'll have them for you next week," said the Doctor. "Come in again Tuesday. Good morning!"

Then John Dolittle got a fine big pair of green spectacles, and the plow horse stopped going blind in one eye and could see as well as ever. And soon it became a common sight to see farm animals wearing glasses in the country round Puddleby; and a blind horse was a thing unknown.

And so it was with all the other animals that were brought to him.

As soon as they found that he could talk their language, they told him where the pain was and how they felt, and of course it was easy for him to cure them.

Now all these animals went back and told their brothers and friends that there was a doctor in the little house with the big garden who really *was* a doctor. And whenever any creatures got sick—not only horses and cows and dogs, but all the little things of the fields, like harvest mice and water moles, badgers, and bats—they came at once to his house on the edge of the town, so that his big garden was nearly always crowded with animals trying to get in to see him. There were so many that came that he had to have special doors made for the different kinds.

He wrote "HORSES" over the front door, "COWS" over the side door, and "SHEEP" on the kitchen door. Each kind of animal had a separate door—even the mice had a tiny tunnel made for them into the cellar, where they waited patiently in rows for the Doctor to come round to them.

So, in a few years' time, every living thing for miles and miles got to know about John Dolittle, M.D. And the birds who flew to other countries in the winter told animals in foreign lands of the wonderful doctor of Puddleby-on-the-Marsh who could understand their talk and help them in their troubles.

In this way he became famous among the animals—all over the world—better known even than he had been among the folks of the West Country. And he was happy and liked his life very much.

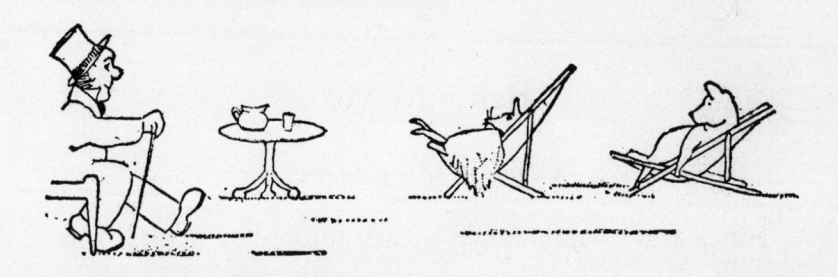

Ben and Me

I Begin My Career

Since the recent death of my lamented friend and patron, Ben Franklin, many so-called historians have attempted to write accounts of his life and his achievements. Most of these are wrong in so many respects that I feel the time has now come for me to take pen in paw and set things right.

All of these ill-informed scribblers seem astonished at Ben's great fund of information, at his brilliant decisions, at his seeming knowledge of all that went on about him. Had they asked me, I could have told them. It was ME.

For many years I was his closest friend and adviser and, if I do say it, I was in great part responsible for his success and fame.

Not that I wish to claim too much. I simply hope to see justice done, credit given where credit is due, and that's to me—mostly.

Ben was undoubtedly a splendid fellow, a great man, a patriot and all that; but he *was* undeniably stupid at times, and had it not been for me—well, here's the true story, and you can judge for yourself.

I was the oldest of twenty-six children. My parents in naming us, went right through the alphabet. I, being first, was Amos, and the others went along through Bathsheba, Claude, Daniel—and so forth down to the babies: Xenophon, Ysobel, and Zenas.

We lived in the vestry of Old Christ Church on Second Street, in Philadelphia—behind the paneling. With that number of mouths to feed we were naturally not a very prosperous family. In fact we were quite poor—as poor as church mice.

But it was not until the Hard Winter of 1745 that things really became desperate. That was a winter long to be remembered for its severity, and night after night my poor father would come in tired and wet with his little sack practically empty.

We were driven to eating prayer books, and when those gave out, we took to the minister's sermons.

That was, for me, the final straw. The prayer books were tough, but those sermons!

Being the oldest, it seemed fitting that I should go out into the world and make my own way. Perhaps I could in some way help the others. At least, it left one less to be provided for.

So, saying farewell to all of them—my mother and father and all the children from Bathsheba to Zenas—I set forth on the coldest, windiest night of a cold and windy winter.

Little did I dream at that moment of all the strange people and experiences I should encounter before ever I returned to that little vestry home! All I thought of were my cold paws, my empty stomach—and those sermons.

I have never known how far I traveled that night, for, what with the cold and hunger, I must have become slightly delirious. The first thing I remember clearly was being in a kitchen and smelling CHEESE! It didn't take long to find it. It was only a bit of rind and fairly dry, but how I ate!

Refreshed by this, my first real meal in many a day, I began to explore the house. It was painfully bare; clean, but bare with very little furniture, and that all hard and shiny; no soft things or dusty corners where a chap could curl up and have a good warm nap. It was cold, too. Almost as cold as outdoors. Upstairs were two rooms. One was dark, and from it came the sound of snoring; the other had a light and the sound of sneezing. I chose the sneezy one.

In a large chair close to the fireplace sat a short, thick, round-faced man, trying to write by the light of a candle. Every few moments he would sneeze, and his square-rimmed glasses would fly off; reaching for these he would drop his pen; by the time he found that and got settled to write, the candle would flicker from the draft; and when that calmed down, the sneezing would start again. And so it went. He was not accomplishing much in the way of writing.

Of course I recognized him.

Everyone in Philadelphia knew the great Doctor Benjamin Franklin, author, soldier, statesman, inventor, scientist, editor, printer, and philosopher.

He didn't look great or famous that night, though; he just looked cold—and a bit silly.

He was wrapped in a sort of dressing gown with a dirty fur collar, and on his head was perched an odd-looking fur cap.

The cap interested me, for I was still chilled to the bone, and this room was just as bleak as the rest of the house. It was a rather disreputable-looking affair, that cap; but in one side of it I had spied a hole—just about my size. Up the back of the chair I went, and under cover of the next fit of sneezes, in I slid. What a cozy place that was! Plenty of room to move about a bit; just enough air; such soft fur; and such warmth!

"Here," said I to myself, "is my home. No more cold streets or cellars or vestries. HERE I stay."

At the moment, of course, I didn't realize how true this was to prove. All I realized was that I was warm, well-fed, and—oh, so sleepy!

And so to bed.

We Invent the Franklin Stove

I slept late the next morning. When I woke up, my fur-cap home was hanging on the bedpost, and I in it. Dr. Franklin was again crouched over the fire attempting to write between fits of sneezing and glasses-hunting. The fire, what there was of it, was smoking, and the room was as cold as ever.

"Not wishing to be critical—" I said. "But perhaps a bit of wood on that smoky ember that you seem to consider a fire might——"

"WASTE NOT, WANT NOT," said he, severe.

"Well, just suppose," I said. "Just suppose you spend two or three weeks in bed with *pewmonia*—would that be a waste or——"

"It would be," said he, putting on a log, "whatever your name might be."

"Amos," said I. "And there'd be doctor bills——"

"BILLS!" said he, shuddering, and put on two more logs, quick. The fire blazed up then, and the room became a little better, but not much.

"Dr. Franklin," I said, "that fireplace is wrong."

"You might call me Ben—just plain Ben," said he. "What's wrong with it?"

"Well, for one thing, most of the heat goes up the chimney. And for another, you can't get *around* it. Outside our church there used to be a Hot-chestnut Man. Sometimes, when business was rushing, he'd drop a chestnut. Pop was always on the lookout, and almost before it touched the ground he'd have it in his sack—and down to the vestry with it. There he'd put it in the middle of the floor—and we'd all gather round for the warmth.

"Twenty-eight of us it would heat, and the room as well. It was all because it was *out in the open*, not stuck in a hole in the wall like that fireplace."

"Amos," he interrupted, excited, "there's an idea there! But we couldn't move the fire out into the middle of the room."

"We could if there were something to put it in, iron or something."

"But the smoke?" he objected.

"Pipe," said I, and curled up for another nap. I didn't get it, though.

Ben rushed off downstairs, came back with a great big armful of junk, dumped it on the floor, and was off for more. No one could have slept, not even a dormouse. After a few trips he had a big pile of things there. There were scraps of iron, tin, and wire. There were a couple of old warming pans, an iron oven, three flatirons, six potlids, a wire birdcage, and an anvil. There were saws, hammers, pincers, files, drills, nails, screws, bolts, bricks, sand, and an old broken sword.

He drew out a sort of plan and went to work. With the clatter he made there was no chance of a nap, so I helped all I could, picking up the nuts and screws and tools that he dropped—and his glasses.

Ben was a fair terror for work, once he was interested. It was almost noon before he stopped for a bit of rest. We looked over what had been done, and it didn't look so bad—considering.

It was shaped much like a small fireplace set up on legs, with two iron doors on the front and a smoke pipe running from the back to the fireplace. He had taken the andirons out of the fireplace and boarded that up so we wouldn't lose any heat up the chimney. Ben walked around looking at it, proud as could be, but worried. "The floor," he says. "It's the floor that troubles me, Amos. With those short legs and that thin iron bottom, the heat——"

"Down on the docks," said I, "we used to hear the ship rats telling how the sailors build their cooking-fires on board ship. A layer of sand right on the deck, bricks on top of that, and——"

"Amos," he shouts, "you've got it!" and rushed for the bricks and sand. He put a layer of sand in the bottom of the affair, the bricks on top of that, and then set the andirons in. It looked pretty promising.

"Eureka!" he exclaims, stepping back to admire it and tripping over the saw. "Straighten things up a bit, Amos, while I run and get some logs."

"*Don't* try to run," I said. "And by the way, do you come through the pantry on the way up?"

"Why?" he asked.

"In some ways, Ben," I said, "you're fairly bright, but in others you're just plain dull. The joy of creating may be meat and drink to you; but as for me, a bit of cheese——"

He was gone before I finished, but when he came back with the logs he had a fine slab of cheese, a loaf of rye bread, and a good big tankard of ale.

We put in some kindling and logs and lit her up. She drew fine, and Ben was so proud and excited that I had to be rather sharp with him before he would settle down to food. Even then he was up every minute, to admire it from a new angle.

Before we'd finished even one sandwich, the room had warmed up like a summer afternoon.

"Amos," says he, "we've done it!"

"Thanks for the WE," I said. "I'll remember it."

We Discover Electricity

It all started with some glass tubes and a book of instructions sent to Ben by a London friend. These glass tubes he would rub with a piece of silk or fur, thereby producing many strange, and, to me, unpleasant effects. When a tube was sufficiently rubbed, small bits of paper would spring from the table and cling to it, or crackling sparks leap from it to the finger of anyone foolish enough to approach. Ben derived great amusement from rubbing a tube and touching it to the tip of my tail. Thereupon a terrible shock would run through my body; every hair and whisker would stand on end, and a convulsive contraction of all my muscles would throw me several inches into the air.

This was bad enough, but my final rebellion did not come until he, in his enthusiasm, used the fur cap to rub the tube. And I was in the cap.

"Ben," said I, "this has gone far enough. From now on, kindly omit me from these experiments. To me they seem a perfectly senseless waste of time, but if they amuse you, all right, go ahead with them. Just leave me out."

"I fear you are not a person of vision, Amos," said he. "You fail to grasp the world-wide, epoch-making importance of these experiments. You do not realize the force——"

"Oh, don't I?" I replied. "My tail is still tingling."

"I shall tear the lightning from the skies," said Ben, "and harness it to do the bidding of man."

"Personally," said I, "I think the sky's an excellent place for it."

Nothing I could say, though, served to dampen Ben's enthusiasm.

I observed that he was developing an unseemly interest in lightning. Every time a house or tree was struck, Ben was the first to reach the scene, questioning all who had been present as to how the bolt had looked, smelled, or sounded, what sensations they had felt, and so on. Then he would go into a brown study that lasted for hours, occasionally murmuring, "I wonder, I wonder."

"Wonder what?" I asked finally. It was getting on my nerves.

"Why, if lightning and electricity are the same."

"To me they are," I said promptly. "They're both annoying, horrid, dangerous nuisances that should be let strictly alone."

"There you go again, Amos. No vision."

"All right," I said, "ALL RIGHT. And if they *are* the same, and if you *do* prove it, then what?"

"Why, then," he said, "why, then, I shall go down in history as he who tamed the lightning, who——"

"If you have any notion of making a house-pet of this lightning," I said, "you can go down in history as anything you please. For myself, I will go down in the cellar—and stay there."

Two days later I was waked from my nap by a terrible clatter overhead. Investigation disclosed Ben seated on the roof, busily hammering. He had fastened a whole collection of sharp-pointed iron rods to various parts of the housetop. There were two or three on each chimney and a series of them along the ridgepole. These were all connected by a tangle of wires and rods that ran down through the trap door into our room.

"You see, Amos," he explained, while connecting wires to various instruments, "the trouble with most people is that they lack the calm observation of the trained scientific mind. Time after time I have rushed to the scene of one of these lightning strokes, and all I could gather from the bystanders was that they were 'terrible skeered.' Now by collecting a small amount of this so-called lightning with the rods which you saw on the roof and conducting it through wires to these jars and instruments, we shall be able to investigate its nature and behavior with true scientific calm.

"We shall be able to settle forever the question which is puzzling all great minds, the question of whether or not lightning is electrical."

"It has never puzzled *my* mind," I said. "Left to myself I wouldn't give it a thought. Moreover," I continued, "you might as well leave out that *we*. I resigned from these experiments a long time ago. Any observing that I do will be done in the cellar. And, as the sky has clouded up rather threateningly, I think I will retire there at once."

The storm was closer than I thought, for I had barely started when there occurred a most horrifying flash of lightning followed by a thunderclap that shook the house to its foundations. The shock threw me bodily into an empty glass jar. This was fortunate, for here I was able to observe all that went on, while the glass protected me from the flashes that followed in rapid succession.

At the first flash the liquid in Ben's jars disappeared in a great burst of yellowish steam and the instruments bounced about wildly. As flash followed flash, blue sparks ran up and down the wires, the andirons glowed as though dipped in phosphorus, and streaks of fire shot from the candlesticks on the mantlepiece. The crashing thunder was continuous, jarring every loose object in the house. There was now no doubt in *my* mind that lightning was electricity—in its most horrid and dangerous form.

In the confusion I had forgotten Ben. Now looking about, I was astonished to find him nowhere in sight.

At this moment a large ball of blue fire emerged from the Franklin stove, rolled across the floor, and descended the stairs, crackling and giving off a strange odor of sulphur. The unusually violent crash that followed brought a faint moan from the bed.

There I discovered Ben, or rather his feet, for they were the only part of him visible. The rest was covered by the bedclothes, while two pillows completely muffled his head.

At first I was alarmed, but as each succeeding crash brought an echoing moan and a violent trembling of the feet, I realized that all that had befallen him was a severe case of fright.

Safe in my big glass jar I thoroughly enjoyed the spectacle of Ben's terror as long as the storm raged.

As the last rumblings died away he cautiously raised the pillows and peered forth. He was a most amusing sight.

"And now, Dr. Franklin," I jeered as he sheepishly rose from the bed, "would you lend a bit of your calm, scientific study to getting me out of this jar? And by the way, what did you observe as to the true nature of lightning?"

"Do you know, Amos," he explained, "that first flash knocked off my glasses, and of course I see very poorly without them."

"So you replaced them with a couple of pillows," I said.

He never answered me—just started picking up the remains of his apparatus.

When, some time later, a scientific writer called them "Lightning Rods," naming Ben as their inventor, he refused to take the credit. This startling display of modesty surprised many people—but not me. I knew all about it.

World Neighbors

Pepperfoot Earns His Name

A Desert Waif

Like a puff of smoke a gray shadow passed behind a rock. Driss sat up, sucking in his breath. A shiver of excitement ran down his backbone. Leaning across from his little donkey, he tugged at the sleeve of his grandfather's cloak. "I have seen four jackals since we left the Singing Brook. You know what that means, Sidi Ahmed? They are all traveling this same way. Please, will you stop and let me see whether there is something among those bushes?"

Driss and his grandfather, having sold all their charcoal at Thursday Market, were hurrying home. They hoped to reach the Berber village of Ali Taza, or High Pastures, before nightfall.

The old man nodded inside his hood. "Look behind those rocks while I keep the donkeys. But hurry. Soon it will be too black to see."

Driss slipped to the ground, lifted the folds of his *jellaba* above his knees, and raced among the palms and jujube bushes. Presently his high, shrill voice shouted, "Come quick, Grandfather! Four jackals are showing their teeth, ready to jump. It is a baby donkey, a very little *behime*, only two or three days old. He is cold and lying down, but he is not dead. Bring one of the charcoal baskets. Oh, come quick! You never saw a donkey of this color before."

As Sidi Ahmed approached, he threw well-directed stones which sent the jackals scurrying to a safer distance. Driss was kneeling and holding in his arms an animal about as big as a setter dog, but all legs and floppy ears.

"Do you think that I can save him, Grandfather?" Driss asked anxiously. "He is so cold and little."

They tucked the helpless animal into the basket and again started the six donkeys on their way up the steep path toward High Pastures. It was a good thing that old Fortunata, the leading donkey, knew every inch and pebble of the trail, for it was now dark. The others heard the clink of her iron shoes and followed obediently.

In Africa the night shuts down like the pulling of a curtain over a window. One minute it is light, and you see everything. The next minute the path is in pitch darkness, and you stumble into the bushes. And the heat of the day goes with the sun, too. One minute you are warm; the next, a cold wind springs up from nowhere.

Driss had never felt so happy, but he was worried, too. Sitting upon his donkey, he reached into the charcoal basket and laid his hand on the little waif. He was nothing but bones. Was he breathing? In all the lands of the Berbers had there ever before been a donkey of this color?

He was the pale gray of the mourning dove when it builds its nest. His nose was white; the insides of his ears were like cotton. His eyes were the color of a saddle that has been rubbed smooth with wax. His body was fuzzy like plush, like the back of a sheep that has just been clipped short.

With a stick Driss prodded his donkey up beside Fortunata, on which Sidi Ahmed rode. "Tell me," he said. "The donkey is a gift from Allah, is he not? Do you think I can keep him alive?"

It was windy and dark, and the old man leaned backward so that the boy might hear. "I am afraid you are too late. He was left to die, I fear, by one of the caravans which bring salt from Egypt. He is an Egyptian donkey, as you see from the cross of the Nazarene upon his shoulders.

"The men of the great desert know animals well. Never would they have abandoned him unless they believed he was about to die. If they think an animal is not strong, they do not waste their time with him. Son of my Son, I fear that your trouble will be for nothing."

Before the path reaches Ali Taza, it skirts the edge of a lower village, Izda Taza, or Low Pastures. Here lived Driss' best friend, Amroo.

Driss was shouting at the top of his voice as the donkeys entered the cedar grove surrounding Izda Taza. "Amroo, you sleepy-headed turtle, come and hear the news. In this basket I have something that never before came to our tribe."

"It is that nest of flying squirrels in the hollow tree," Amroo cried.

"No, it is a baby Egyptian donkey with hoofs no bigger than the eye of a cow. Grandfather thinks he will die, but we *must* keep him alive. Put your hand in the basket and feel him. He is cold, but he is still breathing.

"Listen, Amroo," continued Driss. "Grandfather says that we must give him goat's milk, half a bowlful, all night, every time the rooster crows. Who has a goat with lots of milk?"

Amroo knew. "Cousin You-Seff has a goat whose kid fell over the cliff. She has much milk."

"Run and get her, Amroo. Do not delay. Tell You-Seff that I will work five days for him if he will rent her to me until this donkey is weaned. Bring her to our tent and tell your family that you are going to spend the night with us."

The donkey opened his eyes, but was too weak to stand when Driss carried him inside the tent. His awkward legs folded up like broken sticks.

Soon Amroo could be heard coming up the hill with a bewildered goat bleating at the end of a rope. Driss milked her into a bowl of baked clay, dipped his fingers in the warm liquid and wet the lips of the little donkey. The creature opened his eyes wide and flopped back his ears. But he would not drink, and when Amroo pushed his nose into the bowl, he sneezed and drew his head away.

Now Rabka, little sister of Driss, came forward. "Let me try," she said. "Sit down and hold his head. Open his lips."

The girl filled her mouth with milk, puckered her lips as though she were going to whistle, and blew a stream of milk down the donkey's throat. Soon the bowl was empty, and the donkey was holding his mouth open of his own accord.

"Good, Rabka!" exclaimed Driss. "I didn't think a girl could be so clever." His sister had helped a lot, but it is not the custom of the Berbers to give girls credit for the clever things they do.

"Go to bed, Rabka," Driss said. "Amroo and I will care for our boarder. You lie on that side of him, Amroo, and I will lie on this side. Snuggle up close, under the rug, so as to keep him warm. Sidi Ahmed says that our only chance of saving him will be to keep him warm and to feed him often."

The boys' eyes were dropping shut when Rabka called a question from her side of the partition in the tent. "What will you name him, Driss?"

"I don't know," replied her brother. "I think I will wait and let him name himself. It must be a good name, because I have a feeling that he will be the most wonderful donkey in all Africa." His voice ended in a sleepy sigh as he settled down with his arms firmly about the neck of his new pet.

Later, as Sidi Ahmed retired, he paused to look down on the three heads lying close together, with the red and brown rug drawn about their chins.

The old man smiled into his beard.

"They are good boys," he muttered. "They will save the donkey if anyone can. *Inch Allah*—if it pleases God—they will save the little *behime*."

Sidi Ahmed was right. The little white donkey was saved and grew up rapidly.

Adventures at Market

It was a few months later that the donkey was taken along to Thursday Market.

The markets of Sidi Ahmed's tribe have existed for thousands of years, every week at the same spot, and are named for the day of the week on which they are held. They are the only stores at which things can be bought, and the only places where a farmer can sell his barley, vegetables, and fruit; the shepherd his wool, sheep, and goats; the tanner his leather; the weaver his cloth. It is like going to school, to the store, to the candy shop, to church, to the circus—all rolled into one.

On this particular Thursday, Driss and Sidi Ahmed were early astir. To save time, the night before they had filled with charcoal the baskets which fitted on the saddles of the donkeys.

Thursday Market was fourteen miles away, with three hills and three valleys to cross before one came to the prairie where one could trot. Sidi Ahmed walked first, followed by Fortunata, steadiest of the pack animals. Behind her, in single file, came the five others, with Driss at the rear to see that nothing fell off and that no one lagged. The Egyptian donkey stayed beside Driss like a dog. He was big and strong by this time, but as yet had not been shod and had carried no burdens.

Once at the market, Driss and his grandfather lifted the baskets into the air, while the donkeys walked out from beneath their loads. Sidi Ahmed weighed the charcoal into five-pound and ten-pound lots for Driss to arrange in piles for the customers to choose. Then sitting upon a carpet, he received the salutes of his friends.

Sidi Ahmed was much respected at Market. He was addressed as *Hadj*, or Pilgrim, since he had made the pilgrimage to the holy city of Mecca.

Driss did most of the work. He would put the charcoal into the basket of a customer, collect the money—half a penny for a small pile, a penny for a large pile—and hand it to his grandfather.

Sidi Ahmed's stock would usually be sold out by noon. Then he would fold his carpet and saunter to the teahouse for gossip with old friends. If business had been good, he would give Driss a coin or two to spend for himself before they packed up to return to Ali Taza.

With the coins tight in his fist, and three whole hours in which to amuse himself, Driss would be blissfully happy.

Always Driss had two errands. The first was at the upper end of the market; the other at the lower end. At the upper end sat the doughnut maker, cross-legged, before an enormous pan of boiling mutton fat. Driss stood in line, waiting his turn, holding out a smooth, clean stick. The cook would flip six doughnuts out of the hot fat and over the end of the stick, the cook's wife would take the halfpenny, and Driss would be off on his second errand. This was to the *mishwee* man on the street of the butchers.

Over a fire of cedar roots, on a stout iron bar, this man would be roasting two or three whole sheep. With a flourish of his long knife, he would carve off a halfpenny slice or a penny slice or even a splendid twopenny cutlet.

Driss, his meat in one hand, his stick of doughnuts in the other, would now start upon a general inspection of the whole market, eating as he went.

The shops that served animals were fun: horseshoers, harness makers, rope and saddle makers, and the blacksmiths who hammered out the flat stirrups that were so comfortable for barefoot riders.

Barbers were fun, too. The customer sat upon the ground, and the barber, waving his razor, knelt behind. Berber men let the hair grow on their faces, but every week they shave their heads as smooth as an egg. On the heads of boys the barber leaves a single lock of hair, which is called the Handle of the Prophet. Parents hope that Mohammed, should the boy be sick or have an accident, will pull him up to heaven by that convenient tuft of hair.

On the ride home Driss would think over all of these exciting things so that he could tell Pabka.

One afternoon at Thursday Market—the day on which the Egyptian donkey earned his name—all the shopkeepers were puzzled. They were angry and suspicious as well as mystified. Nour Edden, the grocer, beckoned to his friend, Ben Hassan, the dry-goods man. "Have you been losing things from your shop? I have. For example, I cannot find a package of sugar that was here two hours ago."

"Now that you speak of it," replied Ben Hassan, "a funny thing happened to me today. A tribesman bought a pair of slippers, but he did not want to take them until later. So I laid the slippers at the back of my tent, on the ground, against the canvas wall. When I had taken my nap, I could not find them. Yet I am sure that no customers came to my store."

"Speaking of objects flying away," added Sidi Ahmed, joining the conversation, "no one could be more careful in weighing my charcoal than I am. I put exactly five pounds, or ten pounds, in every pile, and the customer can take his choice. But lately some of my best customers find fault, saying that my piles do not weigh enough. They think that I am not honest. Someone must be tampering with my goods."

There was a second riddle at Thursday Market, and he had been a mystery for a long time. His name was Dillal Ben Abbes, a dried-up man who rode a dried-up donkey and was followed by a little dried-up dog.

This Dillal Ben Abbes never worked. He never brought vegetables or eggs or wool or sheep to exchange for other things. He never bought from the shops. Nevertheless, every Thursday when he left the market, the bags on his donkey's saddle were nicely rounded out, full of many articles.

A number of people had noticed this, but none could explain where his provisions came from.

Today Driss was helping his grandfather as usual. But the charcoal had not sold well. Sidi Ahmed had gone to the teahouse, and during his absence the boy was to guard the remaining piles of charcoal. Driss had eaten his bread and white cheese and was lying under the sun shelter, half-asleep. The white donkey was keeping him company, head down, ears forward, eyelids drooping. The whole market was enjoying a peaceful and refreshing siesta until the sun should be less blistering and until the noon meal should be digested.

But not everyone at Thursday Market was inactive. That dried-up dog of Dillal Ben Abbes was at work. Lying flat upon her stomach, not noticeable against the dust, she was worming her way, inch by inch, to the nearest pile of charcoal. She had already made raids on the sandal maker, the grocer, the butcher, and the candlemaker.

She had had long experience as a thief, that dusty yellow dog, and she was as quick-witted as a desert fox. Whenever a person passed near her, she would lie, barely breathing, her eyes closed. But if anyone should try to lay a hand on her, she would jump and bite, vicious as a hornet. She was there to steal a piece of Sidi Ahmed's charcoal and carry it to her master.

A piercing yelp split the silence. It was a howl, a snarl, a cry of pain, of surprise, and of hate—all uttered together. Instantly the men in the market opened their eyes. A yellow dog and a bundle of charcoal were flying through the air.

"I saw it! I saw it all!" Waving his hands, Ben Hassan waddled across from his dry-goods tent. "It was the Egyptian donkey! He did it with his hind feet. The thin dog came on her belly. Slinking, so, so, so, like that. Not seeming to move, she opened her mouth for the charcoal. Then, *poof*, she was in the air, howling like a devil spirit. I saw it all. This dog is the thief who has taken Nour Edden's sugar and my slippers and El Ghouli's carpet and Berk El Lill's package of candles and Sidi Ahmed's charcoal. Thursday after Thursday she robs us and takes our goods to her master, that rascal Dillal Ben Abbes. Let us find that man and see what his saddlebags contain."

With a cry of approval, fifty angry shopkeepers and their friends pursued the yellow dog around the tent of the pack makers. But they were too late. Dillal Ben Abbes, upon his dried-up donkey, with the dried-up thief of a dog at his heels, was off at a gallop toward the cedar forest where he lived.

Walking back to their tents, the merchants talked it over. "That rogue will not dare return to Market. For he lived by stealing, and the donkey has spoiled that. Isn't that donkey a wonder?"

Ben Hassan clapped his hands. "His feet are sharp, and they bite like red pepper. A regular pepperfoot he is."

"Ha-ha, a pepperfoot," chuckled El Ghouli, the carpet seller. "A good name for that donkey— Pepperfoot of Thursday Market."

The others applauded and separated to their places of business, repeating the name, their faces creased with smiles.

That evening on the way home, Driss and Sidi Ahmed paused to let their donkeys drink at the Singing Brook. A round and smiling moon lifted its face above the snowy summit of the mountain, and in the moon's soft radiance Pepperfoot seemed to Driss to be made of silver.

The Immortal Railroad

A red light on the semaphore brought the powerful locomotive of the express from Moscow to a stop outside the yards, with grinding brakes and hissing steam. Gregory Kholodny, the engineer, looked down from his cab and saw a lanky, freckle-faced boy standing near the tracks gaping up at him. Kholodny's face crinkled into a smile.

"Think you'd like to be a railroad man?" he asked.

"Yes, sir!" the boy replied eagerly. "I'm going to study to be an engineer like——"

His words were drowned out as the locomotive snorted, and the enormous wheels began turning. Shura Trekach looked after the train wistfully, wishing he could see the engineer again.

The very next night his wish came true. There was a public meeting in the town hall to discuss a proposal to build a children's railroad. Shura brought his father and mother, because when a boy sets out to be the very first engineer on the first children's railroad in the world, he has to be sure his parents will back him up.

To Shura's delighted surprise, the engine driver with whom he had talked the day before stepped on the platform. In a deep, pleasant voice, Kholodny began to explain the plan which a group of school directors and railroad men had worked out.

"Fellow citizens, within the memory of the older boys and girls, ours was a sleepy old town on the edge of impassable marshes. Above us were the treacherous rapids of the Dnieper River. In 1928 the marshes were drained and planted in grain. The foaming river was locked between strong walls of concrete to furnish power for our factories. The Dnieper Dam now spans the river. It is the biggest power plant in Europe—the symbol of our nation's dream, the promise of better things to come." He paused, and added softly, "This dream we must share with the children—our future citizens.

"Railway transport is of utmost importance in this program, and many trained workers are needed to run it. We have figured it out this way: Children who like music begin taking lessons at an early age. Why shouldn't children who like railroads do the same? We propose to train selected groups of students at the yards, but that is not all. We want to give these students practical experience by letting them construct and operate their own railroad! Not a toy, but a real railroad, just half the standard size, with a mile or two of track circling our central park."

A wistful sigh from hundreds of young listeners swept through the hall. With a sympathetic smile, the old engineer concluded, "You see, citizens, this is what your children want. I hope you will adopt this proposal."

As Kholodny left the platform, Shura nudged his father, who, taking the hint, shouted, "I move we accept the proposal!"

After a short discussion a Children's Council was named from the list of young people who had signed up for the railroading courses, and Shura Trekach was one of them.

That was early in March. During the next few weeks the children helped select the route, plan railroad buildings, and solve mechanical problems. The problem of trees that grew on the right of way was brought before the council. A girl suggested that the trees could be saved by uprooting and planting them elsewhere. This the youngsters did, assisted by the park landscape gardeners.

While the track was being built, work went on in other places—in the engineering college where plans for the locomotive, cars, and stations were made, and in the shops where the students designed signal apparatus, telephones, and telegraph instruments. Meanwhile, the operating staff was being trained—seven hundred students to serve as switchmen, stationmasters, dispatchers, track walkers, repairmen, conductors, inspectors, and so on.

The most responsible work was that of the engine crew, especially that of the driver, who had to study for four months. Shura was in this group. He was certain that on opening day of the Little Stalinsky Railway he would be the engineer.

The opening date was to be July sixth. On the day school closed, Shura confidently went to look at the list of names of the operating staff posted on the shop bulletin board, but his name was not on the list! He was bewildered. His marks in the railroad courses were excellent—he had put his whole heart into them. He was so disappointed that his father went to the director.

"I'm sorry, but only those with high grades in school qualify for the operating staff," said the director. "Shura neglected his regular studies."

Then Kholodny talked with Shura. "Personal ambition is a good thing," he said, "but it should not be stronger than your desire to be of service."

However, Kholodny proposed a plan to the director. Shura could spend the summer working at various jobs on the children's railroad, from the bottom up. When school opened in the fall, if his scholarship was satisfactory for the first term, he would then qualify as engine driver.

"Very good!" the director agreed. So it came about that on opening day Shura donned a porter's blue uniform and was almost as proud as though he were to drive the engine.

It was a solemn moment when the red ribbon across the track was cut. The waiting locomotive, called the *Young Pioneer*, impatiently blew out sparks as a long line of children, tickets in hand, came out of the station.

The dispatcher struck a gong twice and waved a green flag. The chief conductor blew his whistle. The engineer, a girl, promptly answered with a short blast from her locomotive whistle, and the train began moving.

Shura followed briskly after the chief conductor to punch the tickets and tried not to feel envious that he was not the engineer. And so he began his service on the Little Stalinsky Railway. From porter he was promoted to switchman, switchman to ticket agent, ticket agent to dispatcher, dispatcher to stationmaster. When at last he passed his final examinations he became, at the age of thirteen, the youngest engineer on the new railroad.

For five years Shura drove the *Young Pioneer*. In the summer of 1941 Shura reluctantly climbed down from his cab to accept the highest post on the railway—that of superintendent.

Suddenly the catastrophe for which every schoolchild had been taught to prepare, came upon Russia. The mighty army of a neighboring country invaded their land. The enemy swept over the flat western grain fields toward the first natural barrier, which was the Dnieper River.

One day in early August Superintendent Trekach posted a notice calling an emergency meeting of the Children's Council for that same evening. A few hours later he faced his fellow workers.

"Boys and girls, fellow railroad workers," he began in a grave voice, "this is the last meeting of the Children's Council."

The audience stared at Shura in sudden alarm.

"What I have to tell you should not be a surprise, for you all know that our armies have had to retreat. This morning—" his young voice faltered—"this morning the evacuation of the city was ordered. The dam is to be blown up!"

A murmur went through the room. Then in a dead silence Shura went on, "The enemy is already at the river, and if they're able to reach the dam they can go on across the bridge. But if we destroy the dam, a flood of water and mud will be loosed that will make this whole region impassable. The rapids will then make an even stronger barrier! That will be the gain for our loss——"

He was interrupted by old Gregory Kholodny, who came to the platform. His hair had grown white in the years since he had begun to help the children run their railroad.

"Don't be downcast children," he began softly. "All is not lost. As you know, when territory has to be abandoned, it is necessary to remove everything that might help the advancing enemy. Only when it is impossible to remove a thing, must it be destroyed. That is what we Russians have been doing ever since this terrible war began—

evacuating, removing grain, machinery, and whole factories to the rear, and destroying what remains. That," he added slowly, "is what we are doing with the Dnieper Dam——"

Shura looked up, sudden hope in his face as the old engineer continued more quickly.

"Everyone of you has seen those giant turbines that stand in the pink stone building at the dam. The first of these fine motors came from America. All the others were made in Russia. An American engineer started the construction—and we finished it! We will not let a single one of our turbines or dynamos fall into the enemy's hands.

"When we finally set off the charge which will make the Dnieper Dam a jumble of concrete blocks with the released waters roaring over them, we will be far beyond the east bank. And we will take with us the most valuable equipment, not only in the power plant itself, but in the city and the whole region. Every Russian soldier, every man, woman, and child will be evacuated. We expect you, the young people, to help in this tremendous task!"

As the veteran engineer left the platform, Shura leaped to his feet. "Listen!" he shouted. "If the grown-ups can remove the power equipment piece by piece, why can't we do the same with our railroad? Let's transplant it as we did the trees!"

Applause and cheers greeted his words.

And so began a heartbreaking task—dismantling the little railway and reducing the remainder to a heap of junk and ashes. Thousands of young people worked with but one purpose, while the boom of the big guns sounded ever nearer.

Then, on a day in late August, an odd procession moved over the Dnieper Dam bridge. First, on a truck, came the locomotive, with the coaches following on other trucks. Then came handcarts, wheelbarrows, perambulators, old wagons, and droshkies drawn, not by horses, but by dozens of husky boys, singing as they pulled in unison.

All these makeshift vehicles were loaded with materials salvaged from the children's railroad.

A long line of boys marched briskly, four abreast, carrying the rails and ties. Their firm and swinging steps showed that they expected soon to lay the tracks in some other and safer location.

The signal crew carried telephone and telegraph equipment. Student mechanics carried their tools. Not a plank, not a bolt which could be moved had been left behind. A company of girls transported the furnishings of the stations—draperies, divans, pictures, easy chairs, and rugs—which had been designed with the help of their mothers.

One eight-year-old boy pulled a wagon on whose contents he turned anxious eyes. Packed carefully in the wagon were hundreds of electric bulbs which had been taken from the stations.

On came the procession, heads held high, faces eager, chanting their *Young Pioneer* marching song, while their feet kept time to the tune. Not one of them looked back or even cast a tearful glance at the magnificent stone structure which their parents had built to harness the turbulent river, and which now stood awaiting its doom.

After the children came their elders and also the brothers and sisters who had stayed to help them move the household belongings. Workers, too, drove truck loads of factory materials, although the heaviest machinery had been sent on ahead by freight trains. Finally came the retreating army. As soon as it was safely across the bridge, the commander was to give the signal to destroy the dam.

Hours later, Shura, safe with his brigade of young railroaders in their night's encampment on the east bank of the Dnieper, listened tensely for the first explosion. He no longer dreaded this destruction, for it would mean that their land was safe.

Nevertheless, when it came in the early dawn, his eyes filled with stinging tears. There was a series of dull, echoing reports, followed by a roar as the unloosed river waters rushed over hundreds of square miles of Russian lowlands.

As the last explosion echoed in his ears, Shura cast a farewell glance westward. Behind him were leveled homes and factories and flooded ground. For the time being, at least, the raging torrent would be a shield between the Russians and their foe.

Shura turned his face to the east. The sun was rising, a red ball on the rim of the far horizon across the fields of harvested grain. Before him lay the vast, unconquered lands of his people. Somewhere, beyond that bright horizon, Shura and millions like him, would build new homes and cities, new factories and railroads, and begin life anew.

A Letter for Nikias

On a cold morning near the end of November, Nikias was leading his little black mule along the mountain trail. He was on his way to Demetrios with food. For three weeks now Demetrios and his regiment had been hiding in the mountains, waiting to attack the enemy that had invaded their beloved Greece. And for three weeks Nikias had been carrying daily food supplies—bread, cheese, and cookies—to the brave patriots.

Nikias felt happy and not at all worried, for had not Kyr Mihale, the schoolmaster, such trust in him as a messenger that he was even excused from his lessons? Of course, the other boys and girls wondered at his absence, but when they asked him, Nikias always said, "I cannot say."

Nikias had just come to the steep slope that led to the clearing, when he heard his name called. He spun around, and there were his sister, Penelope, and their neighbor, Theo. Nikias did not speak. He stood still, frowning.

"Why did you follow me, Penelope?" he said at last. "Kyr Mihale will be very angry."

Penelope shuffled her foot in the pebbles, but Theo made a rude face. "Aha," he jeered. "You are not the only boy who can take food to Demetrios. From now on I will carry to our troops the almond cakes and mincemeat that *my* mother makes."

"Why are you not at school?" Nikias asked.

"Oh, Nikias," Penelope begged, "please, don't scold us. You see, the other night I heard Grandmother and Grandfather talking. They thought I was asleep. I heard them say that you were taking food to Demetrios, and I told Theo."

"So you told Theo?" Nikias asked accusingly.

"She had to tell me," Theo said in a bragging tone. "She was afraid to follow you unless I came."

"It was wicked to tell," declared Nikias.

"Nikias," Penelope said, her lip trembling, "I—I told Thalia, too, because I knew she would want to send a message to Demetrios. She wrote a letter. I have it here. You—you would want Demetrios to have his wife's letter. Would you not?"

Nikias leaned his head against the rocky wall that lined one side of the trail. He did not know what to do. Of course, Penelope—and Theo, too—were all right; they would not want any harm to come to the regiment. They just did not know how important it was to keep the hiding place a secret.

Kyr Mihale trusted him. What would he say if he knew that Penelope and Theo had followed him? What would Demetrios say for him to do? Suddenly Nikias knew.

Obey orders and use his head!

Suppose—suppose he let them come as far as the clearing and then told them to go back with the mule? If Theo and Penelope refused to turn back, he, Nikias, would not move a step farther. He would just sit there, if it took all night, and not say a word about where he was going until they would have to go back. Penelope would be afraid when the darkness came, and she would think of how Manitza, their grandmother, would punish her. Manitza had a switch.

"I will let you come just as far as the clearing," Nikias said. His voice sounded strangely grown-up, like Kyr Mihale's. "But when we get there, you must turn back."

"Oho, must we? Well, I'll tell you—Demetrios will soon see there are others in the village besides this Nikias," Theo retorted.

"Come on," Nikias commanded.

Penelope did not say anything; she was looking out of the corner of her eye at Nikias. He looked very stern—not like himself at all.

The little black mule began to pick its way carefully down the trail, and the children followed. Presently they came to a ravine. Nikias was just easing the mule down the slope, making little coaxing sounds with his lips, when there came a sharp rattle of stones. All three of them stood quite still. There was a second trail down the slope, and along it was coming a party of six men dressed in strange uniforms. They were scrambling down, one after the other, and a tall man in front was waving to the children.

Nikias thought he must be dead. His heart had stopped beating; he couldn't feel it at all. He knew who those men were! He had seen a picture of them in a newspaper from Athens.

These were soldiers of the enemy! Nikias could not speak. He felt Penelope's fingers digging into his arm. He saw the terror reflected on Theo's face. *They* knew, too.

"Nikias," Theo whispered, "the—the——"

"Yes," Nikias said. It did not seem as if his lips could move; they were stiff. But, he, Nikias, would have to do something. Demetrios had to be warned! And had not Kyr Mihale said that Nikias might see the enemy soldiers, but that they would not harm a child?

"If they ask us anything," Nikias whispered, "we must pretend that we know nothing. We—we go on a picnic."

The man in the lead was shouting now. He was beckoning to them to wait.

"They'll kill us," Penelope whispered.

"No," Nikias said. "Just—just leave it to me."

Now the men were beside them. They looked smart in their dark uniforms with braid and buttons, and they carried revolvers. The man in the lead was smiling, but it did not seem like a real smile. He spoke in the Greek language to Nikias.

"A good year to you, my lad," he said.

"A—a good year to you," Nikias responded hoarsely.

"You are pale. Are you sick?" the man queried.

"Perhaps one of their Greek goblins has stolen his tongue." It was another soldier speaking. He had queer, angry black eyes.

"I—we go on a picnic," Nikias said. "We—we eat over yonder near that stream."

"Oh, a picnic," said the first man. "Perhaps we can add something to that."

"Look—" it was the first man speaking again— "here is a package of sweetmeats. I have been saving it for just such a pretty little maid as that one there. I think there is enough for all three."

Nikias knew that when anyone offered you food, you must take it for politeness' sake. Had not Manitza told him that many times? Penelope said nothing but pressed up close against Nikias, her hands over her eyes. Theo just looked at the ground without moving.

"I thank you," said Nikias, holding out his hand for the sweetmeats.

"Ho, the cockerel gets more friendly," said the second man, "but the pretty little hen hides under her feathers. Perhaps, Benito, the children of these mountains have no tongues."

"Peace, Rafael," the first man said, frowning. "I can attend to them."

Nikias pretended to bite into a sweetmeat.

"Ah, that is better," said the first man. He was smiling again. "Now, will you do a small thing in return for our gift?"

"What would you have us do?" Nikias asked.

The first man stood curling the ends of his black mustache. "Oh, it is nothing," he said. "We are in quest of a band of soldiers in this vicinity. We wish to give them a friendly message. On your way here, did you see any such?"

Nikias thought again of the words Demetrios had often spoken: *Obey orders and use your head.*

"Yes, we saw them," Nikias said in a whisper.

"Which way did they go?" the man asked. His voice was frightening; he was not smiling at all.

Nikias pointed up the path they had come.

"We met them perhaps a quarter-mile back," he said. "They were headed toward the west."

Demetrios' hiding place was straight *east*, over the next ridge.

The first man came so close that Nikias could feel his breath. His arm hurt where the man held it.

"You would not lie, cockerel?" he said.

"No," declared Nikias.

The man spoke to the others in a language that Nikias did not understand, then started up the trail which the children had just traveled. He began to climb, and the others behind him.

Nobody spoke as they watched the soldiers disappear around the bend. Then Theo whispered, "That was a lie you told, Nikias."

"Yes," Nikias whispered back.

"It was to save Demetrios," Penelope said. "They would kill him if they knew where he is."

"Yes," Nikias admitted.

"Nikias," Theo said, still whispering, "when they find out you lied, they will come back. They will kill us, Nikias."

Nikias did not say anything for a minute. He knew, without being told, what the end would be. The soldiers would return soon; they would guess that Demetrios and the others were close. They would take the only other trail—the one up the mountain. And they would creep up on Demetrios and kill him and the others. He, Nikias, must climb that high mountain and warn Demetrios!

"Theo," he said, "you and Penelope go back home. Take that path to the north; it branches off from the main trail. Watch for it. It is near the two tall balsams. That way you will not meet the enemy. Tell Kyr Mihale what happened."

"But what will *you* do?" Penelope sobbed.

Nikias looked up at the dark wall of the mountain, and he felt afraid—more afraid than he had ever been in all his life. And then suddenly he felt very angry at those soldiers who were looking for Demetrios, and he was no longer afraid.

"I will climb the peak to warn Demetrios," he said. He did not wait to see Penelope and Theo go scrambling down the trail with the mule. Nikias set his foot on the slippery ledge that marked the beginning of the path and began to climb. Every now and then he made a wild clutch at a shrub or tree root to save himself from falling. Occasionally he looked back, but no one was coming.

He climbed on. It seemed as if an hour passed. Then he could see the top of the peak not more than six feet above him. But there seemed no hold right there. He reached out toward a jutting boulder to swing himself up, but the rock was slippery, and his hands were wet with perspiration. His fingers clutched frantically. He heard himself scream. He felt himself fall.

Nikias fell perhaps eight feet before he struck a ledge of rocky soil. This broke his fall, but his body landed hard. For a moment he lay there, while a pain like a red-hot needle went tearing along his shoulder bone. He closed his eyes. . . . Demetrios was waiting for him, and the regiment, too. . . . He, Nikias, must save them all.

Nikias pulled himself up and saw a shelf just above. Perhaps he could reach it. The agony in his shoulder was like a blazing fire in his flesh. Nikias' hand closed about the rock. With a final effort he pulled himself over the top and lay still. He must not sleep. . . .

He gave a feeble shout and waited, but no one replied. Then he remembered the call Demetrios used to make to the sheep. Demetrios could hear that sound; he could hear it a quarter of a mile away. Nikias twisted his lips and gave the sheep call, and ten minutes later Demetrios knelt beside him.

"Demetrios," Nikias whispered, "I had to let you know. The enemy . . . has a scouting band . . . down below. They are looking for you. They asked where you were. I . . . I told them you had gone west. They will know I have lied and come back. They will . . . will bring their regiment around the trail below the pass. I . . . I . . . "

And then Nikias fainted.

Five days later Nikias lay on a blanket in front of the fire at home, with his bandaged shoulder propped against a pillow. Penelope was sitting on a stool beside him. Near her was Thalia. Suddenly they heard the heavy tread of Kyr Mihale's hobnailed brogans coming up the path. In a moment the teacher was in the room.

"May the good year be with you," said Kyr Mihale. He sat down on a chest, looking very important. He cleared his throat.

"What have you in that wallet at your waist?" asked Papous, the old grandfather.

"I have news," said Kyr Mihale, and suddenly he forgot to be dignified and act like a teacher. He jumped up and swung Papous off his feet.

"Papous, Manitza, Nikias—all of you!" he cried. "I have wonderful news! The sixth regiment— Demetrios' regiment—it has driven back the enemy! It is chasing them beyond our borders!"

"And to think Nikias did it all!" said Penelope.

"But of course he did," cried Thalia, "with the aid of Demetrios!"

"It is true that Demetrios led the regiment to the secret pass on which they could cross to outflank the enemy," Kyr Mihale said, "but Nikias warned them of the enemy's presence."

Kyr Mihale was drawing from his wallet a long letter with a red seal. He was smiling. He was handing the letter to Nikias. "I have been ordered to give you this," he said.

"For me!" Nikias exclaimed, staring at Kyr Mihale. "I have never had a letter. What can it be?"

"Best open it and find out," said Papous.

"My—my hand shakes," said Nikias.

"Read it for him, Kyr Mihale," Manitza begged.

Kyr Mihale took the envelope and tore it open. He pulled out the sheet of paper inside and began to read:

> My dear Nikias:
>
> You have done a great, a shining deed for your country. You have saved a regiment. You have shown the courage of a great hero. It is not in my power to thank you properly. But this one thing I say to you:
>
> May you always hold the courage you showed on that day. I salute you, friend of Greece!
>
> Aleko Kalamato
> Colonel of the Sixth Regiment

End of a Quest

At daylight Jorge was awakened by the loud cries of birds and animals. He sat up in bed staring. Everything was strange. Then he remembered that this was the home of *Senhor* Manoel, the kind gentleman who had taken pity on him—a homeless coffee picker—and invited him to stay a few days.

Jorge smiled to himself as he recalled the din and clatter he had caused the night before when he had accidentally knocked over a parrot cage as he entered the gate to the *Senhor's* courtyard.

That parrot had reminded him of Chiquita, his own parrot that he was looking for. If he could find his friends, the Gomes family, who lived in this great bustling city of São Paulo, Chiquita would be with them. For Maria Gomes had promised to keep Chiquita until Jorge had finished his work on the Gomes coffee plantation in the hills of Brazil. He was glad he had found a home in which he could live while he hunted for the Gomes family.

Jorge dressed and hurried out to the courtyard. His new friend, *Senhor* Manoel, was there feeding his collection of rare Brazilian animals which he sold for pets.

"What a wonderful business!" thought Jorge, as he joined the animal dealer in the court. Never had he seen so many different kinds of animals.

Adapted from *Jorge's Journey* by Alice Desmond. By permission of The Macmillan Company, publishers.

There were cages of solemn monkeys, herons, and canaries, and crates and crates of blue and yellow parakeets. In a cage lay an armadillo, an odd, interesting little animal covered with thick, shell-like armor. The armadillo had a comical face, small eyes, long nose, and big ears.

There was a tapir, which resembled a pig and had a long trunklike snout. A howling monkey joined the bright-colored macaws in chattering a welcome to the visitor.

Before a pair of toucans Jorge stood enchanted. Wings, tails, and the upper part of their heads were black. The orange of their throats reached up to their eyes.

"Here, feed them, Jorge," *Senhor* Manoel said and gave him some bread.

The toucans caught the bread in their enormous beaks balanced in front of them like long, heavy noses. Throwing back their heads, they allowed the bread to slide down their throats.

Then Jorge approached a blue and yellow macaw sitting with great dignity on a perch. All the other animals had greeted the boy with cries and shrieks and grunts. But this ancient bird looked at him gravely and blinked its eyes.

The macaw reminded Jorge of his own Chiquita, grown old and wise. "And how do you feel today, *Senhor?*" he asked the solemn bird.

The macaw cocked its head, moved from one foot to another, then as if conferring a favor, bent its neck and offered its head to be caressed.

"Animals like you, Jorge," said *Senhor* Manoel with a smile. "I have had that macaw for a long time. He has never before taken to a stranger."

The macaw was the animal dealer's personal pet, just as Chiquita had been Jorge's. "It is not easy to part with the birds, once you've grown fond of them, is it?" asked the boy.

The *Senhor* threw up his hands. "I must make a living," he said. "I have far more animals here than I can sell, Jorge. My brother lives on the Amazon River. His Indian hunters collect these animals for me to sell, but few people come to buy. If I had two good strong legs, I would go from door to door and sell many more. Street peddling is the only way to conduct a business in Brazil.

"Brazilian women seldom go shopping," explained the animal dealer. "They like to stay at home all day long and let the merchants come to their doorsteps."

As proof of *Senhor* Manoel's words, there came from the street outside the cries of other vendors. Jorge ran to the gate. A peddler with a basket of towels, ribbons, and spools of cotton was clapping wooden sticks to announce his arrival. A whistle announced the cake-and-sweets man, a showcase of goodies on his head. Then came a musical cry of "*Verdura!*"—the vegetable hawker.

A bellow of "*Vassoura!*"—and the brush-and-broom fellow marched along, nearly lost under his baskets and woven chairs. Hardly had he passed till Jorge heard the high wail of "*Gallinha Gorda!*"—and a man shuffled past with baskets of live chickens swinging from a pole across his shoulders. He was followed by a fish-and-shrimps man calling, "*Peixe! Camarão!*"—an army of cats at his heels.

"*Abacaxi!*" sang a man with pineapple. Jorge was thinking how good a fresh pineapple would taste, when an idea popped into his head. Why not repay *Senhor* Manoel for his kindness by hawking his animals on the streets of São Paulo as these street vendors did their wares? This plan would have an added advantage, for everywhere he went he would ask for the Gomes family. Perhaps in this way he would find his friends and Chiquita.

When the boy suggested his plan to *Senhor* Manoel, the animal dealer looked doubtful. Jorge was very young to be entrusted with his precious menagerie. But it was an honest pair of eyes that pleaded, and finally *Senhor* Manoel consented. He helped Jorge load boxes and cages onto a pushcart. The smaller cages were strung on a long pole, which the boy balanced across his shoulders. With the *Senhor's* blessing, the new street hawker set out proudly with his noisy load.

Many a long block the boy covered along the streets that stretched from the center of the city out to the newer residential suburbs of São Paulo. These streets were broader than the older streets downtown, but their cobblestones were just as hard under Jorge's bare feet.

Sales were slow. At first he was too shy to shout as did the other vendors when they spied a housewife seated in a doorway. He hoped people would see his wares and offer to buy canaries or parrots or the lively baby leopard, playful as a kitten, that reached out its claws from the cage to scratch his cheek.

By studying the tricks of the ice-cream man, the flower man, the tin man, and the scissors grinder, Jorge began to acquire the art of street hawking.

He learned to engage in long-winded bargaining to the delight of Brazilian women, who, peering out of their windows, considered shopping of this kind the greatest of fun. By noon Jorge's load was lighter. He had sold a pair of canaries, a toucan, and a marmoset. When a stout housewife stopped him to ask the price of a honey bear, Jorge said quickly, "Sixty *milreis* to you, *Senhora*."

"Too much," cried the woman, shaking her gold earrings. "I'll give you forty—not a *milreis* more."

Stubbornly Jorge held out for sixty.

His customer pretended to be shocked. "For that little honey bear?" she said.

"The finest in Brazil," Jorge asserted, growing more and more sure of himself, "and for only sixty *milreis*. My master will beat me for giving it away."

"Your master must be a robber, like yourself."

The woman tossed her flounced skirt and turned aside. But Jorge saw a pleased gleam in her eyes. He waited. "What, *Senhora*, would be your idea of a fair price?" he asked sweetly.

When she admitted that she might go up just a bit, Jorge offered to sell for fifty. "I'm giving it away at that. Here, *Senhora*, hold this little fellow."

As his customer took the cuddly honey bear in her arms, Jorge knew he had won. She stroked its soft brown fur. "All right. Fifty," she sighed. And Jorge went off whistling.

Thus far Jorge had been mostly in the poorer parts of the city. But two days later the young vendor came to a broad and beautiful boulevard on one of São Paulo's hills. Marble houses as big as palaces lined the wide street, standing proudly behind high walls among shade trees on green lawns.

Beside Jorge stood an open gate from which a drive led up to a big white house.

"Didn't you see the sign, peddler? It says 'Use the Tradesmen's Entrance.'" A girl's voice stopped him as he turned into the drive.

The smile of the pretty, dark-haired girl lessened the harshness of her words.

Jorge did not know the meaning of *Tradesmen's Entrance.* He had never before been in the fashionable part of the city, where vendors must go to the kitchen entrance. But it did not matter now. The *Senhorita* was cooing over Jorge's lovebirds.

"What darlings!" she cried. "If they're not too expensive, I might buy them."

His lovebirds were the rarest in all Brazil, Jorge told her—yet he would let her have them for eighty *milreis.*

"No, that's too dear. Sixty is enough."

Jorge smiled. "Well, since it's you, I'll take off ten *milreis.*"

The girl laughed. "I'll be fair with you, too. We'll split the difference."

Then Jorge made bold to ask her a question: Did the young lady know the Gomes family?

"Of course I know them. That's their house next door." The *Senhorita* pointed across a hedge to a red-roofed, deep-verandaed white house standing back from the street on a wide lawn.

There stood a marble palace, far bigger and finer than the Gomes home on their coffee plantation. Staring at this house with its beautiful gardens, its flower beds, and ornamental shrubbery—the finest house Jorge had ever seen—he was too awed to speak. Then his eyes began to glisten. In that house was Chiquita, his parrot. Soon he would see her! Happy tears ran down his cheeks, for he realized that he had come to the end of his quest.

The Good River

The River Brings Food

All her life Lan Ying had lived by the river with her father and her mother and her three younger brothers. The Good River, they called it, because the river helped them in many ways; although its name was Yangtze, or Son of the Sea. In spring the river brought swelling tides down from the snow melting on the mountains where was its source.

Many an hour had Lan Ying wondered about that source as she sat watching the fish net for her father. The river ran so wide and deep and yellow here at her feet, below the great net spread out on bamboo poles, that it seemed impossible to believe that it was ever a small stream somewhere, tumbling down some rocky cliff, or running small and sluggish through some sandy desert. The only way she could realize it was to think of her baby brother, newly born three years ago. How small he was and how different from a man, and yet he, too, would grow out of that smallness, even as the river did, until it was so great it could be called truly a Son of the Sea.

Sitting by the fish net and waiting patiently until it was time to pull the rope that lifted it again, Lan Ying stared across the river. She could see the opposite shore only as a line of green. On misty mornings she could not see it at all, and she might have been sitting beside a muddy ocean.

Nearly all her days did Lan Ying sit here beside the river, and it had come now to mean something like a person to her. Her father was a farmer. He planted rice and wheat on his land that edged the river and ran back an acre or two to the hillock where the hamlet was—where they lived with half a dozen or so other families.

They were families of farmers like Lan Ying's father, but they had nets tended, too, by children or by grandfathers who had grown too old to work any more in the fields. Fish brought in the extra pennies they could spend for the various holidays and for incense to burn before the gods and for new clothes, sometimes, and besides all this, fish was good meat to eat, as well.

Lan Ying rose suddenly from the little bamboo stool where she sat and pulled with all her might at the rope. Up came the net slowly. Many a time there was nothing in it. Sometimes there were tiny fish that she had to scoop up with a long-handled dipper. Sometimes there was a big fish; once in several days or so. But there was none now; only a flash of minnows. She stooped and dipped them up. Her mother would pin each one by a sliver of bamboo to a bit of matting and dry them in the sun, and then they were salted and were very good to eat with morning rice. She lowered the net slowly and sat down once more.

Sometimes the days were very long, sitting here alone. She came just after her breakfast and sat until noon, when she could go home again. But she liked it better than the other things the children must do on the river farms. She liked it better than herding the buffalo and sitting astride its hard and hairy back all day as her second brother did. She liked it better than herding the ducks in the little inlets from the river as her eldest brother did.

Yes, she liked it because there was something very companionable about the moving river, about the boats that passed by her there, and the coveys of wild duck that floated down, great flocks of them, carried askew by the current.

There was always something to see. As for boats, there was every kind, from small fishing sculls to the junks with their painted eyes staring out at her from their bows. Once in many days low-set foreign craft came by and sometimes smoking steamers. She hated these, and the river hated them, too. It always swelled into angry waves and rocked back and forth as they passed.

Sometimes waves grew so high that the little fishing boats almost capsized, and the fishermen shouted loud curses at these foreign ships. Seeing the river angry like this, Lan Ying was angry, too, and ran to hold her net. Still, oftentimes, after these steamers passed there would be fish in her net, frightened there into commotion. Lan Ying, when she saw the silver bodies flapping in the bottom of the net, gave thanks to the river in her heart for sending her the big fish. It was a good river.

It brought them food from the land and meat from its waters, and to Lan Ying it came to mean something like a god. And staring out over it day after day, she could read its face and catch its mood for the day.

It was, indeed, the only book she could read, for she did not dream of going to school. In their hamlet there was no school, but she knew very well what a school was, because in the market town to which she and her mother went once a year there was a school. There were no pupils there on that day, but she had looked curiously into the empty room and had seen the empty seats and the tables and pictures hung on the wall. She had asked her mother, "What is it they do there?"

To this her mother said, "They learn the books."

Now Lan Ying had never seen a book, and so she asked with great curiosity, "Did you so learn when you were a child?"

"No, indeed!" said her mother loudly. "When did I ever have time for such stuff? I have had to work! It is only idle people who go to school—city people and such like. It is true my father talked of sending my eldest brother to school for the looks of the thing. He was a proud man, and he thought it would look well to have one of the family who could read and write. But when my brother had gone three days, he grew weary of so much sitting and begged to be sent no more and wept and pouted so that my father did not make him."

Lan Ying had pondered a while longer on all this and had asked again, "And do all city people learn books, even the girls?"

"I have heard it is the new fashion," said her mother, shifting her load of cotton thread she had spun and brought to the market to sell. "But what use it can be to a girl, I do not know. She has but the same things to do—to cook and sew and spin and tend the net—and when she is wed she does the same things over again. Books cannot help a woman." She went along more quickly then, for the load on her back grew heavy, and Lan Ying, seeing the dust on her new shoes, stooped to brush them and forgot about books.

Nor did she think about them any more when she went back to the river. No—books had nothing to do with her life here by the river. To lift the net and lower it again; to go home at evening and burn the grass fuel in the earthen oven upon which two iron caldrons were set and in which the rice was heated for their supper; and when they had eaten it with a bit of fish, to run with the bowls to the river's edge and rinse them there and back again before the night was too dark; to creep into bed and lie and listen to the soft rush of the river among its reeds—this was all her life of every day.

Only on a feast day or a market day did it differ, and then but for that one day. It was a quiet life thus spent, but a very safe one.

Sometimes Lan Ying heard her father say that in the market town where he went to sell his cabbages and grain, he had heard of famine to the north because there had been no rains, and he would add, "You see how fine it is to dwell beside a good river! Whether it rains or not is nothing to us, who have only to dip our buckets into the river and there is water for our fields. Why, this river of ours brings us the water from a hundred valleys, and rains or none is nothing to us."

When she heard this, Lan Ying thought that theirs was surely the best life in the world, and life in the best place, where everything came from the river. No—she would never move away from this river so long as she lived.

The River Changes

Yet there came a spring when the river changed. Who could have foreseen that the river would change? Year after year it had been the same until this year. The yellow water ran high against the clay banks. It curled in great wheels and tore at the earth, so that often a great clod would shudder and tear itself away from the land and sink. Then the river licked it up triumphantly.

Lan Ying's father came and moved the net away to an inlet's mouth, lest the bit of land upon which she sat might sink and bear her away. For the first time she was afraid of the river.

The time came for the river to go down. Surely by now those upper snows were melted, for it was summer and the winds were hot, and the river ought to lie quiet beneath the bright skies. But it did not lie quiet. No, it tore on as though fed by some secret and inexhaustible ocean. Boatmen who came down from the upper gorges, their craft buffeted by high rapids, told of torrents of rain, when the times for rain were past. The mountain streams and the lesser rivers all poured into the great river and kept it high and furious.

Lan Ying's father moved the net still farther up the inlet, and Lan Ying did not look over the river any more. For it was a cruel river now. All during the hot summer months it rose—each day a foot, two feet. It crept over the rice fields where the half-grown grain stood. It covered the grain and took away the hope of harvest. It swelled into the canals and streams and flooded their banks. Stories came of dikes falling; of great walls of water rushing over deep, rich valleys; of men and women and children engulfed and swept away.

Lan Ying's father moved the net far back. Again and again he moved it back, cursing the river and muttering, "This river of ours has gone mad!"

At last there came a day when he tied the handle that lifted the net to one of the many willow trees that grew at the edge of the threshing floor that was the dooryard to Lan Ying's home. Yes, the water had risen as high as this, and the little hamlet of a half dozen earthen houses, thatched with straw, was on an island surrounded by the yellow river.

Now they must all fish, for there could be no more farming.

It did not seem possible that the river could do more than this. At night Lan Ying could scarcely sleep, the water rushed so near the bed where she lay.

At first she could not believe that it would come nearer than this. But she saw the great fear in her father's eyes. It was true the water was rising nearer. Was it halfway across the threshing floor the day before yesterday? Yes, it was rising. In three days it would come into the house.

"We must all go to the innermost dike," said Lan Ying's father. "Once before in my father's father's time the river did this, and they had to go to the innermost dike, where the water does not come once in five generations. It is our curse that the time has fallen in our lifetime."

The youngest boy began to howl in a loud voice, for he was suddenly afraid. So long as the roof of the house was over them and its walls about them, it was only a strange thing to see the water everywhere and be like a ship perched above it. But when he heard they must live on a dike, he could not bear it. Lan Ying's tears came in sympathy, and she drew him to her and pressed his face against her breast.

"But may I take my black goat?" he sobbed.

"We will take all three goats," answered the father loudly, and when his wife said, "But how can we get them across all the water?" he said simply, "We must, for we will have them as food."

On that very day, then, he took the door from its wooden hinge, and lashed it together with the wooden beds and with the table. He tied the rude raft to a little scull he owned, and upon the raft climbed Lan Ying and her mother and the boys.

The buffalo they tied to a rope and let it swim, and the ducks and geese, also. But the goats were put upon the raft. Just as they left, the yellow dog came swimming after them, and Lan Ying cried, "Oh, my father, look! Lobo wants to come, too!"

But her father shook his head and rowed on. "No," he said, "Lobo must look after himself and seek his own food now, if he lives."

It seemed a cruel thing, and the eldest boy said, "I will give him half my bowl of rice!"

Then did the father shout as though he were angry, "Rice? What rice? Can a flood grow rice?"

The children were all silent then, not understanding, but afraid. They had never been without rice. At least the river had given them rice every year.

When at last Lobo grew weary and swam more and more slowly and was farther and farther behind, there came a time when they could not see his yellow head against the yellow water.

Across the miles of water they came at last to the inner dike. It stood like a ridge against the sky, and it seemed a heaven of safety. Land, good dry land! Lan Ying's father lashed his raft against a tree, and they climbed ashore. But there were many there before them. Along that ridge stood huts of mats and heaps of furniture—benches and tables and beds—and everywhere were people.

But even this inner dike had not stood against the water. It had been a hundred years since it had been so attacked by the river, and in many places people had forgotten there could ever come such an attack, and they had not kept the dike sound and whole. The river crashed its way through the weak places and swept behind into the good lands beyond the dike. The dike was then an island, and upon it clung these people from everywhere.

Not people only, but the wild beasts and the field rats and the snakes came to seek this bit of land, too. Where trees stood up out of the water, the snakes crawled up into them and hung there. At first the men battled with them and killed them and threw their dead bodies into the flood.

Through the summer and autumn did Lan Ying live here with her family. The basket of rice they had brought was long since eaten. The buffalo, too, they killed at last and ate, and Lan Ying saw her father go and sit alone by the water when he had killed the beast. When she went near him, he shouted at her surlily, and her mother called her and said in a whisper, "Do not go near him now. He is thinking how will he ever plow the land again with the buffalo gone."

"And how will he!" said Lan Ying, wondering.

It did not seem possible it was the Good River that had done all this. They had eaten the goats before the buffalo, and the little boy had not dared to complain when he saw his pet kid gone. No, there was the grim winter ahead of them.

No boats ever passed in these days. Lan Ying, sitting by habit and looking over the water, thought of all the boats that had once passed by in a day. It seemed they were the only people left in the world—a little handful of people perched upon a bit of land in the midst of a flood.

Sometimes the men talked together in faint tones. Not one of them had his old strong voice now. Each man talked as though he had been ill a long time. They talked of when the flood would abate and of what they would do to find new beasts to pull their plows. Lan Ying's father would say, "Well, I can harness myself to my plow, but what is the good of plowing when there is no seed to put into the ground?"

A Dream Is Fulfilled

Lan Ying began to dream of boats coming. Surely somewhere there were people left in the world who had grain. Might not boats come? Every day she sat looking earnestly over the waters. If a boat would come, she thought, at least there would be a living man in it, and they could call to him and say, "Save us who are starving. We have eaten nothing but raw shrimps for many days."

Even though he could do nothing, he might tell someone. A boat was the only hope. She began to pray to the river to send a boat. Every day she prayed, but no boat came. It is true that one day she saw on the horizon, where the yellow water was dark against the blue sky, the form of a small boat, but it came no nearer. Yet the sight heartened her. If there was *this* boat, might there not be others?

She said timidly to her father, "If a boat should come——"

But he did not let her finish. He said sadly, "Child, and who knows we are here? No, we are at the mercy of the river."

She said no more, but she still looked steadfastly over the water.

Then one day she saw, sharp and black against the sky, the shape of a boat. She watched it, saying nothing. She waited lest it fade away again as that other boat had faded. But this boat did not fade. It grew larger, clearer, more near.

At last it came near enough so that she could see in it two men. Then she ran to her father who lay sleeping. She shook him, panting a little, plucking at his hand to waken him. She was very faint and too weak to cry aloud.

"There is a boat coming," she gasped.

He rose, fumbling and staggering in his feebleness, and peered out over the water. It was true there was a boat. It was true it came near. He pulled off his blue coat and waved it weakly, and his bare ribs stood forth like a skeleton's. The men in the boat shouted. But not one among those on the land could answer, so feeble they were.

The boat came on. The men tied it to a tree and leaped up the bank. Lan Ying, staring at them, thought she had never seen such men as these—so fat, so well-fed. What were they saying?

"Yes, we have food for all! We have been searching for such as you! How long have you been here? Four months—heaven have pity! Here, eat this rice we brought cooked—no, not too fast—remember to eat just a little at first, then a little more!"

Lan Ying stared as they dashed into the boat and brought back rice gruel and loaves of wheaten bread.

She stretched out her hand without knowing what she did, and her breath came as fast as a spent animal's does. She did not know what she did except that she might have food at last—she must have food.

One of the men gave her a piece of the loaf he tore off. She sank her teeth into it, sitting down suddenly on the ground, forgetting everything except this bit of bread she held. So did they all, and so did they eat. When all had something, the two men stood and looked away as if they could not bear to see this famished eating. No one spoke.

No, not one voice spoke, until suddenly one man said, having eaten as much as he dared, "Look at this bread, how white it is! I have never seen wheat to make such white bread!"

Then they all looked, and it was true; the bread was white as snow.

One of the men from the boat spoke and said, "It is bread made from wheat grown in a foreign country. They have heard what the river did and have sent us this flour."

Then they all looked at the bits of bread that were left and murmured over it. How white and good it was! It seemed the very best bread they had ever eaten. Lan Ying's father looked up, and he said suddenly, "I should like a bit of this kind of wheat to plant in my land when the flood goes down. I have no seed."

The other man answered heartily, "You shall have it—you shall all have it!"

He said it easily as though he spoke to a child, for he did not know what it meant to these men who were farmers to be told they had seed to plant again.

But Lan Ying was a farmer's daughter, and she knew. She looked at her father and saw he had turned his head away and was smiling fixedly, but his eyes were full of tears. She felt the tears knot together in her throat, too, and she arose and went to one of the men and plucked at his sleeve.

He looked down at her and asked, "What is it, child?"

"The name—" she whispered, "what is the name of the country that has sent us this fair wheat?"

"America," he answered.

She crept away then and, unable to eat more, sat and held the precious bit of bread she had left and looked out over the water. She held it fast, although the man had promised them more. She felt suddenly faint, and her head was swimming. She would eat more bread when she could—only a little at a time, though, this good bread! She looked out over the river and feared it no more. Good or bad, they had bread again. She murmured to herself, "I must not forget the name—America!"

The World of Nature

Adventures of Chut

An Orphan Is Rescued

The big moon poked up through the trees along the backwash of Tom Henton's dam, its golden face reflected in the still waters. The moon was immense, and as it rose the landscape took on pale colors: gray and silver, lilac and faint green; a splendid silver shining that paled the stars.

A group of teal stirred in the growing radiance. A heron on a high, bare tree changed from one leg to the other. Innumerable elephant moths in quest of honey became gray, darting, velvet blurs instead of unseen, humming, brushing bodies. The faint scent of thin-petaled white spider lilies all along the waterway filled the Australian night like some invisible flood.

Presently, down a little dusty path through the bleached silver grass came a kangaroo family on its way to water, moving with tranquil undulation upon hoppers and hands.

The "old man" of the mob came first—an immense red warrior, velvet-furred in pale chestnut across back and thighs, tawny cream on chest and belly, weighing three hundred pounds, and standing seven feet when he rose upright on toes and tail to face an enemy. Sixteen wives and several small fat joeys followed. The does were much smaller than their lord, and, with the exception of one who was a beautiful dove-blue, all had fur of a brownish mouse-color. Their ears were large and quivering;

their eyes dark, deerlike, and sad. Yet in reality they were very happy creatures.

Seeking for shoots or seeds beside the path, they chittered conversationally and caught with tiny dark hands at each other's heavy, muscular tails which dragged in the dust. Soon they came out upon the sod by the dam and tasted the green grass. And here Chut took his first good look at the world.

He had lived in his mother's pouch for a long time, changing there from the semblance of a pink new-born mouse to a plump, small ten-pound creature of an exquisitely delicate loveliness. He was gentle, velvety, trembling-eared, with huge dark eyes and little dark clutching hands. Tonight, for the first time, he was dissatisfied with the warmth and security of the pouch. His tiny legs with their two well-polished ebony toenails rebelled at being neatly tucked above his head.

"*Chut!*" he called sharply. "*Chut! Chut!*"

His mother, the little blue doe, answered with a reproving "*Ch-ch!*" and drew shut her pouch-mouth. But Chut had glimpsed a world of magic brightness and keen new scents. He wanted to get out. He kicked; he clawed; he made strange commotions beneath his mother's cream-velvet pinafore until she opened the pouch with her horny-palmed hands and spoke sternly to him. Chut just reached up and caught her nose, touching his to it as if with a kiss.

Then the doe tucked her hands down against him, lifted him out, and set him upon the grass. He staggered clumsily, the moonlight glinting on the cowlick in the middle of his plump back and shining in pinkish-coral through his quivering ears. He clutched at his mother as he tried to steady himself upon his slender hoppers. He wobbled and fell with his legs sticking up absurdly.

In this posture the little joey felt more secure. In a moment he grasped at one of his hoppers as a baby might at its foot. He stretched out to his full length and grasped his toes again as he looked about him with bright, knowing eyes.

Had his mother been older, she would never have let him out while he was so little. But she was a very young doe, and he was her first baby. She sat up to her full height and snatched playfully at a passing elephant moth. Then she, too, lay down and rolled in the sand and across the short, fragrant carpet of green. Another doe came and rolled beside her. They grappled; they turned and twisted like playful children. They leaped up and played tag through the trees.

Suddenly a shot rang out—a jarring agony of sound—and the little blue doe lay still.

Chut was frightened. He wanted to go back into the despised pouch. He wanted food. He called and called, but his mother did not answer.

When presently he found her, he nibbled at her nose, but as he did so, something told him that she no longer lived. He did not know what had happened, but he knew that this was the end of warm softness and food, of nubbled noses and tender chittering. He sat up, holding his little hands as a small dog does when it begs. He chittered with all the energy of his baby voice. Then he slept, holding to the fur of his dead mother.

He woke with an overwhelming shock of panic. As he sat there unhappy and shelterless, the shadow of an eagle swept across him. The bird altered its course, poised, and then came hurtling toward the furred baby in the grass. It clutched at Chut, leaving a knifelike cut across the russet fur, missed his hold, and rocketed up again.

Chut fled wobblingly. The grass tripped him; the barbed leaf edges cut his skin across the back and thighs; the twigs poked him in the stomach. He jumped at shadows and twittered with fear at the sound of the wind. On and on he traveled, making tiny hopper-marks in the dust as he went.

Then Chut stumbled up a dusty path. It smelled of kangaroos! Instinct told him that the path led to the dam, and he took it. The day faded through the long afternoon, and dusk had come before he scented the dam. His sides were pinched with thirst, and his fur was draggled, but he stumbled on.

Led by blind instinct, Chut, who had never tasted water, hurried toward it. But at the margin he did not know what to do. He was terribly thirsty, but he had never drunk anything except milk, and this he had drunk lying flat upon his back in his mother's pouch.

Instinct told him that the water might soothe the torture of his thirst, but he had not learned to stoop and drink. Instead, after a wary look about, he placed his little hands on the sod, lowered his head between them, and turned a somersault. Once on his back, his hands reached up, but no food and drink awaited them. He called. There was only silence. So he crept away into the shadows.

As he did so, a voice close by said, "Jove!" And a light flashed into the eyes of the trembling joey.

In an instant Chut was surrounded by some men. Tom Henton, who had found Chut, seemed pleased.

"He's a little beauty," said Tom. "I'm going to take him home to my wife." He held Chut up by the scruff of the neck and poked him with a finger. Then the man looked puzzled. "He has a lot of nasty scratches, poor little nipper! I guess he belongs to that dead doe we found."

The other men pressed around. "Let's take him and give him a drink," said one.

Gathering up their things, they moved on, Chut hanging limp and helpless under Henton's arm.

At the camp back over a ridge there was discussion as to how the baby should be fed. One man said, "He won't drink unless he's upside down." So they got a pair of trousers, tied a knot in one leg and hung the trousers on a tree by the backstrap. Then they held Chut up before it. He looked at it as if he were puzzled.

"Better let him get in himself," said Tom, and he gave Chut a push. It worked. Instinctively Chut grasped the edge of the trousers, lowered his head, and, bracing his hoppers against the man's stomach, turned an expert somersault into the depths of the leg.

Once again he was swinging as a little kangaroo should swing. He was enclosed, safe. He gave a feeble chitter.

One of the men stepped forward and presented him with the end of a bit of rubber tube whose other end was in a tin of milk. Chut sucked. Milk was in his mouth. He gave little ticking sounds of bliss, and, still drinking, he fell asleep in the warm embrace of the trouser leg.

Chut Is Adopted

Chut's wounds healed. The men were good to him. He learned the new smells of fire smoke and potatoes roasting in ashes; the mellow smell of coffee and the sharp tang of tea; the odors of sizzling bacon and broiling chops; tobacco smoke by a campfire under the stars; the sneeziness of raw flour and the smell of men. He learned that fire was hot and kerosene nasty. His ears attuned themselves to many new sounds. Soon the clatter of plates, loud jests and louder laughter, galloping of horses, and clanging music of horse bells ceased to frighten him.

When, after a month's work on the farthest part of the great ranch, Tom Henton returned to his home, Chut went with him—swinging securely in one leg of the old trousers attached to the man's saddle. Only when the horse's trotting caused the trouser leg to bounce, did he chitter in protest. Arriving at the tree-set homestead, Tom Henton was met by his young wife.

"I've brought you a baby," Tom said, untying the trousers from the pommel of the saddle and holding them out.

She took the bulging garment hesitatingly as the man dismounted and stood beside her.

"Oh, the darling!" she said. "He's so *little*, so *soft!* What shall we call him?"

Squeezed between the big man and his wife, Chut gave a loud cry, "Chut! Chut! *Chut-ch-ch-ch!*"

So he was called "Chut." During the day he followed Mrs. Henton about like a little dog. He slept in the trousers, which swung from a tree, and this garment was referred to as "Chut's pants."

He would come whenever the woman called him and somersault neatly into her lap as she sat on the steps. There, lying on his back, he took his supper to the accompaniment of tiny kicks of pleasure. Soon he was allowed to use a baby's bottle.

There was soft green grass in which he might roll, and many pepper trees beneath which to play. His world was satisfactory—save for one thing. At the homestead was a fat and bumptious lamb named William Mutton. To William had belonged the baby's bottle before Chut took it over, and to see Chut using it seemed to enrage William.

Chut saw in the greedy lamb a possible playfellow. So, poised upon the arch of his lower tail and the tips of his toes, Chut gave a few stiff, bouncing side-hops—a kangaroo's invitation to play.

"Chut-chut!" he barked sociably.

William's gaze dropped to Chut's round stomach, and then he charged. His round, woolly head met Chut's silk-furred stomach with a resounding *plop*.

Chut grunted and fell, kicking, while William went on without even looking back.

After that the lamb seemed to take care to make the kangaroo's life wretched. He knocked Chut down every time he had a chance. He learned his victim's weaknesses and took advantage of them.

If Chut was asleep in the sun by the kitchen door, it was only necessary for William Mutton to sneak up on him and give a loud "Baa" to bring Chut to his feet in the most convenient position to be butted into the ash pit.

He was also fond of waiting near the pepper trees for the kangaroo to go hopping past in one of his games—and then charging out and catching him in mid-hop. Still, the "stomach-butt" seemed to be his favorite.

Persistent persecution will, of course, develop wariness in the most trusting creature, and as Chut grew older, he became harder to catch. On the other hand, if William's butts became less frequent, they became harder; for William was a particularly hefty young sheep and in addition he was growing horns—only nubby buds as yet, but very uncomfortable when applied to Chut's body.

About the time that Chut outgrew his trouser leg, Tom Henton brought in two little does that were just a trifle smaller than Chut had been when he had been captured. Mrs. Henton christened them Zodie and Blue Baby, and Chut promptly adopted them both. He would often sit chittering and whispering to them when they were in their sleeping bags. He nosed them and pulled at their ears in a manly, masterful way.

When they were old enough to come out to play, he romped with them and at times put his little arms round both their necks so that the three small heads were drawn close together. Often he led them on little gallops beneath the trees.

Of the two young does, Blue Baby was his darling. Blue Baby was furred to an exquisite shade of smoke-blue, brighter than the bluest of squirrel fur, and her stomach and chest were clear cream-velvet. Her slender little tail, hoppers, and hands were dark; her eyes, dark and dewy-soft. But for some reason she was slightly lame.

She could travel on her hoppers and hands, but when she tried to hop in an upright position, she stumbled and fell. Hence she was always left behind in the races. Chut would circle back for her as though he did not want her to be left out. He seemed to feel responsible for her.

When she, too, outgrew the trousers, he slept with one arm about her neck, their postures like those of sleeping children.

Chut was growing miraculously fast now, and his chubbiness had gone from him. He was strong and erect, with muscles swelling deeply beneath the skin of his forearms and back. When he drew himself up, he was almost as tall as Mrs. Henton. But at her call his great body still somersaulted into her lap, and, when he could entice her into giving it to him, he still adored his bottle. He still lay on his back in the sun and played with his toes, and he was still very fond of the pair of trousers which had been his foster mother.

After the manner of kangaroos, he was exceedingly curious. He wanted to see everything. He tasted everything and loved bread and sugar.

The three kangaroos often came begging to the dinner table for pieces of sugared bread, which they had been taught to carry outside before eating.

One day, just as they had gotten their sweetened bread and carried it out beneath a big pepper tree, the bullying Mutton spied them. Chut and Zodie hopped out of the way, but Blue Baby was clumsy and dropped her bread. William, who had always attacked Chut, suddenly turned on Blue Baby. With an evil "Baa" he charged her—sending her sprawling on the grass, chittering with fright.

Chut dropped his bread and drew himself up with a few bouncing steps.

"Chut," he cried harshly. "Chut! Chut! *Chut!*"

"Baa-aa," answered William. Next moment he was grabbed, and one of Chut's hind toes kicked him expertly in the side, tearing out a hunk of wool as it ripped downward.

Like most bullies, William was a coward. Bleating, he leaped for safety. The swimming pool lay before them, and at its edge William tried to wheel, but this was fatal.

A kangaroo cannot kick well unless it embraces the thing it is kicking, and William's leap brought him to the perfect height for Chut's best attentions. Chut clutched the sheep's neck, and with chuts and nickers of rage he delivered a whirlwind of kicks straight to his victim's stomach. When Chut released his hold, William Mutton made a frantic leap—right into the pool!

He emerged a sadder and a wiser sheep, to whom a kangaroo's stomach was, forever after, sacred.

Enchanted Island

Douglas Spencer had been standing at the rail of the *Falcon* watching Captain Jensen bring the two-masted schooner into Academy Bay, when his father told him the exciting news. He, Doug Spencer, was to go ashore on Indefatigable Island on a collecting trip with his scientist-cousin, Randall!

"While I hunt about in the waters near here for those rare fish I'm to get for the aquarium in San Francisco," Mr. Spencer said, "you and Randall have a chance to explore Indefatigable. It's said to be enchanted, you know."

All during their trip Randall had talked of the specimens he hoped to collect for the museum, once they reached the Galápagos group of islands. Douglas had listened enviously—and now he was going along!

Early next morning the two boys carefully loaded the dory with their equipment and sufficient water for a five-day camping trip and set out from the *Falcon* for Indefatigable Island, a half mile away.

A short time later Randall and Douglas rowed up to the island and, helped by a friendly fisherman, made the dory fast to the stout wharf. Learning that the boys were to camp on the island, the man offered them rooms in his home and helped carry their things up to their new quarters.

"I'll have a look around," Randall said, when everything had been brought up from the dory. He went out, leaving Doug to stow away their gear.

His task finished, Doug sat down to await his cousin's return. One hour passed—then two—and still no Randall. Douglas finally tired of waiting. He put into his knapsack the lunch he had brought from the ship, his first-aid kit, and some matches. He attached his sheath knife, his scout hatchet, and a canteen of water to his belt. Then scribbling a note to Randall, he slung the knapsack over his shoulder and set off along the deserted beach.

It was an hour later when Randall found the note:

> Couldn't wait any longer. Have gone for a hike. Think I'll take a look at the wreck we passed below here. Back soon—Doug.

Knowing how dangerous it was to wander alone on these islands, Randall was alarmed. He shouldn't have loitered so long, since he was responsible for his cousin. Making sure his canteen was full of water, he set out in the direction Doug had taken.

Douglas, meanwhile, kept to the shore as much as he could, trying to locate the wreck. It couldn't be far, he thought, for it seemed to be only a few minutes from the time he had first seen it until the *Falcon* moved into Academy Bay.

"What crazy plants there are on this island," he said to himself, squinting at a giant cactus rearing directly out of the lava. Apparently these plants didn't need soil, but flourished on bare rock.

Balancing himself for just a moment before jumping across a chasm, Doug thought that this was really an awful place. There wasn't a thing enchanting about it. He knew now what was meant in stories that spoke of one's being shipwrecked on a desert island. When he had read about it, he had imagined an island with waving palms and plenty of coconuts to eat and a rippling stream of water purling over the rocks. He was glad he was going just for a hike and would be back safely for dinner.

Picking his way gingerly along the rough lava, he suddenly saw a large black iguana rise up in front of him. The animal appeared so suddenly that it seemed to spring out of the rock itself. It was not only the suddenness of its appearance that startled Douglas, but its immense size. About four feet long from the tip of its nose to the end of its tail, its whole length was made ferocious looking by a long series of spines which ran like a dragon's mane along the back. The body was thick and heavy and spotted with green and black and daubs of orange. The scaly feet ended in five fingers, which gave the grotesque appearance of a monster's hands.

Douglas stared, his mouth open with surprise. The iguana stood still on a protruding shelf of the volcanic rock and gave him a fierce glare. Poised and unmoving, it looked at Douglas attentively. Then its great head began to shake up and down, and its ugly mouth opened, showing rows of sharp teeth looking like bits of white coral.

Douglas pulled his hatchet out of its sheath and held it tightly in his hand. Into his mind sprang a remembrance of some story he had read of explorers discovering a lost world which was still inhabited by dinosaurs. That was what he felt like—someone in a lost world suddenly faced with dinosaurs or dragons. Yet he knew this was only a lizard. Taking a step forward, he watched the iguana closely, ready to defend himself if necessary.

As Doug moved, the iguana ran quickly to the water and plunged in. The waves broke over the black lava, making it as shiny as wet coal. A short way out from the shore were rocks covered with seaweed. Suddenly the big iguana came up from below the surface of the water and swam to the rocks. Its feet were held close to its body, but its long tail moved strongly from side to side, propelling it rapidly through the water. Aided by its claws the iguana climbed up onto the seaweed-covered rocks, where after resting a moment it began to eat. When Douglas saw the ferocious-looking animal calmly munching seaweed, he laughed. Scared of the vegetarian lizard!

His momentary fright over, Douglas stood there watching the iguana crop the seaweed. Waves occasionally rose over the rocks, and he expected to see the iguana washed off, but after each wave it was still there, holding tight and eating.

In a few minutes Doug started on. He climbed around the side of a hill that extended to the sea and came upon thousands of these same iguanas, some black, some with orange spots of all shapes and sizes. As the boy approached, they stopped basking in the sun and dashed for the sea.

Emboldened by his success with the lone iguana, Douglas went on toward them. They ran like leaves blown over the ground, some of the little fellows taking refuge in the crannies of the rocks to escape this two-footed monster who pursued them. Douglas noticed that the smaller ones refused to enter the sea, but that the larger ones didn't mind the water.

After driving off the thousands of iguanas, Douglas soon grew tired. His feet had begun to hurt from constant contact with the sharp, rough lava, and he sat down a moment to rest. He could feel through his shoes the hard outlines of the rocks.

As he sat, he heard a snorting and scraping that seemed to come from the other side of the rock he rested on.

He turned around and peered anxiously over. In a level spot between the rocks, two great crested male iguanas were locked in combat. Lying close to the ground they put their heads together, the pyramid-like spikes meshing in their two heads like gears of a machine. Thus locked, they were pushing each other back and forth.

The earth flew; the combatants snorted; while a little farther away, watching from a pile of rocks that looked over the arena, a great bevy of female iguanas stared at them. Douglas wondered what the outcome would be. Would they fight to the death the way deer did when they fought? Apparently not, for time was called occasionally, and the iguanas would withdraw from the struggle to wipe their noses on some rocks, for they pushed so hard that blood was flowing from their nostrils as well as from their mouths.

Separated, they would nod their heads up and down and open their mouths savagely. Then they moved up to each other again, always nodding and snorting, until once more they were locked in combat. As the battle showed no signs of ending, Douglas decided to go on.

He continued to walk along the shore toward the wreck, but new things constantly drew his attention. It was well past noon when he decided suddenly that he was hungry. He reached into his knapsack and took out some sandwiches. When he had finished them, he drank heavily from the canteen.

"I guess I shouldn't drink so much," he said to himself, "but I'll be home soon, and at the harbor we have plenty." He took another drink.

As he sat there looking out over the water, he decided that it would be nice to soak his smarting feet. He walked carefully over the sharp stones to a little beach of white sand. There, sitting on a rock, he pulled off his shoes and dangled his feet in the water. Gazing at the Pacific, he noticed how the blue sky and water were almost the same color. The entire seascape seemed empty and quiet. But on the beach it was different.

Whole platoons of red crabs ran along the shore, their bodies as big around as saucers. Like the iguanas, they were sunning themselves. Some were walking alongshore, feeding on the jetsam of the beach. Their tireless pincers were constantly going up and down as they reached into the sand and put things into their mouths.

When one crab bumped another, they would fight. Holding their pincers in front of their bodies and using them as if they were boxing gloves, the crabs sparred back and forth. One would swing out and crash his pincer against the other's head. Back would come the pincer of the other. One of them lost his pincer, and there it lay in the sand, opening and closing even though it no longer had any contact with its owner. The crab who had lost his pincer left the fight and ran for the sea.

Suddenly the crabs stopped their play as if they all had been enchanted and turned to stone. Some held their pincers in mid-air. Their telescopic eyes rose to their full height, and very slowly the crabs began to retreat. What was happening? They must be afraid of something.

Just then, around the corner of a rock stalked a small powder-blue heron. About ten inches high and armed with a long stiletto-like beak, it moved slowly toward a crab. Quickly it sprang—and missed. Before the bird could turn, the crab had dashed for safety, slipping between the rocks.

The heron ran angrily up to the rocks and pecked at the crab, but the crab flattened out and backed further into the crevice. Seeing no hope of capturing that meal, the heron turned on the others. All the crabs retreated in good order, without hurry, but little by little they moved toward the rocks away from the beach. Every forward move of the heron brought a backward move by the crabs. Again the heron singled out a retreating crab for special attention and began stalking it.

Slowly the eight legs of the crab felt for a foothold on the lava rocks. The heron poised and flew at it. Equally agile, the crab leaped backward into the rocks. Again outwitted, the heron raised his crest in anger and flew off down the beach. Free of their enemy, the crabs came slowly out of hiding and resumed their play.

Douglas put on his shoes and started off again along the shore. The rocks became larger and their surfaces sharper, and the toes of his tennis shoes were soon cut as if by a jagged instrument. In full glare of the sun the island seemed to become very quiet. Everything seemed more parched than it had been that morning. Two black finches, looking like English sparrows with big beaks, were struggling over a pad of cactus from which they were trying to squeeze a few drops of moisture.

Douglas recalled a description of these islands from a book: "No voice, no low, no howl is heard. The chief sound of life here is a hiss."

From the top of an unusually tall mound of rock, he stood up to survey the interior of the island. Back of the lava-rock coast was a sandy area where the cactus began. Behind that was a slight rise of ground which seemed to have some trees.

About a half mile back in the interior, Douglas saw a large lagoon, and toward it he made his way, believing that he might find some earth on which walking would be less painful. He began to wonder how much farther he had to go to find the wreck. Coming to the edge of the lagoon, he noticed the coarse soil. The trees, although not high, did afford some shade. As he walked along, each step cushioned in deep soil, he gave a sigh of relief, for the walking was much better. But he noted that the vegetation had a curious sameness, and that the landscape had no juts of rock or groups of trees to guide him.

Halfway around the lagoon, Doug saw some birds wading in the water. As he came closer, they waded faster—broke into a quick walk, then into a run, and then were off in flight. After flying around the lagoon a few times, they settled near the edge again. Moving up more cautiously, Doug parted the plants that lined the shore and peered through.

He saw that the birds gathered close to some strange conical mounds apparently made of mud. As he stared, Douglas realized that the birds were flamingos. There was no mistaking them, for he had seen pictures of them. They were about three or four feet high, with pink and white feathers and curious beaks. Their long necks curved down to the water, where they searched for food.

Looking again at the mounds, Douglas could hardly believe his eyes. In the center of each mound was a single egg. And not a mother was on her nest!

"The eggs will get cold," he thought.

The flamingos walked slowly as if they sensed some danger. A mother flamingo approached her nest and put a webbed foot on the side of the mound, which rose about twelve inches from the ground. Then she shook her other foot as if to free it from water and dirt. After shaking one leg, the bird shook the other and poised for a moment on the edge like a diver at the end of a diving board about to make a back dive. Then plump down on the egg the mother lowered herself. Douglas wondered how the egg could stand such rough treatment.

Suddenly the flamingo gave a start and, raising herself, left the nest. She turned the egg over with her beak and tapped it sharply. "What can she be doing?" Douglas wondered as the flamingo tapped the egg again and broke a bit off. Douglas watched carefully while the mother bird broke off another piece. From within the egg came a faint chirp as the shell cracked a bit more from the contortions of the bird inside.

The mother flamingo stepped back, watching. She walked past the others who were now sitting on the eggs, strutting up and down as if to say, "There you are, old long-necks. *My* little one is coming first."

The others were jealous, Douglas decided, for they pecked at the proud mother when she came too near.

The small flamingo now began to break out of the egg, assisted by its mother's beak. Finally it gave a harder shake, and the last of the shell came off.

"Well, you got out of that!" Douglas said aloud. As he moved to go, the birds were startled, and with a great cackling and fuss they left their nests.

"I must have been sitting a long time watching those birds," Douglas said to himself. He looked at the sun. It was sinking, and realization of his situation came to him. Night was almost here.

He knew that it grows dark very quickly in the tropics—almost directly after sunset. He must hurry to get back to the harbor before night.

Douglas began to retrace his steps. Suddenly he knew that he was not sure which way he had come. At the same time he realized that he could never cross those chasms that split the rocks except by daylight. At the thought he began to feel panicky. Fear gripped him, and he could feel a cold shiver run over his back, spreading throughout his whole body. What a fool he had been!

He began to talk out loud to himself to calm his quickly beating heart. "What have you to be afraid of?" he admonished himself sternly. "There are only lizards and birds here. Remember what Father said—*people get lost only if they become panicky.* If I can't make it tonight, I can get back sometime tomorrow morning."

He felt better at that and began to gather fuel to build a fire. All the trees were dry and burned easily. He gathered a great deal of wood, for the night would be chilly. Already it was colder. The sun had disappeared, and the last faint rays of day lighted the sky. Things became gray and indistinct. The roar of the sea kept up a steady pounding in his ears as the fire leaped and crackled.

Reaching into his knapsack, Douglas took out the lone sandwich and the piece of chocolate saved from lunch. He wondered how much water he had. Raising the canteen, he swallowed what was left. Now he was sorry he had drunk so much at lunch.

The fire did make things seem more cheerful, but as the daylight faded, the shadows from the flames took on weird, flickering shapes. Douglas drew closer to the fire, no longer a bold explorer, but a tired, frightened boy.

Sitting huddled beside the fire, Doug tried not to listen to the strange night noises. Above the sound of the waves of the sea he thought he heard animals moving about. Once or twice he thought he heard voices, but though he called he got no reply. Finally he was positive he heard the scrabbling of uncertain footsteps in the dark. He took out his hatchet, gripping it tightly. Yes, he did hear footsteps and someone stumbling through the brush.

He raised himself, ready for he knew not what.

"Doug—are you all right?"

"Randall," Douglas shouted, going to meet him.

"Are you all right, Doug? What happened?"

"I was interested in things and forgot the time, and then the sun went down so fast I couldn't get back," blurted Douglas all in one breath.

"There's no sense in trying to get back tonight," Randall advised. "We might as well sit by the fire and try to get some sleep. It's too dangerous walking in the dark."

Douglas agreed and began to relate the day's events. Long before he had finished, he had fallen asleep. His first day as an explorer was over.

Sharp Wits in Bronze Armor

It was not until the moon floated above the pine trees that a procession of large, powerful brown ants filed out of their nest. The moonlight gave such metallic luster to their bodies that they appeared to be dressed in bronze armor.

At the tip end of their bodies were long spears that stabbed and poisoned at the same time, and on either side of their mouths were powerful cutting tools that gave them a grim and terrible look.

Heading the army was the scout ant. After her poured the rest of the hungry horde, racing across the grass-blade bridges. Every ant appeared to know where it was bound and what it was to do, just as if the scout were issuing orders to them through a megaphone. So it was not long before they came to an orange grove and to the beehive that the scout had discovered that very morning. The scout and her army now began skirting round the base of the beehive in search of a crack. A moment later they found one, a mere thread of a crack, but large enough for the honey smell to pour out in warm, perfumed waves.

At once the ants fell to work, scraping and chiseling with their gnashing jaws. The larger the crack grew, the louder did the orange-blossom honey shout to their noses.

The bees inside heard nothing, for they had worked all day, and most of them were sleeping, unaware of the danger that was steadily drawing closer to their hive.

When the crack had been sufficiently enlarged, the first ant to enter was the scout herself. After her crept her followers. Once inside the hive, the ants found that the beehive was very differently planned from the narrow corridors of their own nests.

Here the roof rose above their heads until it was lost to sight in the shadows, while all the space beneath was filled with gigantic frames on which were stretched the honeycombs. Most of the honeycomb cells were sealed by lids of wax, but beyond these were thousands of open cells filled with rich yellow honey.

Put yourself in the place of a hungry ant and try to imagine what that meant: the sweetest food in the world, perfumed with the most enticing scent—masses, oceans, mountains, worlds of it!

This was the delightful part of the sight that met the eyes of the ant army as they peered about at the vast walls of sweetness surrounding them. But the unpleasant part was alarming enough to frighten even a famished ant, for sleeping in clusters on the combs were uncounted numbers of huge creatures in striped furry coats. The size of these creatures would make the coming fight seem about as uneven a battle as if an army of tomcats tried to rout a herd of buffalo. Yet the ants were equal to the occasion, for they knew the only way in the world that a bee can be made helpless and defeated by an ant.

The advance guard of the ant army now clustered on the floor of the hive, talking things over with their feelers. And all the time they talked, they were tantalized by the enchanting odor of honey.

The wonder is that the ants resisted the desire to plunge instantly into those vats of amber liquid and die of sweetness. But ant armies must follow commands just as do the armies of men.

So the ants awaited the orders that were to give the ant word "Charge!" But even when it came, the ants moved forward as stealthily as a black shadow smudges across the light, without making a sound on the wax walls of the frames. In this way they were able to reach quite a distance up the side of the nearest comb before the sleeping bees noticed them. For bees trust the sentries that they keep on guard and go to sleep as calmly as you would if you were quite sure that a squad of policemen was on duty, faithfully patrolling the street in front of your house.

Closer and closer crept the ants. All was going well with them until a drone, hanging on the outside of a bee cluster, moved in his sleep. Perhaps he had a bad bee-dream. However that may be, the drone turned his head and, looking down the comb, saw a thick, dark wave that was lapping nearer and nearer to him every moment. The drone rubbed his eyes with his paws and looked again.

The dark wave was coming closer. On its rim the drone could see the feelers of the ants thrashing the air in mad excitement! Now he could plainly distinguish the faces below the feelers, with their cutlass jaws that moved continually in a terrifying chewing motion.

The drone was frightened, but he did not advance to meet the enemy—not he! What he did was to wake up his nearest sister and communicate the dreadful news to her. Then he rushed to a place of safety on the very tiptop of the hive, while his sister charged down the comb, her wings and air holes shrilling the battle hymn of the bees.

She was really a majestic sight—her wings roaring, eyes blazing, and her sting dripping drops of strong-smelling poison. But menacing as her figure was, the dark wave never faltered. On it came. It reached her. It lapped about her. Then she began the tactics of bees attacked by ants. She kicked wildly with all her six legs.

She kicked and kicked and kicked, flinging ants into the air about her like a shower of rockets! But it was useless. In an instant she was buried under a mass of attackers who were sawing through her wings and pulling off her legs. She fought bravely, but she had no chance to escape. A moment more of horror, and she fell to the floor, far below the honeycombs, crippled and useless.

The ants had done the one and only thing that they could do to defeat a creature so much more powerful than themselves—the thing that ants have been doing ever since the first small ant tackled the problem of the first large bee.

Though the drone's brave sister was lost—as far as her ability to fight was concerned—she kept up the shrill trumpeting that had, by this time, waked the whole hive. And not one of them buzzed more defiantly than the drone who had crawled up on the roof out of danger. In his buzzing bee-language he continued to warn his sisters that something was happening.

Something was—and bees rushed to the defense from every part of the hive. They kicked! They churned the ants with their feet! Brown ants shot through the air like bits from an explosion.

But every ant who went up came down again not much the worse for the kicking, and the advance continued until the bees were struggling beneath a squirming sea of enemies. They fought valiantly enough, but they could not kick if they had no legs.

The uproar in the hive had now grown deafening. The ants were beginning to pay for their appetites with their lives. Thousands of them were crushed; thousands were torn to pieces. Yet for every one who fell, ten came to take her place; for now the endless procession from the nest was not only marching in at the open crack, but straight through the front door of the hive as well. Bees were piled high—a mangled mass of living insects who could neither crawl nor fly.

Hours passed. The moon shrank and began to slide down among the stars toward the earth again, and still the battle of the bees and ants raged on. Now the last frame was covered by the ants. It was on this spot that the poor queen was crouched, hidden under a mass of her ladies-in-waiting ready to sacrifice their lives for her when the time came. She had been wakened by a noise that had begun as a far-off hum, but which had soon grown to the roar of battle. Now she continued to lie still under the pile of her ladies-in-waiting until the din should subside.

More and more frantic grew the bees as they were steadily driven backward by the advancing waves of ants. So the battle continued. Beautiful combs were clawed open. Honey dripped everywhere, running in slow, shining rivers down the frames, gluing dead bees and their enemies in one sticky mass.

Now a dreadful moment struck for the battling bees. The queen was being attacked! From every side the ants leaped upon her. Great cutlasses sank into the royal body from a dozen places at once. The queen, who had never known a moment's unkindness, felt her legs being ripped from her body. Her wings were now draggled ribbons of lace, never again to lift her skyward. She called for help, and her voice rose high and shrill above the din of battle. Her loyal subjects, hearing it, were full of panic. Then her cries stopped short. And with that silence, dreadful news swept through the hive. Every bee knew that the queen was dead!

The queen was dead—and it seemed as if the hive had suddenly been stripped of some spirit of courage, some impulse of work, some urge to live. One by one her daughters gave up. Her sons had never fought at all. And there stood the hive in the moonlight, a sacked city, with the dead lying in heaps in its narrow streets. Yet no newspaper carried the news next morning that a city had been destroyed, that a queen had been murdered, and that a host of faithful, honest workers was forever lost.

The Shining Gateway

At last, after heavy rains, Willow Creek began to clear, and Flash was venturing home. The great rainbow trout had left the river at dusk the day before and now, with six miles of winding creek behind him, he lay at sunrise in a reach of water just below a deep pool. The pool was the feeding place where for many summers he had been the undisputed ruler.

But a tragic change had come to Willow Creek. No longer did clear cold water seep into it from feeder streams through miles of forest floor. The big trees had been cut, the undergrowth uprooted, and fire had done the rest. These improper logging methods had changed the very nature of Willow Creek. Erosion had set in, and after every big rain the water was charged with silt. Many of Willow Creek's superb rainbow and cutthroat trout had been driven out, and others had been left stranded when the level of the stream suddenly dropped.

Uncontrolled spring floods had played havoc with the eggs and fry of the survivors. But silver-flanked Flash always returned to Willow Creek. For in spite of the tragic changes that had taken place along the miles of his underwater kingdom, Flash had always found food in the pool below the falls.

The light breeze of that June morning touched the leaves of overhanging willows, and golden sunlight dappled the smooth water above the big trout. A caterpillar, shaken by the breeze from a twig tip, fell to the surface with a soft plop. There was a sudden swirl, and an instant later Flash nosed up the coiling eddy again. The glint of his closing gill covers told that the tasty bite had not been missed.

At the head of the reach a moth was whirling on the surface with bedraggled wings. A quick tail-thrust, and the rainbow trout shot ahead to snatch it under. Only for a moment did Flash linger in the fast water; then, surging grandly up the ripple, he pressed on, for the call of the home pool was strong upon him. Something seemed to tell the giant trout that there would be abundant feeding in his old lurking place—the falls pool.

That morning Ron Lincoln left the ranch house and hurried toward the falls. Ron was anxious. This was the fifth day since the freshet, and Flash, the trout he had fed for two summers, had not returned. Stopping where black ants swarmed on a log, he broke open the rotten wood and scooped a handful of the plump white egg-clusters into the rusty tin can he carried.

As he neared the creek he stepped cautiously. Below the small falls over which the water churned, Ron crouched behind a screen of willows fringing the bank. He tossed the ant eggs upstream, turned quickly, lifted a trap door in the ground and eased himself down into a pit no wider than a big packing case.

Ron reached up and slid the door into place, so that no light from above came into this observation post he had built. Beyond the wide sheet of window glass set in a concrete wall against the riverbank, the pebbly bottom faded into cloudy, shimmering shadows.

Then against the glass window a silver picture sprang to life. Out of the bubbles upstream, Ron saw the first clump of ant eggs come drifting past. A few yearling trout drove at them, one darting against the glass in its lusty eagerness. As a big school of salmon fingerlings rushed in, a savage squawfish shot forward and tried to seize one. But Flash, the superb ruler that Ron had loved to watch, did not appear.

During the low water of late winter when Ron had built his one-man marine studio, he had thought of it mainly as a hobby. Gradually the thrill and strange beauty of this underwater world had gripped him. For Ron had been born with the love of wild things in his heart, and this crude marine studio, copied from some magazine pictures of a tropical aquarium, had become a shining gateway to adventure. Here his exploring mind had let him glimpse a new and exciting world.

Ron, crouching with his face to the window, sat up suddenly. From somewhere he heard a muffled shout. He pushed back the trap door and looked out to find his younger brother coming toward him. Jimmie, his eyes bright with excitement, had Ron's box camera under his arm. Pulling a newspaper from the pocket of his overalls, he thrust it at Ron.

"Talk about luck!" he cried. "Soon as I read it I came a-running. The Tourist Bureau in town is giving fifty dollars for the best—but here, you read it!"

Ron scanned the startling announcement in the newspaper Jimmie had brought:

> As a part of our advertising program, we are offering fifty dollars for the best wild-life photograph taken within twenty miles of River City. All the photographs must be clear, unusually interesting, and they must be capable of being reproduced and enlarged.
> Professor I. J. Howard, scientist at River College and a well-known conservationist, will be the judge. The contest closes at Saturday noon, June 30.

Fifty dollars! With money from other jobs, that would pay his room and board for one term at the college where Ron meant to go someday. It would mean the start of a course in science to prepare for the career as a naturalist he craved.

"Old Flash's picture will win that prize easy," Jimmie exulted. "Why, what's wrong?" he demanded, looking at his brother's gloomy face.

"I'm afraid Flash is gone for good," answered Ron. "Last time the creek silted up he was back in three days. But now it's been five days and——"

At that instant the sound of a mighty splash came through the willows. Ron grabbed the camera, and his sun-bleached hair vanished down the pit like a startled groundhog diving into his hole.

"I see Flash! He's back!" Jimmie heard Ron shout as the lid dropped over his head.

Ron knew nothing of underwater photography, but during the next two hours each time the great rainbow drifted near the window, the shutter on Ron's camera clicked. The perfect streamlining of this superb fish was beautiful to see. To Ron with his eager curiosity about wild life, what he beheld was more exciting than any man-made motion picture ever filmed. His woodsman's patience was richly rewarded that morning.

Flash had come back hungry from the river. While squawfish might have gorged on the small trout that inhabited the falls pool, this speckled aristocrat would feed only in the swift current that swirled past the observation window.

Thousands of clumsy flying ants were swarming across the meadow that morning; hundreds of them had fallen into the upper reaches of the creek and were being carried down. When one of the drifting forms showed through the cloudy bubbles below the falls, Flash drove at it swiftly and with a confidence that was thrilling to watch.

Once a big squawfish, attracted by the rich feeding, tried to poach on Flash's preserve. But as it came drifting along the bottom, the trout took after it like an angry terrier, battering its flabby flanks with open jaws as he drove it off.

Ron snapped picture after picture until the last film on the roll had been exposed. It was nearly noon when he straightened out his cramped legs and pushed back the trap door. In the pit his eyes had grown used to the dim light. Now he was surprised to see that a haze hid the sun.

"It's lucky we got those pictures while it was bright," said Jimmie. "Think they will turn out all right?"

"Hope so," Ron replied. "It'll be late Monday before the prints can be developed and be back from town. If not, maybe I can get better ones next week."

But bad weather broke, and Monday when Ron came home from high school, Willow Creek was

320

coming into freshet. Later he saw the prints that had come by mail and learned the worst. Four of the negatives were complete blanks, and in the other Flash showed but faintly through the gray fog of underexposure.

Ron had not an hour to lose. Silt was starting to cloud the water, and by morning Flash would be driven downstream. It would be days before he came back. Ron had to get a good picture of the big fish before the contest closed Saturday.

When Jimmie came home from the country school, he found Ron in the workshop, fitting a cover to a cage of wooden slats that he had made. Later he saw Ron carrying the cage and a fishing rod toward the falls pool.

Grimly silent, Ron stood at the head of the pool and cast. All too well he knew what he was doing. Now the freedom that Flash had known in his mountain stream throughout his life was to end.

Almost to an inch, Ron knew where Flash would be lying, and as the gaily colored fly touched the water, the rainbow rose from his lurking place.

With a quick lift of his forearm Ron struck, the rod tip bent, and Flash was hooked.

Like a silver arrow he shot away, curved upward in a leap that shattered the surface like a small explosion, and fell with a sharp twist as in his fury he slapped the water with his widespread tail.

The reel sang, and Flash leaped again. He swerved and dodged, made one long dazzling rush, and jumped three times in quick succession. But always the thin, transparent leader on the fish line kept its steady drag on his head.

At first Ron let him have all the line he wanted. The reel shrilled as Flash charged down the pool. Ron was on the defensive during that first enraged flurry. Soon, he thought, the power of those broad fins must lessen. He gained some of the line he had lost.

But the big rainbow was only beginning to fight. Up the pool he surged in a terrific rush, and Ron, knowing that a slack line often means victory for a fish, reeled frantically. Would the big fellow never tire?

Time after time Flash renewed his struggle. A few minutes more of savage give and take, and his flanks weakened, and with heaving gills Flash lay on his side at the surface.

Ron kept wishing there had been another way. To defeat this courageous, untamed fighter that he had so long befriended seemed like treachery. But he knew that because of the freshet it had to be this or failure. Because of the prize, he dare not fail. Gently he guided the exhausted rainbow into the cage, freed the hook, and wiring down the cover, sunk the cage so that it lay against the lookout window of the pit below the willows.

"He'll be all right," Ron told himself. "I'll feed him well, and in a day or two, when the water clears, I'll let him go and get a good picture."

But when the lamp was out he lay wide awake, haunted by the thought of the trout's having his spirit broken by captivity. Argue with himself as he might, the truth was that he had selfishly deprived a splendid creature of its freedom.

Ron did not sleep well, and at daylight he stole from the house and hurried to the pool. There, vague and ghostly in the silt-laden water, lay the great trout in his cage, gasping for breath. Ron did not hesitate a moment. He quickly lifted the sunken cage, wrenched off its slat cover, and his prisoner was free.

On Saturday evening Ron listened to the radio announcer at River City name the winner of the Tourist Bureau's prize. As a last resort, Ron had sent in the best of his photographic failures—the one of Flash's putting the invading squawfish to flight. The names of several contestants were given, but there was no reference to Ron's picture.

The next Monday evening a car drove up, and a gray-haired man got out and came to the house.

"My name's Howard," the stranger said with a smile. "Are you Ron Lincoln?"

Ron could only nod dumbly. He was too astonished to speak. Why had the famous head of the Conservation Board come to see him? What could it mean?

"I believe you took this photograph," Professor Howard was saying. Ron looked at the blurred snap of Flash and the squawfish. He nodded.

"Will you tell me why you took it?" asked Ron's visitor.

Ron spoke hesitatingly at first. But the kindly manner of his visitor reassured him. As the man listened, he nodded encouragingly now and then, and led the youth to reveal much about himself.

"But tell me," the man urged at last. "How did you come to be so interested in wild life?"

"I don't know, sir," Ron answered. "I was born that way, I guess. Sometimes I sit at that pit window and imagine I can pretty nearly tell what those fish are thinking. You see, I don't know the scientific names or anything——"

"Mere labels," the professor broke in. "Anyone can learn them. Training's needed, of course, but you have something that no amount of training can give. In conservation we've always room for lads like you. Fact is, that's why I came." And to the astonished boy he offered a summer's job with the Conservation Board. Ron was to observe and collect specimens for pay!

The Wild Goat's Kid

Her nimble hoofs made music on the crags all winter as she roamed along the cliff tops above the sea. During the previous autumn she had wandered away, one of a small herd that trotted gaily after a handsome fellow with gray-black hide and long winding horns. Then with the end of autumn, farm boys had come looking for their goats, and the herd was broken up.

The gallant buck was captured and slain by two hungry dogs from the village of Drumranny. The white goat alone remained uncaptured. She had wandered too far away from her master's village. He couldn't find her. She was given up as lost. So then she became a wild one of the Irish cliffs, where the sea gulls and the cormorants were lords, and the great eagle soared high over the thundering sea. Her big, soft yellow eyes became wild from looking down often at the sea, with her long chin whiskers swaying gracefully in the wind.

She was a long, slender thing, with short straight horns and ringlets of matted hair trailing far down on either haunch. With her tail in the air, snorting, tossing her horns, she fled when anyone approached. Her hoofs would patter over the crags until she was far away. Then she would stand on a high crag and turn about to survey the person who had disturbed her, calmly confident in the power of her slender legs to carry her beyond pursuit.

She roamed at will. No wall however high could resist her long leap as she sprang on muscular thighs that bent like new silk. She was so supple that she could trot on top of a thin stone fence without a sound except the gentle tapping of her delicate hoofs.

She hardly ever left the cliff tops. There was plenty of food there, for the winter was mild, and leaves and grasses that grew between the crevices of the crags were flavored by the strong salt taste of the sea brine that was carried up on the wind. She grew sleek and comely.

Toward the end of the winter a subtle change came over her. Her hearing became more acute. She took fright at the least sound. She began to shun the sea except on very calm days, when it did not roar. She ate less. She was very particular about what she ate. She hunted around a long time before she chose a morsel.

Winter passed. New green leaves began to sprout. Larks sang in the morning. There was sweetness in the air and life was pleasant. One morning a little after dawn, the white goat gave birth to a gray-black kid.

The kid was born in a tiny glen, under an overhanging ledge of low rock that sheltered it from the wind. It was a male kid, an exquisite, fragile thing, tinted with delicate color. His slender belly was milky white. The insides of his thighs were of the same color. He had deep rings of gray, like bracelets, above his hoofs. He had black knee-caps on his forelegs, like pads, to protect him when he knelt by his mother to take food into his silky black mouth. His back and sides were gray-black. His ears were black, long, and drooping with the weakness of infancy.

The white goat bleated over him, with soft eyes and quivering flanks, gloating over her exquisite treasure. She had this delicate creature all to herself in the wild solitude of the glen, within earshot of the murmuring sea, with the birds whistling spring songs round about her, and the winds coming with slow whispers over the crags. In absolute freedom, she watched with her young.

How she maneuvered to make him stand! She breathed on him to warm him. She raised him gently with her forehead, uttering soft sounds to encourage him. He rose, trembling, staggering, swaying on his curiously long legs. She became excited, rushing around him, bleating nervously, afraid lest he fall again. He fell. She was in agony. Bitter wails came from her distended jaws, and she crunched her teeth. But she renewed her efforts urging the kid to rise, to rise and live.

He rose again. Now he was steadier. He shook his head. He wagged his long ears as his mother breathed into them. He took a few staggering steps, sagged to his knees, and rose immediately. Slowly, gently, gradually she pushed him toward her flank with her horns. At last he sank to his knees and began to feed on her milk.

She stayed with him all day in the tiny glen, just nibbling a few mouthfuls of the short grass that grew about. Most of the time she spent exercising the kid. With a show of anxiety and importance she brought him on little expeditions across the glen to the opposite rock, three yards away, and back again.

At first he staggered clumsily against her flanks, and his tiny hoofs often lost their balance on tufts of grass, such was his weakness. But he gained his strength with amazing speed, and the goat's joy and pride increased in consequence. She fed him and caressed him after each tiny journey.

When the sun had set he was able to walk steadily, to take little short runs, to toss his head. They lay all night beneath the shelter of the ledge with the kid between his mother's legs against her warm body.

Next morning she hid him in a crevice of the neighboring crag in a small groove between two flagstones that were covered with a withered growth of wild grass and ferns.

The kid crawled instinctively into the hole without any resistance to the gentle push of his mother's horns. He lay down with his head toward his doubled hind legs and closed his eyes.

Then his crafty mother scraped the grass and fern stalks over the entrance hole with her forefeet and ambled away to graze as carelessly as if she had no kid hidden.

All morning, as she grazed hurriedly and fiercely around the crag, she took great pains to pretend that she was not aware of the young kid's nearness. Even when she grazed almost beside the hiding place, she never noticed him, by look or by cry. But still she pricked her little ears at every distant sound.

At noon she let him out and gave him his dinner. She played with him on a grassy knoll and watched him prance about. She taught him how to rear on his hind legs and fight the air with his forehead. Then she put him back into his hiding place and returned to graze. She continued to graze until nightfall.

Just when she was about to fetch him from his hole to the overhanging ledge, to rest for the night, a startling sound reached her ears. It came from afar—from the south, from beyond a low fence that ran across the crag on the skyline. It was indistinct, barely audible, a deep purring sound. But to the ears of the mother goat it was loud and threatening as a thunderclap. It was the heavy breathing of a dog sniffing the wind.

She listened, stock-still, with her head in the air and her short tail stiff along her back, twitching one ear. The sound came again. It was nearer.

There was a patter of feet. Then a clumsy black figure hurtled over the fence and dropped onto the crag with awkward secrecy. The goat saw a black dog, a large curly fellow, standing by the fence in the dim twilight with his forepaw raised and his long red tongue hanging. Shutting his mouth suddenly and raising his snout upward, he sniffed several times, contracting his nostrils as he did so as if in pain. Then he whined savagely and trotted toward the goat sideways.

She snorted. It was a sharp, dull thud, like a blow from a rubber sledge. Then she rapped the crag three times with her left forefoot loudly and sharply. The dog stood still and raised his forepaw again. He lowered his head and looked at her with narrowed eyes. Then he licked his breast and began to run swiftly to the left. He was running toward the kid's hiding place, with his tail straight out and his snout to the wind.

With another fierce snort the goat charged him at full speed in order to cut him off from his advance on the kid's hiding place. He stopped immediately when she charged. The goat halted, too, five yards from the hiding place, between it and the dog, and facing the dog.

The dog stood still. His eyes wandered around in all directions with the bashfulness of a sly brute caught suddenly in an awkward position. Then he raised his bloodshot eyes slowly to the goat. He bared his fangs. His mane rose like a fan. His tail shot out. Picking his steps like a lazy cat, he approached her without a sound. The goat shivered along her left flank, and she snorted twice in rapid succession.

When he was within six yards of her, he uttered a ferocious roar that came from his throat with a deep, rumbling sound. He raced toward her and leaped clean into the air as if she were a fence that he was trying to vault. She parried him subtly with her horns without moving her forefeet. Her sharp straight horns just grazed his belly as he whizzed past her head.

The slight blow deflected his course. Instead of falling on his feet between her and the kid as he had intended cunningly to do, he was thrown to the left and fell on his side with a thud. The goat whirled about and charged him.

But he had arisen immediately and jerked himself away, with his haunches low, making a fiendish scraping and yelping and growling noise. He wanted to terrify the kid out of its hiding place. Then it would be easy to overpower the goat, hampered by trying to hide the kid between her legs.

The kid uttered a faint fretful bleat, but the goat immediately replied with a sharp, low cry. The kid muttered something indistinct; then he remained silent. There was a crunching noise among the ferns that covered him. He was settling himself down farther.

The goat trotted rigidly to the opposite side to face the dog again.

The dog had run away some distance and lain down licking his paws. Now he meant to settle himself down properly to the prolonged attack after the failure of his first onslaught. He yawned lazily and made peculiar mournful noises, thrusting his head into the air and twitching his snout.

The goat watched every single movement and sound, with her ears thrust forward past her horns. Her great, soft eyes were very wild and timorous in spite of the valiant posture of her body and the terrific force of the blows she delivered occasionally on the hard crag with her little hoofs.

The black dog remained lying for a half hour or so, continuing his weird pantomime. Then night fell. Everything became unreal and ghostly under the light of the distant myriads of stars. An infant moon had arisen. The sharp rushing wind and the thunder of the sea only made the silent loneliness of the night more menacing to the white goat as she stood bravely on the limestone crag defending her young. On all sides the horizon was a tumultuous line of crag dented with shallow glens and seamed with low stone fences that hung like tattered lace curtains against the rim of the sky.

Then the dog attacked again. Rising suddenly, he set off at a long swinging pace, with his head turned sideways toward the goat, whining as he ran. He ran around the goat in a wide circle, gradually increasing his speed. A white spot on his breast flashed and vanished as he rose and fell in the undulating stretches of his flight.

The goat watched him, fiercely rigid from tail to snout. She pawed the crag methodically turning around on her own ground slowly to face him.

When he passed his starting point, he was flying at full speed, a black ball shooting along the gloomy surface of the crag, with a swift, sharp rattle of claws. The rattle of his claws, his whining, and the sharp tapping of the goat's hoofs as she turned about were the only sounds that rose into the night from this sinister encounter.

He sped round and round the goat, approaching nearer and nearer each round, until he was so close that she could see his glittering eyes and the white lather of rage on his half-open jaws. She became slightly dizzy and confused, turning methodically in a confined space, and was amazed by the subtle strategy of the horrid beast.

His whining grew louder and more savage. The rattle of his claws was like the clamor of hailstones driven by a wind. He came in a whirl on her flank. He came with a savage roar that deafened her.

She shivered. Then she stiffened in rigid silence to receive him.

The kid uttered a shrill cry. Then the black dog hurtled through the air, close-up, with hot breathing, snarling, with reddened fangs, and—smash!

He had dived for her left flank. But as he went past her head, she had turned like lightning and met him again with her horns. This time she grazed his side, to the rear of the shoulder. He yelped and tumbled sideways, rolling over twice. With a savage snort she was upon him.

He was on his haunches when her horns thudded into his head. He went down again with another yelp, rolled over, and swept to his feet with amazing speed. He whirled about on swinging tail and dived for her flank once more.

The goat uttered a shriek of terror. He had passed her horns. His fangs had embedded themselves in the matted ringlets that trailed along her right flank. The dog's flying weight, swinging onto the ringlets as he fell, brought her to her haunches. She was ferocious like the dog himself, ferocious and fearless, defending her young. She wriggled to her feet beside the rolling dog that gripped her flank.

She wrenched herself around and gored him savagely in the belly. He yelped and loosed his hold. She rose on her hind legs in a flash and, with a snort, gored him again. Her sharp horns had penetrated his side between the ribs. He gasped and shook his feet in the air. Then she pounded him with her forefeet.

Her little hoofs pattered with tremendous speed for almost a minute; then she stopped suddenly. Her eyes were dazed. She bleated slightly and looked down. The dog was still. He was dead.

For a moment or two she stood shivering and sniffing him. Then she lifted her right forefoot and shook it with a curious movement. She uttered a wild joyous cry and bounded toward her kid's hiding place.

Night passed, with a glorious dawn that came over a rippling sea from the east; a wild, sweet dawn scented with dew and perfumes of the flowering earth. The sleepy sun rose brooding from the sea, golden and soft, searching far horizons with its shafts of light. The dawn was still—still and soft and pure.

The white goat and her kid were traveling eastward along the cliff tops over the sea. They had traveled all night, flying from the horrid carcass of the beast that lay stretched on the crag beside the little glen. Now they were far away on the summit of a giant white precipice of Cahir. The white goat rested to give milk to her kid and to look out over the cliff top at the rising sun.

Then she continued her flight eastward, pushing her kid before her gently with her horns.

Defenders of Freedom

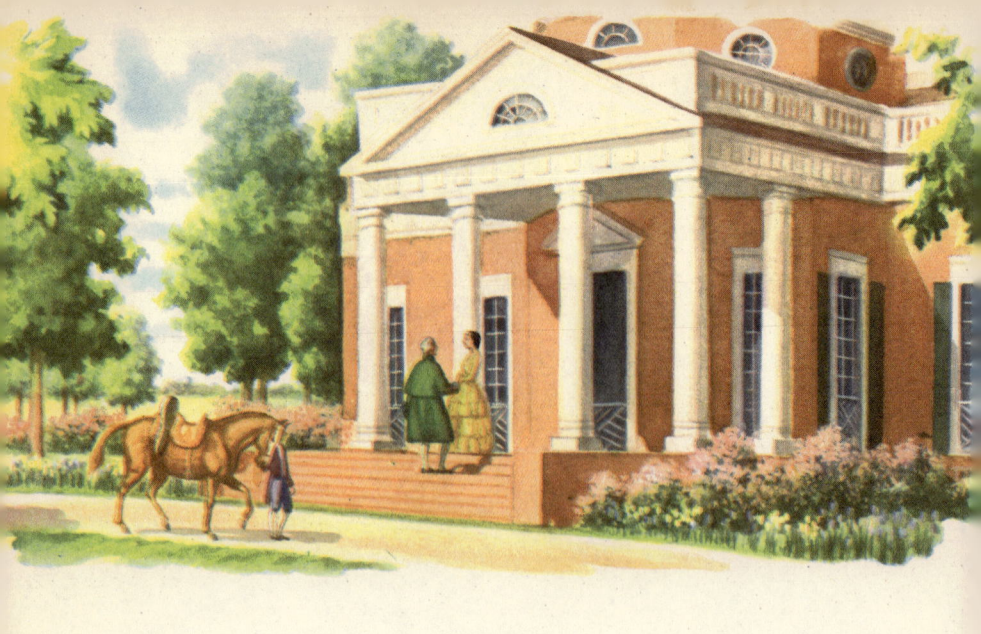

Thomas Jefferson

The birds were singing in the trees; the Virginia sky stood high and golden blue. The azaleas were in bloom, and blue and yellow iris shone in the dew-drenched grass on the lawn of Monticello this May morning. On the gravel path a horse, saddled and laden for a journey, stood pawing the earth while a faithful servant held the bridle.

"My heart is full of dread, Thomas," whispered Martha Jefferson. "Revolution—it is a terrible word, and everyone is talking of it."

"It is the wish of the people," said her husband. "A revolution is like a pot that's come to a boil. If the fire's too hot, it boils over—and so is it with people. If the suffering is too great, there comes

From *The Way of an Eagle* by Sonia Daugherty, Copyright, 1941, published by Oxford University Press.

a revolution. And then a better life to all alike must be the outcome."

"God willing," said Martha. "I shall no longer fear."

"Then I shall go back to Congress with a lighter heart," her husband told her.

Martha watched him as he rode away. At the turn of the road he looked back at Monticello standing there stately and elegant. He urged his horse to a gallop. This was no time for vain longings for the home he cherished. He must go and take his place in an important meeting of Congress.

It was a seven days' journey over rough roads, stopping at inns overnight. Reaching his lodgings in Philadelphia, Jefferson washed, donned fresh clothes, and set out for a dinner at the tavern. The streets were full of people, all jostling each other as they passed, and the keen, brilliant eyes of Thomas Jefferson took in everything, the elegant rich, as well as the shabby poor. He walked briskly to the tavern where many members of Congress met daily at dinner. It was a jovial place, and it stood conveniently near to the brick Statehouse, where Congress held its meetings.

John Adams from Massachusetts was there, and so was his cousin, Samuel Adams. They were carrying on a heated discussion with Richard Henry Lee of Virginia, and they greeted Jefferson with cordial exclamations of welcome as he found a place.

"What are we waiting for?" Samuel Adams demanded, his mouth full of food that he had forgotten to swallow in his excitement. "The battle of Lexington was proof of how the farmers feel. Didn't they give the redcoats a merry chase?"

"Aye," said John Adams, "I'm for separation, but we must make sure Spain and France are allies."

"'Tis to their benefit to be on our side," protested Samuel Adams. "We can't afford to wait; the battle of Bunker Hill made people certain we have the ability, and now that George Washington is Commander in Chief of the Continental Army, we are able to call out the militia from all the colonies and make our army powerful."

Jefferson, partaking hungrily of his meat pie, listened with quiet earnestness. The members of Congress were used to his silence. He spoke rarely, but they all knew that if he should speak, it would be worth hearing.

The business of Congress absorbed Jefferson, and work on numerous committees left him little leisure. Since the colonies would buy nothing from England, ways must be found to manufacture needed goods. Opinion in the colonies must be united, and they must find ways to trade among themselves. There were Indian uprisings to settle, there was the training of armies, and still there was correspondence with England concerning a possible peace.

The debaters in Congress never flaunted the word *revolution*. A definite break with England was unavoidable, thought each one, but they spoke of revolution only at the tavern or on the streets. In Congress, Benjamin Franklin sat listening, offering advice now and then, but never arguing. No one mentioned the fateful word.

On the streets, knocking from door to door, were men asking housewives to part with everything made of lead, to make bullets for the soldiers. And yet many members of Congress were still in doubt. "The halfways," Jefferson called them. To declare independence, they must all be of one mind.

"If we don't hang together, we'll each hang separately," drawled the humorous Dr. Franklin, with a twinkle in his eye.

On the seventh day of June, in the year 1776, Richard Henry Lee rose from his seat in Congress and read a resolution: "Resolved, That these United Colonies are, and of right ought to be, free and independent . . . ."

Virginia was taking the lead, Jefferson realized with a beating heart. But, to his keen disappointment, the voting on the resolution was postponed for the time being. Meanwhile a committee was to prepare a declaration on the subject of independence. John Adams, Benjamin Franklin, Thomas Jefferson, Roger Sherman, and Robert Livingston were chosen to write the paper for Congress.

"I am of little assistance on this committee," John Adams protested. "I've argued so much for the right to govern ourselves that my name is obnoxious to those who are undecided, and they will be less critical if my name does not appear."

Thomas Jefferson meekly accepted the extra responsibility. He knew only too well from past experience that the aged Franklin would find little time to spare for this work. Thomas was on many committees. It always fell to his lot to do the most tedious work, for he was not a speechmaker.

He walked back to his lodgings to consider the task before him. A declaration of rights—it was a task near to his heart.

In his apartment, he stood before the window thinking, his beloved old violin pressed under his chin. His thoughts went roaming across the ocean, up and down the world. What were the rights of men? He passed the bow softly across the moaning strings.

What words would express to others the things he himself felt about the glorious rights of freedom? How weak were words! How pale and inadequate! They should be flaming missiles to rouse the sleeping dreams in the hearts of men.

He sat at his desk, quill pen in hand, thinking— words, words. They came forth from deep within him. Slowly, methodically, he arranged them into sentences, weighing each one.

> When in the Course of human events, it becomes necessary for one people to dissolve the political bands which have connected them with another, and to assume among the powers of the earth the separate and equal station to which the Laws of Nature and of Nature's God entitle them . . .

He walked up and down, musing deeply. Then he went back to the desk, and again the quill raced over the paper.

> A decent respect to the opinions of mankind requires that they should declare the causes which impel them to the separation . . .

His pen hung suspended again. What were these causes, the true causes that made the caldron of human strife boil over? Greed, ambition—ignorance of the sublime nature that lay hidden deep within each breast.

Late into the night he mused, long after his candles burned out. Day after day went by as he weighed his thoughts and the words that came to shape the sentences.

> We hold these truths to be self-evident, that all men are created equal, that they are endowed by their Creator with certain inalienable Rights, that among these are Life, Liberty, and the pursuit of Happiness.

The words flamed on the white paper. Visions rose before his eyes of a free people, a people of equal privilege and opportunity.

> That to secure these rights, Governments are instituted among Men, deriving their just powers from the consent of the governed . . .

He plied his quill over the paper, enumerating the trials of his people. He minced no words. It must be plain and clear. He wrote and rewrote the sentences. He would be wise; he would be just, he promised himself, but he would not be weak.

Days were going by; he no longer counted them. It was the end of June, and in the heat of his struggle with himself and with the words that failed when his thoughts soared, he forgot to look at the thermometer or to ponder any longer on the consequence of the paper spread before him.

> And for the support of this Declaration, with a firm reliance on the protection of Divine Providence, we mutually pledge to each other our Lives, our Fortunes, and our sacred Honor.

It was finished. His heart beat fiercely as he read the words. Whither would it lead?

The deep silence of the night called to him. He walked the streets restlessly. The hustling city lay shadowy in the starlight, and the great bell in the dome of the Statehouse shimmered dimly in the darkness. He stood still and lifted his eyes to the stars that burned high in the deep canopy of heaven. A whisper in the stillness of the night reached him like the rustling of far-off wings. What would men do with this independence for which they were ready to die?

But in the cold reasoning of debate that followed the reading of his paper in Congress, no one seemed troubled by these questions.

From the stable nearby came flies to torment the silk-stockinged shins of the bewigged delegates as they argued and debated over every word and sentence in the paper Jefferson submitted for their approval. He sat in their midst, motionless and silent. It did not matter to him what they said, so long as the paper proclaimed the dignity of men's rights. John Adams defended each sentence, word by word, but Congress omitted a part that Jefferson had taken great pains to compose.

Noting his discomfort as the debate grew warmer, the kindly Benjamin Franklin came to sit beside this young member, in whose words he sensed great things. "I will tell you a story," he offered.

"A friend of mine set up a shop and hung a sign above his door. 'Twas handsome—on it was painted the picture of a hat and above the hat was printed in large letters: JOHN THOMPSON, HATTER, MAKES AND SELLS HATS FOR READY MONEY. Friends and customers came to offer criticism of the sign. One said omit this word, another said omit that—in the end all the words were omitted except his name and the picture of the hat. You can guess now why I avoid the writing of state papers."

Thomas smiled ruefully at Dr. Franklin's story. He saw the point of it, nevertheless—that which mattered in the declaration would remain. Let them debate. Let them change what words they chose, the declaration of rights would remain and proclaim to the world that they were about to embark on the greatest adventure a people can dream of—the birth of a free nation, a democracy.

His lips curved in a humorous smile as he watched the flies swarm around the legs of the ponderous men who were mopping perspiring brows under their powdered wigs. Flick, flack went the white handkerchiefs, striking at the greedy insects that tormented the stout calves.

"These flies are my friends," thought Thomas to himself. "They will help me."

Fidgeting in their chairs, the delegates stopped debating early in the afternoon. John Hancock, president of Congress, boldly called for a vote.

But it was not everyone who voted so freely as did John Hancock. Some made their "Aye" very meek and soft. But it was an accomplished fact nevertheless. The Declaration of Independence was adopted and sent posthaste to the printer. It must be ready the next morning, he was told.

The weary and excited printer, who had worked all night, had enough copies to send out at the right time to all the colonies. A postrider dashed off bearing the fateful words. The Declaration would be read to all the troops and proclaimed in cities and towns from every courthouse. It was the fourth day in July, 1776.

Later, in the Statehouse at Philadelphia, a copy of the proclamation lay on the table. The printed words looked back from the white paper boldly at the members of Congress who gathered about the table to gaze with wonder at what they read, as if they had never seen these words before. But they were laughing and jesting now, their fear forgotten.

John Hancock was the first to write his signature. He wrote his name in large letters.

John Hancock

"There!" he roared. "John Bull can read my name without his spectacles!" He looked about him mockingly. "Gentlemen, we must hang together."

Benjamin Franklin joined his laugh to Hancock's; "Yes, we must hang together, gentlemen, as I've said many times, or we shall all hang separately."

Jefferson wrote his name in a hasty scrawl. He knew what it had cost so far for them to come to this point, and he guessed all it would cost, now they had made an open break.

Th Jefferson

The spirit of revolution was afoot in the streets. Soldiers paraded, sidewalks were jammed with people hurrying to and fro, and groups of men gathered to thrash out the wrongs and rights of it.

They heard the Declaration of Independence read at last from a platform in the Statehouse yard, on July 8, by Captain Hopkins, a young navy officer who had been chosen for the task. His fine voice made the words ring out like bells to the people who had gathered to hear him. Those who had been indifferent became inspired. They rushed to the Statehouse and snatched the King of England's coat of arms from the hall and set it afire in the square amid cries, shouts, songs, and gun salutes. Bells rang, drowning out the voices and the songs, making a great chorus.

Proclaim Liberty were the words inscribed on the great bell in the steeple of the brick Statehouse. "Proclaim Liberty," it rang late into the night. Thomas Jefferson could hardly go to sleep. A new nation was born—the United States of America—a democracy.

Lafayette Meets His Hero

On August first, 1777, the dream of a certain young Frenchman came true. He was not yet twenty years old, but for two years he had been trying to join the brave American Army. Because he considered George Washington the greatest man in the world, and because he loved liberty more than life, he had resolved to help America's Revolution.

But the young man's wife belonged to a rich, powerful, and noble family who wished him to stay at the court of the French King Louis. So he had to come to America in secret.

With a small party of friends he landed on the coast of South Carolina, and it took thirty-two days to ride north to Philadelphia, where the Continental Congress was meeting. When the eager youth offered to serve without pay, he was given a commission as Major General by the Board of War. "Now, comrades," he exclaimed triumphantly to his friends, "I am enrolled in the cause of freedom!"

On the next day the rest of his dream came true. General Washington rode into Philadelphia from his camp, six miles away. The British fleet had been sighted, and the General had many things to talk over with the Board of War. At the end of the lengthy discussion he was handed a list of the new officers who were to serve under him.

Putting a finger against a name he did not know, Washington asked, "When will this officer be presented to me?"

"This afternoon, General," was the reply. "We sent him an invitation to meet you at dinner."

When the invitation had come to the gallant young Frenchman, his heart almost burst with happiness. He could hardly wait until time to go. On reaching the mansion where the dinner was being held, he found it crowded with officers and congressmen. Suddenly a door opened, and in walked a tall man in the blue coat, buff waistcoat, light breeches, and high boots which composed the uniform of an American officer. The way he carried himself and the noble calm of his face made the young Frenchman gasp, "It is he! This is the great Washington, my hero!"

Slowly he drew near the General. And then Washington was looking straight into his eyes, while somebody said, "Your Excellency, this is our new Major General, the Marquis de Lafayette."

Washington saw a tall, athletic young man with a foreign look and an attractive face. The intense joy blazing in his eyes told Washington that the youth had long looked forward to this moment and that it was a true love of freedom which had drawn him across the seas. Deeply affected, the General held out his hand.

Heads turned. The buzz of voices ceased. All eyes watched the two greet one another. It was no ordinary meeting. For that day George Washington clasped the hand of a man who was to become one of the most picturesque persons in the Revolution and one of the dearest friends of his life.

Lafayette was overcome to be face to face with his hero. For a moment he blushed and stammered when Washington asked him a question. But soon he was relating some of the adventures of the long, hard journey from Paris to Philadelphia. Smiling, tossing back his head of reddish hair, flinging his slender hands, he tumbled out his words at a rapid rate and with a definitely foreign accent.

"Oh, that long, long way!" he concluded. "Fifty-two days of sea travel and then the dark forests of Carolina and Virginia! Almost, *mon général*, I lose hope of arriving!"

He laughed at the marvel of succeeding, of being there with the man whom he had wanted to meet above all others in the world.

Before the dinner was over, Washington invited the Marquis to stay at headquarters. "My staff is called my family, and I shall hereafter, my dear sir, regard you as a member of it."

Lafayette departed as if on wings. The next day he was asked by the General to go with him to inspect the Delaware River forts. Afterward they drove to the camp at Germantown, and the General reviewed the troops. In dismayed silence the Frenchman watched the ragged, poorly drilled men go through their crude maneuvers. Could this really be the American Army? Then he heard Washington's grave voice:

"We ought to feel embarrassed in presenting ourselves to an officer from the French Army."

At this Gilbert de Lafayette's heart leaped up in admiration of the man beside him. With only half-clothed, shabby companies to oppose the superb British troops, he had been able to defy them. By glorious leadership he had performed daring feats at Trenton and Princeton. With a humbleness which went straight to Washington's tender heart, the Marquis said, "I came here to learn, not to teach, *mon général*."

Two weeks later, attired in his elegant new Continental uniform, and astride a horse he had just purchased, Lafayette came galloping into the American camp. He brought to serve as aides two of the men who had accompanied him from France.

Watching his arrival, the old troopers grinned and whispered to one another, "He thinks this war is a play and he's dressed for a hero's part!"

But soon the young man won everyone's respect by his shy and modest ways.

One of the officers, Nathanael Greene, came in from helping Lafayette drill a company and said to Alexander Hamilton, "Perhaps this Frenchman will make a good officer in time."

Meanwhile fresh enemy troops had landed from their ships, and in the battle that took place near Brandywine Creek, the Americans proved no match for the well-armed foe. Washington was forced to retreat, and the enemy marched into Philadelphia.

One by one the forts along the Delaware River were captured. In order to watch the British, who had settled down for the winter in that vicinity, Washington made his camp at Valley Forge. Long before the soldiers could build their rough cabins, snow and icy cold set in.

The Board of War seemed unable to send food or clothing, and many of the soldiers went barefoot in the snow. They faced a cruel winter with nothing to encourage them except the wonderful spirit of their leader and his faithful officers.

In the retreat from Brandywine Creek, Lafayette had been wounded in the leg. When his wound healed, he was assigned to command the Virginia Company and did all he could to help the soldiers under him. He gave a sick man some of the blankets from his own bed and made hot tea in his copper kettle for those suffering most from the cold. His odd way of pronouncing the English language made them laugh, and he laughed with them. They loved him for sharing their hardships so bravely.

As Washington watched the gallant officer at work, he grew more and more fond of him. Quite often they had long talks, and each one added to Lafayette's admiration of the courage and patience of his hero.

Once Washington said to him, "If the enemy ever guesses how sick and hungry the American Army is, if they find out how many men have died of cold and disease, they will attack. If they do, they can wipe out our forces in a single battle."

In addition to other worries Washington knew that there were plots against him in the American Army of the North and in Congress. But the devotion of Gilbert de Lafayette filled him with gratitude and gave him new faith in his own power.

Never was spring so welcome at Valley Forge as in 1778. In the warm sunlight sick soldiers began to get well. General Greene was at last able to get wagonloads of wheat, corn, and potatoes to feed the men, and another officer secured uniforms. They were now able to drill again and liked serving under the Frenchman, who was a good drillmaster.

Now when Lafayette stood beside his commander to watch the troops go by in good marching order, he marveled at what they had accomplished. The great Washington had held fast to a dwindling army until it once more became a fighting unit.

But there was more than all this to give new life to America that spring. In May came great news. The moment he heard it, Lafayette rushed to headquarters, pushed aside all who blocked his way, seized General Washington in his arms, and kissed him on both cheeks.

"*Mon général!* Thank God! Now we are one country! Oh, my friend, I have just heard the glorious, marvelous news!"

That wonderful news was speeding across the land. France was to be an ally of America! Now King Louis of France was to send ships, supplies, and money to help the Americans.

For weeks Lafayette had been thinking that he should go home to see his dear wife and baby. But now he knew that, as a Frenchman, it was his plain duty to stay and fight for the cause he had adopted. As for reward, he could want nothing better than the words General Washington spoke to him one happy day in May.

Clasping the hands of the joyous young officer, Washington said, "Your example, Marquis, has done more than any other one thing to bring about this alliance with France."

Thus it was that Gilbert de Lafayette, champion of freedom, shared America's darkest hour of the Revolution and the glorious turning point of the war.

Simón Bolívar, Liberator

In South America one name stands above all others—the name of Simón Bolívar, the Liberator. He was born July 24, 1783, in the city of Caracas, the capital of Venezuela. Although the family was very wealthy, they and the other native South Americans were denied many of the rights of free men by their rulers from Spain.

When Simón grew up, he, like other patriots, deeply resented the unjust laws passed by the Spanish officers and made a resolve to give his life to the freeing of his country from the chains which bound her to Spain. He felt that the time had come for her to follow the example of her northern neighbors, who had freed themselves by the American Revolution some thirty years earlier.

Full of enthusiasm for revolution, Bolívar worked toward the Venezuelan Declaration of Independence of July 5, 1811, and for thirteen months he, with other patriots, fought to maintain the Republic.

The Republic failed. The patriots were defeated, and young Bolívar was sent into exile.

Bolívar did not go far. From an island north of Venezuela he continued to plan for freedom. He saw that it was not just Venezuelan freedom for which he must work, but the freedom of other provinces in South America as well.

In a few weeks he was back on South American soil, but not in Venezuela. He had crossed by sailing ship to Cartagena, which was the northern port of New Granada, to try to persuade the patriots of that province to go across the mountains and help the Venezuelans. He appealed to the people of Cartagena to look beyond their own borders. He warned them that they should act for their defense by sending an army across the mountains instead of waiting for the Spanish forces to come over and attack them.

The black-haired young patriot won the people to his way of thinking. In three months Simón was on his way up Magdalena River with a small force of New Granadans who were ready to follow him across the Andes mountains to Venezuela.

This march was a triumph of human endurance. The soldiers came up from the hot green jungle into cold wind-swept heights.

The mountains to be crossed were ten, twelve, and fifteen thousand feet high. For ten long days and nights Bolívar and his loyal men pressed on, wandering without shelter and with little food along the trails through the passes. The painful *soroche*, the mountain sickness, attacked them. The cold chilled them to the bone. But always the young commander was helping and inspiring the weary men.

Haggard, worn, with his black eyes burning like lights in his face, he was at the front of the line, in the middle, at the rear—wherever the need of him was greatest.

The little army came over the crest of those northern Andes and should have halted for a few days to get back their health and strength. But they could not stop. Spanish troops were waiting for them, and the patriots had to begin to fight at once, before they recovered their full strength. Yet they won those skirmishes and marched on through western Venezuela. The Spaniards were defeated, and Bolívar was ready to help the Venezuelans set up the Second Republic.

Ninety days after he left New Granada, Bolívar arrived in triumph at the gates of Caracas.

At the city gates he exchanged his ragged uniform for one more suitable for a parade and stepped into a flower-decked carriage which was waiting for him inside. Twelve beautiful daughters of the leading citizens were there to draw that carriage through the streets, while the people crowded the sidewalks and shouted from windows and housetops their welcome to "The Liberator."

That was the first time he was greeted by the title which was to become almost as much a part of him as his name. His honors were shared by the ragged, exhausted soldiers from New Granada.

The men of the West had come across the mountains to help the patriots of the East! These two parts of the South American continent had been brought together as never before.

That triumph was brief. The patriot armies were soon fighting again, this time against all the forces that the aroused Spanish generals could throw against them.

For six months the patriots held out, disputing every mile of the advance. Then Bolívar was forced to yield.

Again the Liberator must go into exile. He went by sailboat to New Granada, where he was warmly welcomed even though he was a defeated man. This reception was healing to his spirit, but was all too brief. The enemy, reinforced from Spain, gathered their armies and inflicted disastrous defeats on the patriots of New Granada. Spain was determined to wipe out all traces of revolution in the entire northern portion of the continent.

Once more Bolívar must leave South America, now with a price put upon his head by Spain. He took refuge in the British island of Jamaica. This was a time of deepest despair. But courage came back to him, and with it greater visions. He was now convinced that not only Venezuela and New Granada but all South America must be liberated.

"I wish above all else," he declared, "to see the formation in America of the greatest nation of the world—the greatest not so much because of its size as because of its glory and liberty!"

He was dreaming not of the single continent of South America. He was dreaming of a congress at Panama, where all the republics of America, both North and South, would meet with representatives of the other parts of the world. He was talking of a "United America, the Mother of Republics."

Spain now considered that the revolutions in her South American colonies were entirely put down, but she was reckoning without the exile in Jamaica.

General Bolívar returned to stage his attack from a new place. He was making a new headquarters on the Orinoco River and calling a congress there to set up once more the Venezuelan Republic. At this place, two hundred fifty miles inland from the Atlantic, he awaited supplies by water from other countries and planned new campaigns.

The congress met and formed a constitution. It was at a dinner for members of the congress that he told his plans. Excited by his own thrilling dreams, the Liberator leaped from his seat to stand on the table top. Between the lines of his fascinated guests he walked its length, with dishes breaking beneath his feet.

"Even so," he shouted, "I shall march from the Atlantic to the Pacific, from Panama to Cape Horn, until the last Spaniard is expelled!"

But Bolívar's armies again suffered a succession of crushing defeats in northern Venezuela. The odds were heavily against the patriot leader, so heavily that his defeat seemed a matter of months, if not of weeks.

Bolívar called his leaders to a conference at a hut in a small village. English and Irish officers were there, as well as South American leaders, for a great number of foreign soldiers had come across the ocean to fight with the Liberator.

There was no furniture in the hut except the skulls of cattle, dried and bleached in the sun, which could serve as seats for those who did not stand or sit on the floor. General Bolívar walked back and forth, gesturing nervously with his long, slender hands as he outlined a new plan.

"Over in the province of New Granada the enemy troops are not so numerous," Bolívar argued. "There are patriot troops, too, under good leaders.

Why should we not go there, leaving a small force to harass and deceive the Spaniards into thinking the Venezuelan Army still in the region?"

The answer could be read in the faces of the men. Between them and New Granada stretched hundreds of miles of llanos, broad treeless plains now turned into swamps by the rainy season, with the mountain slopes of the high Andes at their end. Nature had given the answer to the question as to why the two countries should not join hands.

Then Simón Bolívar repeated the remark that he had made at the time of a terrible earthquake in Caracas: "If Nature opposes us, we will battle with her and compel her to obey us."

Hours passed while the men argued. Through all the discussion Bolívar held to his point. "We must cross the Andes if we are to gain the victory," he declared. In the end he won them over. It was an Irishman named Rooke, one of his lieutenants, who swung them to the final yielding.

"Lead the way," he cried. "Say the word and I'll march with you not only over the Andes but right down to Patagonia—even to Cape Horn!"

For weeks the men made their way across the llanos; struggling through the wet lands, trying to ford the swollen rivers, losing lives all along the route by one tragedy and another. Then they came to the mountain slopes, and again, as he had on that first march of his, the Liberator was leading men of the tropic plains up into the bitter heights of the Andes. But as they neared their goal, a scout brought word that the pass through which they had expected to go was held by a small Spanish force, on guard to keep any enemy troops from marching through.

With that crossing locked, there was only one other way. That very night they must do the impossible. They must go over a lofty, wind-swept region of eternal snow, where only the bravest of mountain climbers had ever ventured. All previous hardships were in vain if they could not get over into New Granada, and this was the only way.

Many died during that wild night; falling from precipices as they tried to cling to the narrow paths, dropping by the way and freezing, perishing from mountain sickness. But the remnant of the troop came over and staggered down the other side of the mountain to the villages below. The men were stared at as if they were ghosts—surely living men could not have crossed by that route which was not a route, but an impassable barrier.

Within a few days these same men revived to fight. Patriots of New Granada, enlisted by one of Bolívar's officers whom he had sent ahead, joined them in time to win one of the decisive battles of the Wars of Independence.

Bolívar and his victorious troops soon entered the capital city, Bogotá, from which the Spanish governor fled in haste at their approach.

Meanwhile General San Martín of Argentina was attempting to deliver Peru from Spanish control. Bolívar went there to complete the work.

In 1824 a great and final victory ended the Wars of Independence, and a new republic established in Peru was named Bolivia in honor of the Liberator, who had led five South American countries to freedom.

Bolívar's dream of a Pan-American Congress did not come to pass. To him it seemed as if he had failed. But he had not failed, for others were to carry on the work, so that nations of the Western World have moved closer to the realization of his dream. And today the Americas are banding together to work for a better world.

First Lady of China

A Woman Makes a Brave Decision

Madame Chiang Kai-shek looked at the men around a conference table in Shanghai. These were the leaders of war-torn China. On each face she read an echo of the words she herself had just uttered, "We must work together for China!"

There was plenty of work to do, for the enemy was threatening a new attack. Wounded soldiers must be cared for. Shelter must be found for the homeless; rice for hungry children. There would be fighting, too, but she would leave that to her husband, Chiang Kai-shek, Generalissimo of the Chinese Army. But work or fight, they must all act *together*. A thousand times she had said it.

Somehow, all the many different provinces of the great, sprawling land of China must learn to work and fight as one nation, truly united.

The Generalissimo was now in the North at Sian, seeking to win over a rebellious young officer. This officer was not willing to wait for Chiang's slow, careful planning. He wanted to attack the enemy without delay, and he had persuaded others to follow him and defy the Generalissimo.

Busy as Madame Chiang was with the problems of the conference in Shanghai, she could not help wondering about her husband. Would he be able to persuade that young rebel to wait, so that China might face the enemy united, not a nation divided against itself?

Abruptly the door of the room was flung open. Through it burst Madame Chiang's brother-in-law, an important official in the government.

"There has been mutiny in our force at Sian!" he cried. "Nothing at all has been heard of the Generalissimo!"

Instantly the room was in a turmoil. Madame Chiang rose slowly to her feet. She tried to speak calm words of courage, but her heart was thumping wildly. Fear, not only for her husband, but for her country also, filled her mind. How could China fight without Chiang Kai-shek's wise, strong leadership?

A soldier rushed in with a late news bulletin: The Generalissimo had been captured by the rebels. He was a prisoner at Sian.

"Send regiments at once," demanded an officer.

"Send bombers," suggested another.

Suggestions and threats flew thick and fast.

"Wait," advised Madame Chiang calmly. "Suppose you *do* start an attack—what will happen? The rebels at Sian will fight back. That means civil war, and China will be divided when the enemy is at our gates. The rebels may, if you attack them, kill the Generalissimo, just when China needs his leadership most. Our attack would condemn him to death at the hands of the rebels—if not by our own bombs and bullets."

The officers listened to what she said, but some were unwilling to give up the idea of fighting for the leader they loved and honored. Days passed. The arguments swung to and fro. And no word came from the rebel troops in the North.

"The Generalissimo is dead," whispered the people. They did not say it in Madame Chiang's presence, but she knew what they were whispering, and she refused to believe it. Dark as the hour was, she kept her faith, the simple, childlike faith in God that her parents had taught her.

Many times in these sad days Madame Chiang thought of how her father had faced loneliness and discouragement when he had been a young Chinese boy in the United States, struggling to acquire an education. Through the help of generous people he had been able to study at college, and he came to believe in the Christian religion. When that Chinese boy, Charles Soong, returned to China, he had spent all his time trying to make the Christian faith known to his people.

Because he had wanted his children to share the blessing of an education like his, he had sent his sons and daughters to the United States. Not to stay always, but to study and learn so that they, too, might return to China and help their country become a strong, united, and educated nation.

Ever since Madame Chiang had been the schoolgirl Mayling Soong, she herself had worshiped God with all her heart. Would she now find the courage and strength that her father had found? Would her faith equal the faith of her Christian mother?

Thinking of these things and praying for strength and wisdom brought new courage to the wife of the Generalissimo. When the army officers again urged an attack on the rebels who held her husband, she faced them calmly.

"What you want to do," she said, "endangers the life of the Generalissimo. Believe me, I am not only a woman trying to save her husband's life. I am a Chinese woman, striving to save my country's leader. No effort must be spared to secure his release by peaceful means. I myself will fly to Sian to see what can be done."

Dead silence met her proposal. She looked at the men about her with a faint smile. "If peaceful means fail," she added, "you can still use force."

There were protests from the officers: The rebels were desperate men; they would kill her, torture her. But Madame Chiang was firm.

Then the young rebel officer who had captured the Generalissimo sent her a telegram: "Come to Sian. Bring your brother-in-law, Dr. Kung. We do not wish to harm your husband."

But then came an urgent telephone call from a friend who had talked with the Generalissimo.

"Your husband pleads with you not to join him in Sian," said the friend. "Your life will be in peril. The Generalissimo is convinced that the rebels mean to kill him. You must not come."

But Madame Chiang did not alter her purpose. Her own life seemed of little value when compared to the hope of a united China. She would go.

Dr. Kung was ill and could not accompany her, but Madame Chiang's own brother sent word that he was already on his way to Sian and would meet her there. Despite protests from the government officials and army officers, Madame Chiang went calmly on with her preparations for her flight.

Suddenly another message came from Sian. The Generalissimo himself had declared a truce and had ordered no bombing or attack on Sian for three days. With a great sigh of relief, Madame Chiang hastened her plans. The truce was short, but it gave her a chance. Could she, in seventy-two hours, work the miracle of her husband's release?

A Dangerous Mission Is Undertaken

The Chinese pilot of the powerful plane bearing Madame Chiang on her dangerous mission opened the throttle to the full. The machine climbed into the wintry sky and headed northward. The face of the woman who sat by the window was strangely calm for one who was about to face grim, mutinous soldiers. Villages, cities, and rice fields of China slid by beneath her. Madame Chiang gazed at them with eyes that saw not. Her thoughts concerned only the desperate peril that hung over her husband, on whom rested the fate of the nation. Would she find the Generalissimo alive?

On the seat across the narrow aisle of the plane sat Mr. Donald, an Australian and her husband's loyal friend. The two sat in silence for a time. Then Madame Chiang spoke, softly as if to herself. "I will not lose my temper when I meet my husband's captors. I will deal with them as man to man—talking naturally and calmly."

The plane was now over Sian. Twice it circled over the city, giving those below fair warning of its arrival. Then it turned toward the air field and swooped down onto the runway.

Cars dashed to the field as the plane taxied to a stop. Madame Chiang—dignified, serene—remained seated in the airplane. The rebel chief climbed aboard. He looked tired, embarrassed, and somewhat ashamed thus to be meeting a woman who had often been his charming, gracious hostess.

Madame Chiang greeted him as she had always done. He returned the greeting with awkward courtesy, and then asked, "You wish to go at once to see the Generalissimo?"

Her heart leaped into her throat. She longed to go to her husband, but the fate of China was in her hands. "I would first like some tea," she replied gently, seeking in this fashion to show the mutineer that she trusted him and had no fear.

After the cup of tea, she walked to the walled garden in which was the house where her husband was a prisoner. Guards were at the gate with machine guns. She found the Generalissimo in bed. He was ill and worn with injuries he had received when trying to escape. He had fallen from the top of a ten-foot wall into a ditch three feet deep. His back had been badly injured by the fall, and he could scarcely sit up.

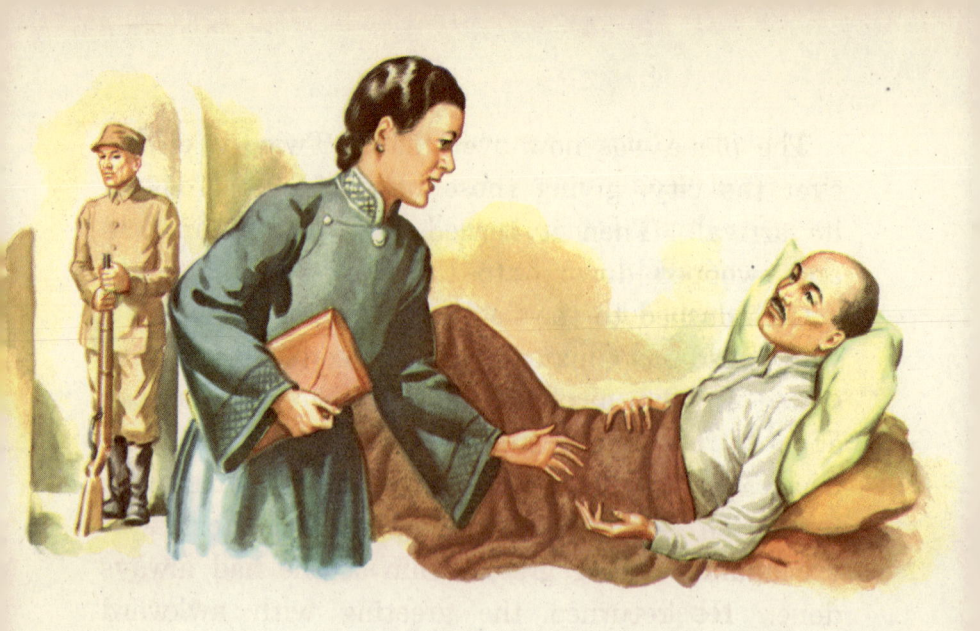

"Why have you come?" he exclaimed in alarm as his wife walked into the room. "You have come into a tiger's lair.

"Although I urged you not to come," he went on, "I felt that I could not prevent it. As I opened the Bible this morning, my eye fell on the words, 'Jehovah will now do a new thing, and that is, He will make a woman protect a man.'

"But do not ask me," the Generalissimo added sternly, "to give in to the rebels."

"I agree,'" she replied. "Our country comes before even your safety. But to save the country there is more need than ever before for you to live. I am here to share your fate and to die with you, if God so wills it; and if He wills otherwise, to live and work with you for the sake of China."

Madame Chiang Kai-shek had several talks with the rebel leader, who was uneasy. "I realize," he said, "that I did the wrong thing in capturing the Generalissimo. I did not mean to do him actual harm," he protested over and over again.

He now desired to release Chiang Kai-shek. He could not, however, get the other rebels to agree. "If we free him, he will have us executed," they declared. For they knew that would be the usual military discipline for such outrageous rebellion as the imprisonment of their own army chief.

The rebel told of the proposal that they had tried to put before the Generalissimo—their urgent wish to attack Japan. Chiang Kai-shek had, however, shown himself so strict in army discipline that he refused to discuss his plans with those of lower military rank. So they had misunderstood him and had turned against him in extreme anger.

"But after we had captured him," said the rebel to Madame Chiang, "I read the letters and military papers of the Generalissimo. I was startled to find that all the reforms that we desire have long been in his mind. We wanted them at once, but he was wisely awaiting the right time.

"Please, try to make the Generalissimo less angry," implored the rebel officer. "Tell him that we do not want anything now. When we seized him we thought it was for the good of China."

"We wanted the reforms to come immediately. We thought he was not employing stern enough tactics against China's enemy," went on the rebel.

"You are too impatient," Madame Chiang told the apologetic officer. "China cannot be changed in a day. The Generalissimo takes the only way, that of painstaking, steady work."

"I tried again and again to talk things over with him," asserted the young officer, "but each time he scolded me violently."

"You do not understand the Generalissimo," said Madame Chiang consolingly. "He scolds only the people of whom he has hope. If he thinks people are useless, he will not take the trouble to scold them."

"In a letter to the Generalissimo which I read," said the repentant rebel, "you told him that you both must strive harder to carry out the vows you made on your wedding day to work for the people. These words genuinely moved me," he confided.

"You must," Madame Chiang admonished him, "ask God to guide you on all occasions if you wish to help China. It was only by the mercy of God that my husband did not die from the bullets of the machine guns or from pneumonia. But let us not talk about that. The thing to discuss is how to bring this to a happy ending. How shall we proceed?"

Off went the officer to confer with his fellow rebels and try to persuade them to free Chiang Kai-shek. With them sat Madame Chiang's own brother, who was making an effort to help them come to the right decision.

"No," declared the stubborn rebels, "we will not release the Generalissimo. Our heads would not be safe. Let him sign a paper to say that we shall not be executed; then we shall release him."

But Chiang Kai-shek would not agree to sign any paper while he was held a prisoner. No chief of staff could make promises as a condition of being released by his own lower-ranking officers. His authority would be destroyed.

"Your heads will be quite safe," Madame Chiang assured the suspicious mutineers. "You know that the Generalissimo has a kind heart. So you must depend upon his generosity."

Time sped by. Christmas Day was approaching. If the Generalissimo were not released on that day, the truce would be over, and the forces in the South would then attack Sian. Madame Chiang would have failed.

Generalissimo and Madame Chiang woke early on Christmas morning and exchanged Christmas greetings, but neither one felt really merry. Their minds were filled with unspoken questions as to what the day might bring forth.

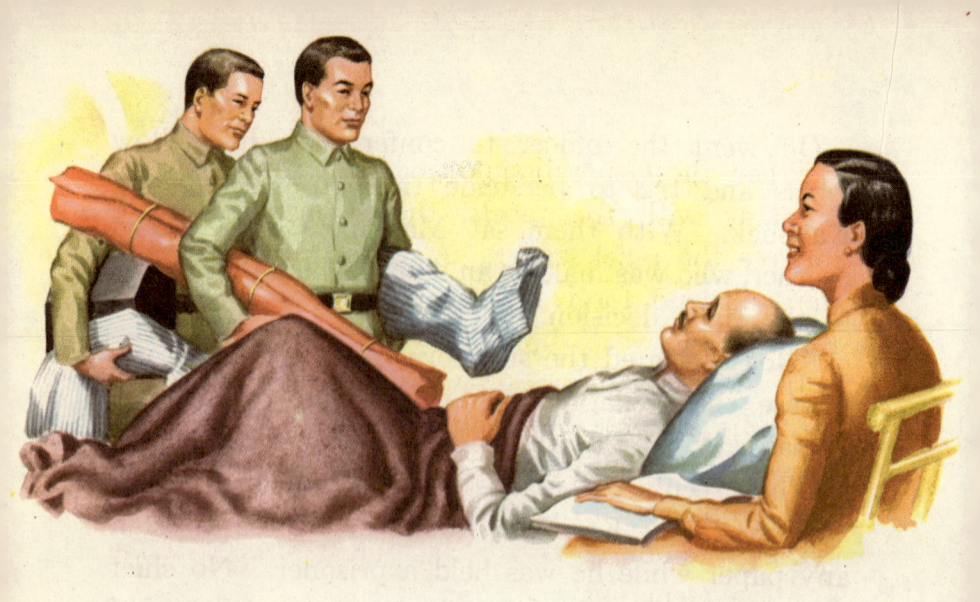

Suddenly the door opened to admit two men. Each held a golf stocking stretched to giant size. Besides small gifts there was a portable typewriter for Madame Chiang, and for the Generalissimo there was a traveling rug. Even in the midst of their anxieties, Mr. Donald had remembered Christmas Day and its present-giving.

Later that day they received the most thrilling present of all their lives. They were told that the Generalissimo was free. The stubborn mutineers had at last agreed to let him go. They came and stood beside his bed while he reminded them of their duty to China, and of his own responsibilities.

"You must obey all orders of our government," he said. "You have confessed that you are sorry for your rebellion. So I will recommend that you should not be punished."

When the Generalissimo and his wife arrived at Nanking with the rebels, the government heads forgave the rebel leader. All his fellow mutineers were likewise forgiven—at the request of Chiang Kai-shek.

In the city of Nanking great rejoicing broke out. By radio and by telegraph, the news spread, "The Generalissimo is released!" Fireworks were set off, and people cried for joy. Students and soldiers marched about waving flags and shouting, "Long live the Generalissimo!"

Chiang Kai-shek had united the country in love and respect for him.

The excitement over the successful outcome of Madame Chiang's dangerous mission gradually died down, but for her the work of serving her country knows no end. Every day—indeed almost every hour—brings new responsibilities.

She supervises the special herds of cattle that she has introduced so that China can produce more milk for the children. Then she raises money to support a Chinese agricultural college whose staff of teachers was trained in America to speed up the improvement of poultry, so that China may have more and bigger eggs. She flies to inspect the many homes which she has established in China to try to bring health and happiness to more than twenty thousand orphaned boys and girls.

But courageous as she is, Madame Chiang could not care for all the children in these orphanages alone. That she has had help is told in this letter to some friends in the United States:

> I can hear you ask—where do all these twenty thousand children come from?
>
> Well, the answers are very sad. The homes of these children, and thousands of other children like them, are no more. Their fathers and mothers, as we say in China, have mounted the back of a dragon and have gone far, far into the skies for a long and peaceful sleep.
>
> When their homes were destroyed and their parents were no more, these little children got lost. They did not know what to do. How could they? Many of them starved for days. They tried to eat the bark of trees and the leaves of plants. They drank water out of the fields. They were dirty and very ill.
>
> But by and by, people in distant cities heard of their plight, and they formed an association to help them. People were sent to the war zones to collect the children who were lost and alone and bring them back to homes in the mountains where they could be cared for.

Nothing is too small or too great for the first lady of China to grapple with if it will help the sum of happiness and the good of China.

Stories That Never Grow Old

Robin Hood

Robin Meets a Stranger

In olden days there lived in Merry England a man named Robin Hood. Now Robin was an outlaw by the King's decree, and with a price on his head to boot, for he had slain the King's deer. No towered castle gave Robin refuge, but only the shadowy glades of Sherwood Forest. There he dwelt with his band of loyal followers.

Though Robin was an outlaw, no man in England was more beloved, for no one ever asked his aid in vain. Rob the rich and help the needy was bold Robin's motto, and many a poor man passing through Sherwood Forest found his pockets lined with gold that had lately been jingling in a fat merchant's purse. Robin Hood's band vowed to do as he bade them and to answer promptly the summons of his hunting horn. They were clad all alike in suits of

Lincoln green, and each carried a stout bow of yew. Skillful archers they all were, but none sent arrow flying with such skill and cunning as Robin.

Plowman, tinker, minstrel, or yeoman traveled in Sherwood Forest unharmed, but rich men with money bags trembled as they neared the outlaw's domain.

One midsummer day as Robin strolled through Sherwood Forest, he came to a stream whose only bridge was a fallen log. Not till he had set foot upon the log did he realize that a stranger faced him from the opposite end. Now Robin was of no mind to back down to any man, even though the stranger stood full half-a-head taller than himself.

"Ho, there!" quoth Robin. "Stand thou back and let the better man cross first."

"Stand back thyself!" retorted the stranger, "for I own no man my better."

"So?" replied bold Robin, fitting arrow to bow. "Perchance an arrow between the ribs will change thy tune."

"A coward's challenge," scoffed the tall stranger, budging not a whit. "Wouldst thou draw a bow when I have naught but a stick to defend me?"

Then Robin blushed with shame, for in his hasty pride he had failed to note the stranger's weapons. Without a word he tossed his bow and arrows on the bank and unbuckled the oaken stick at his belt.

"Now," quoth he. "Meet me if thou darest, and we will fight until one of us tumbles into the water."

And fight they did, belaboring each other roundly, but each turned the other's blows so deftly that neither gave way an inch. So the two stood and fought for nigh onto an hour, and many a stout blow found its mark, but neither man was willing to call "Enough." Each one kept his footing upon the log as nimbly as a tight-wire walker at a fair. In truth it seemed that they would still be fighting at sunset, when suddenly the stranger clouted Robin squarely upon the ribs and sent him head over heels into the water.

"Now where is the better man!" called out the tall stranger, roaring with gusty laughter.

"Cooling in the water," returned Robin merrily, stumbling to his feet and splashing his way to the bank. "Faith, but thou art a stout hand with a cudgel." He shook the water from him and held out his hand.

"Give me thy hand," he cried. "I must own thou art a brave soul and a sturdy fighter."

"And I," quoth the stranger with a merry twinkle, "must grant that thou hast a good heart. For never a man took a drubbing with such good spirit."

"A good heart I may have and more besides," returned Robin, and lifting his hunting horn to his lips, he blew three strong blasts.

Before the stranger could do more than ask the why and the wherefore of such a trumpeting, a score of archers, all clad in Lincoln green, burst from the surrounding forest.

"Good master!" cried Will Stutely, staring aghast at Robin's dripping figure. "How now?"

"Why, naught of any matter," said Robin slyly. "Except that this stranger hath tumbled me into the water and thwacked me soundly besides."

Without more ado, the archers fell upon the tall stranger, and though the big fellow was well able to use his cudgel, Robin restrained them with a merry shout.

"Nay, nay, men! I summoned you not to fight, but to welcome a brother." Then turning to the stranger, Robin told his own name and the purpose of the band and asked him to be one of them.

"That will I be right gladly," said the stranger. "And here is my hand and my heart with it to seal the bargain. My name, if you would know it, is John Little."

"John Little!" chortled Will Stutely in high glee, for the man was seven feet in height and at least an ell around the waist. "That must be altered. A new name you shall have, John Little, and that as speedily as I can perform a christening."

"A christening! A christening!" cried all the outlaws, and before the tall stranger could do more than stare at them in amazement, seven bold fellows had seized him, while still another of their band ran straightway to the outlaws' lair and brought out a brimming tankard of fresh-brewed ale.

"Nay! Nay!" spluttered poor John, guessing their purpose, but all his cries were to no avail. Seven feet tall though he was, and with muscles like steel, he was no match for seven of Robin's men. Laughing and shouting, they held him fast while Will Stutely pushed his way through the cavorting throng, holding aloft the tankard of ale.

Instantly the outlaws ceased their wild antics, lest they miss a single word.

"I now christen thee *Little John*," cried Will, who doted on such merry pranks, and forthwith he emptied the tankard of foaming ale over the tall fellow's head.

"Little John he is," cried Robin, "and Little John he shall be." And all the outlaws laughed so wholeheartedly at their prank, that the big fellow could do naught but laugh with them.

So *Little John* the stranger became to all the band, in spite of his size and his protests. And they all made merry under the greenwood trees and feasted upon the King's deer.

"Now, look you, Little John," said Robin Hood when the feast was over. "Rob no tiller of the fields, nor any yeoman. But if a fat merchant or rich landowner passes by, then take care to relieve him of his ill-gotten wealth. And above all, keep a sharp lookout for the Sheriff of Nottingham."

Little John nodded, for everyone in the country round knew that the Sheriff of Nottingham had sworn to capture Robin Hood by fair means or foul. For the sheriff was a man with fingers greedy for gold, and the price on Robin Hood's head was a good two hundred pounds.

Little John Proves His Loyalty

One Sunday morning Robin asked Little John to come with him to church in Nottingham. As was their custom, they took their bows, and on the way Little John proposed an archery contest. Robin Hood laughed haughtily and said that Little John might have three tries to his master's one.

Robin soon repented this offer, for Little John speedily won the contest. At this, Robin struck his friend. Now Little John was not the man to bear such treatment. He told Robin that he would never more own him for master, and he walked away. Then Robin was ashamed, but his pride prevented his saying so; and he went on to Nottingham.

Well he knew that to enter the church alone was dangerous. However, there he was, and there he meant to stay. As he knelt down, one man recognized him, and that man ran to tell the sheriff.

The sheriff quickly summoned all his guards and marched to the church. Their noisy entrance caused

Robin to look around. "Alas and alack," he said to himself, "now do I need Little John." But he drew his sword and fought so savagely that twelve of the sheriff's men lay prone before him. Then Robin found himself face to face with the sheriff and dealt him a fierce blow, but his sword broke on the sheriff's head. So the guards closed about Robin and bound him hand and foot.

Ill news travels swiftly, and soon the outlaws heard that their master was in prison. They cursed and moaned till Little John bade them take courage and unfolded a plan to outwit the sheriff.

The next morning Little John hid with a comrade till they saw a messenger riding by. It was the sheriff's man carrying a letter to the King, telling him of the capture of Robin Hood.

"I pray you," asked Little John, going up to the messenger, "can you give us tidings of the outlaw, Robin Hood, who was captured yesterday?"

"You may thank me that he is captured," said the rider, "for I laid hands on him first."

"We thank you so much that we will go with you," said Little John, "for Robin Hood's men are in this forest, and you ride at the peril of your life."

So they started on together, but suddenly Little John grasped the horse's bridle and pulled down the messenger. Seizing the letter, the two outlaws carried it to the King's palace in London town.

When Little John and his companion were brought before the King, the two foresters fell on their knees and held out the letter.

"God save you, my lord," they said. "We are humble messengers from the Sheriff of Nottingham, and we have come to bear this message to you."

Breaking the seals on the letter, the King read it carefully. Then he handed his royal seal to the foresters and commanded them to bear it to the Sheriff of Nottingham and to bid him without delay bring Robin Hood unharmed into the presence of the King. "There never was yeoman in Merry England that I longed so much to see," said the King. He then bade his royal treasurer give the messengers twenty pounds each, and he made them his yeomen.

Little John took the King's seal to the sheriff, who made him and his companion welcome because he thought they were the King's men. Then the sheriff set a feast for them, and the sheriff himself ate and drank so heartily that he fell asleep.

Creeping away stealthily, the two outlaws set out for the prison. Once there, they overpowered the guard, and, taking his keys, hunted through the dungeon cells until they came upon Robin Hood. "Follow us," whispered Little John.

The three stole out of the prison and crept along until they reached the lowest part of the city wall, from which they jumped and were safe and free.

"Farewell, Robin," said Little John. "I have done thee a good turn for a bad one."

But Robin Hood would not let him go and begged his pardon so humbly that Little John once more consented to be his friend and his comrade.

Robin Meets the King

Now the King heard of Robin's adventure, and he did not intend that Robin Hood should keep on doing as he pleased; so the King called his knights to follow him to Nottingham, where they would lay plans how best to capture the bold outlaw.

But though the King dwelt in Nottingham for six weeks, he could hear nothing of Robin. The outlaw seemed to have vanished into the air with his men, though one by one the deer were vanishing, too.

At last one day a forester came to the King and told him that if he would see Robin he must come with him and bring along five of his bravest knights. The King made ready, and the six men, disguised in monks' robes, mounted their steeds and rode merrily along. The King wore an abbot's embroidered hood over his crown, and he sang as he passed through the greenwood. Suddenly at the turn of a path, Robin and his archers appeared.

Seizing the King's bridle, Robin said, "You will stay awhile with us, Sir Abbot. We are yeomen who live upon the King's deer and have no other food. Now you have abbeys and churches and gold in plenty; therefore give us some of your wealth."

"I have only forty pounds," answered the King, "but if it were a hundred, you should have it all."

So Robin took the forty pounds and gave half to his men. Then he told the disguised King that he would detain him no longer.

"I thank you," said the King, "but I would have you know that our ruler has bidden me give you his seal and pray you to come to Nottingham."

At this message Robin bent his knee. "I love no man in all the world so well as I do my king," he cried. "For your tidings, Sir Abbot, which fill my heart with joy, you shall dine with me for love of my king."

Then Robin led the King into an open place, and lifting his horn, he blew it loud. At its blast seven score young men came speedily.

"They are quicker to do his bidding than my men are to do mine," said the King to himself.

The foresters set out huge roasts of venison and loaves of white bread, and Robin and Little John served the King. "Make good cheer," said Robin. "And then, Sir Abbot, you shall see what sort of life we lead, so that you may tell our king."

When all had finished eating, the archers made ready their bows and hung a rose garland up with a string, for every man was to shoot three arrows in turn, each arrow to be sent straight through the center of the rose wreath. If any man failed, he should have a blow on the head from Robin.

The archers took their places with many a jest and boast, but good bowmen as they were, few could stand such a test.

Little John and even Robin's cousin, Will Scarlet, shot wide of the mark, and the others fared no better. At length no one was left but Robin himself and Gilbert of the Wide Hand.

Once, twice Robin's arrow sped straight to its mark. Robin bent his bow for the third try, but a sudden breeze tweaked the feathered tip, and the arrow fell to earth three fingers from the garland.

"Master," said Gilbert, "thou hast lost; stand forth and take thy punishment, as 'twas agreed."

"I will take it," answered Robin, "but, Sir Abbot, I pray that I may receive the blow at your hands."

The King hesitated. "It is not fitting for me to smite such a stout yeoman," he said.

"Smite on and spare me not," quoth Robin. So the King turned up his sleeve and gave Robin such a blow on the head that he lost his feet and rolled upon the ground. As the King struck this blow, his hood fell back, so that Robin saw his crown.

"'Tis the King of England! Now I know you well," cried Robin and fell on his knees, and all the outlaws with him. "Mercy, I ask, my King, for all my brave foresters and me."

"Mercy I grant," said the King, "and therefore I came hither, to bid you and your men leave the greenwood and dwell in my court with me."

"So shall it be," answered Robin. "My men and I will come to your court and spend our time in your service."

"Have you any green cloth," asked the King, "that you could sell to me?"

Robin brought out thirty yards and more, and the King and his men threw off their monks' robes, and Robin clad them all in Lincoln green. "Now we shall all ride to Nottingham," said the King.

The good people of Nottingham saw them coming and trembled as they watched the dark mass of Lincoln green drawing near. "I fear lest our king be slain," whispered one to another, "and if this wild band of outlaws gets into the town, there is not one of us whose life is safe."

The King laughed aloud when he saw their fear, and called them back. Right glad were they to hear his voice, and they feasted and made merry.

A few days later the King returned to London, and Robin and Little John and all the merry outlaw band went with him.

Robin dwelt in the King's court for a twelvemonth and a day. But his men, who had lived under the open sky of Sherwood Forest, could not dwell contentedly amid streets and houses. One by one they slipped away, till only Little John and Will Scarlet were left. Then they went also, and Robin himself yearned for the greenwood glades. At last he went to the King and begged leave to go on a journey.

"I may not say you nay," answered the King. "Seven nights you may be gone and no more."

Robin thanked him and that evening set out for his old haunts in Sherwood Forest.

It was early morning when at last he reached the greenwood glade, and all about him he could hear the sweet notes of the larks and of other birds, great and small. "It seems long since I was here," he said to himself. "How happy I would be if only I could see my loyal band once more!"

So he blew on his horn three blasts loud and clear, and all the outlaws of the forest came flocking round him.

"Welcome, our dear master, back to the greenwood tree," they cried, and they fell on their knees before him in delight.

Nothing the King could say or do would tempt Robin back again, and he dwelt in the greenwood for two and twenty years. Come good fortune or ill, he was ever a faithful friend and kind to the poor.

Tom and the Treasure Chest

Tom Encounters a Mystery

All day long a strange sloop had been lying just offshore. No one sought to board her, for these were pirate days, and the folk of Delaware Bay minded their own affairs.

There had been a thunderstorm that afternoon, and Tom Chist had gone down the beach to bail out the boat in readiness for the next day's fishing with his foster father, Matt Abrahamson. It was full moonlight now as he was returning, and the sky was full of clouds. Now and then there was a dull flash to westward, and once a muttering growl of thunder, promising another storm to come.

Tom could see the sails of the mysterious sloop glimmering in the moonlight. He was walking up the shore homeward when he saw at some distance ahead of him a ship's boat drawn up on the narrow beach and a group of men clustered about it. He hurried forward with a good deal of curiosity to see who had landed, but it was not until he had come close to them that he realized that they were pirates. With a shudder, half dread, half thrill,

Tom wondered if Captain Kidd, the most famous pirate of all, was among them.

They had evidently just landed, and two men were lifting a chest from the boat. One was a Negro, naked to the waist, and the other a white man in shirt sleeves, wearing petticoat breeches, a black hat upon his head, a red bandanna handkerchief around his neck, and gold earrings in his ears. He had a long plaited queue hanging down his back, and a sheath knife dangling from his side. Another man, evidently the captain of the party, stood at a distance as they lifted the chest out of the boat.

He had a cane in one hand and a lighted lantern in the other, though the moon was shining as bright as day. He wore jackboots and a handsome laced coat, and he had a long, drooping mustache that curled down below his chin. He wore a feathered hat, and his long black hair hung down on his shoulders.

They were so busy lifting the chest from the boat that at first they did not notice Tom Chist. It was the white man with the long plaited queue and the gold earrings who called to him.

"Boy, what do you want here?" he said in a rough, hoarse voice. "Where did ye come from?" Then dropping his end of the chest and without giving Tom time to answer him, he pointed off down the beach and said, "You'd better be going about your own business, if you know what's good for you; and don't you come back, or you'll find what you don't want waiting for you."

The pirates were looking at him, and so, without saying a word, Tom turned and walked away. The man who had spoken to him followed him threateningly for a short distance, as if to see that he went away as he was bidden. But presently he stopped, and Tom hurried on. Then he stopped also, turned, and looked back whence he had come.

There had been something very strange in the appearance of the men he had seen, something very mysterious in their actions, and he wondered what it all meant and what they were going to do. He stood for a little while thus, looking and listening. He could see nothing and could hear only the sound of distant talking. What were they doing on the lonely shore thus at night? Then, following a sudden impulse, he retraced his steps across the sand, his object being to spy upon them and to watch what they were about from behind the low sand hummocks that fronted the beach.

Tom had gone some distance when he became aware of voices that seemed to be drawing closer to him. He stopped and stood listening, and instantly the voices stopped also. He crouched there silently in the glimmering moonlight, and the stillness seemed to press upon him like a heavy hand.

Then suddenly the man's voice began again, and Tom heard someone counting. "Ninety-one," the voice began, "ninety-two, ninety-three, ninety-four"—the slow, monotonous count coming nearer and nearer—"ninety-five, ninety-six, ninety-seven," and so on.

Suddenly he saw three heads appear above the sand hill, so close that he crouched down quickly with a keen thrill. His first fear was that they might have seen him in the moonlight; but they had not, and his heart rose again as the voice went steadily on. "One hundred twenty," it was saying—"and twenty-one and twenty-two and twenty-three and twenty-four," and then he who was counting walked out from behind the sandy hill into the shimmering brightness.

It was the man with the cane whom Tom had seen before—the captain of the party. He carried his cane under his arm now. He was holding his lantern close to something that he held in his hand, upon which he looked closely as he walked with a slow, measured tread in a straight line across the sand, counting each step as he took it.

Behind him walked two other figures; one was the half-naked Negro, the other the man with the plaited queue and earrings whom Tom had seen lifting the chest out of the boat. Now they were carrying the heavy box between them, laboring through the sand with shuffling tread as they bore it onward. As he who was counting pronounced the word *thirty*, the two men set the chest down on the sand with a grunt, the white man panting and blowing and wiping his sleeve across his forehead. And immediately he who counted took out a slip of paper and made a mark on it. The others stood there while Tom lay behind the sand hummock watching them.

One, two, three minutes passed, and then the men picked up the chest and started on again; and then again the other man began counting. "Thirty and one, and thirty and two, and thirty and three, and thirty and four"—he walked straight across the open space, still looking at that which he held in his hand—until the men disappeared, and still Tom could hear the counting voice far in the distance.

Just as they disappeared behind the hill there was a flash of light; and by and by, as Tom lay still, listening to the counting, he heard, after a long interval, a faraway muffled rumble of distant thunder. He waited for a while and then arose and stepped to the top of the hummock behind which he had been lying. He looked all about him, but there was no one else to be seen.

Then he stepped down and followed the pirates. He crept along cautiously, stopping now and then to make sure that he still heard the low counting voice, and when it ceased he lay down upon the sand and waited until it began again.

Presently, still following the voice, Tom saw the three men again in the distance. Skirting a hill covered with coarse sedge grass, he came to a point where he could see an open level space gleaming white in the moonlight.

The pirates had been crossing the level of sand and were now not more than twenty-five paces from him. They had set down the chest, upon which the white man with the long queue had seated himself to rest, the Negro standing beside him. The moon shone as bright as day, full upon his face. He was looking right at Tom, every line of his face as keenly cut with white lights and black shadows as if it were carved from ivory and jet. He sat so still that Tom drew back, thinking he had been discovered.

Tom lay silent, his pulse beating heavily in his throat; and presently he heard the counting begin again. When he looked, he saw they were going straight across the open. A soft, sliding hummock of sand lay in front of them, and they did not turn aside but went straight over it, the leader still counting and still keeping his eyes fixed on that which he held in his hand. Then they disappeared again behind the white crest of the hill.

Tom followed the men cautiously until they had gone almost a half mile inland. When next he saw them clearly it was from a sandy rise. The white man who had helped carry the chest was kneeling and whittling the end of a stick into a long wooden peg. When he had finished, he rose and stepped to the place where the man who seemed to be in charge had stuck his cane upright into the ground as if to mark the particular spot. He drew the cane out of the sand, thrusting the stick down in its stead. Then he drove the peg down with a wooden mallet which the Negro handed to him.

The sharp rapping of the mallet sounded loud in the perfect stillness, and Tom lay watching and wondering what it all meant. The man drove the peg farther and farther down into the sand until it showed only two or three inches above the surface. Just as he finished, there was another flash of light followed by a deep rumble of thunder.

The two white men were now stooping over the peg, the Negro watching them. Then presently the man with the cane started straight away from the peg, carrying the end of a long measuring line, the other end of which the man with the plaited queue held against the top of the peg. When the pirate captain had reached the end of the measuring line, he marked a cross upon the sand; and then again they measured out another stretch of space.

So they measured a distance five times over, and then, from where Tom lay, he could see the man with the queue drive another peg just at the foot of a tall white sand dune which stood sharp and clear against the night sky behind. As soon as the man with the plaited queue had driven the second peg into the ground, they began measuring again. Still measuring, they disappeared in another direction, which took them in behind a sand dune where Tom no longer could see what they were doing.

Presently from behind the hill there came, for the third time, the sharp rapping sound of the mallet driving still another peg. Then after a while the two pirates emerged from behind the sand dune into the space of moonlight again.

They came direct to the spot where the chest lay. The white man and the black man, lifting it once more, walked away across the sand and on behind the edge of the nearest hill and out of Tom's sight.

Tom Chist could no longer see what the pirates were doing; neither did he dare to cross over the open space of sand that now lay between them and him. He lay there speculating on what the pirates were about; and meantime the storm cloud was rising higher and higher above the horizon, with louder and louder mutterings of thunder. In the silence he could hear an occasional click as of some iron implement, and he supposed that the pirates were burying the chest, though just where they were at work he could neither see nor tell.

Tom lay there watching and listening. By and by a puff of warm air blew across the sand; a thumping of thunder leaped from the storm cloud, which every minute was coming nearer and nearer.

Suddenly the three pirates came out again from behind the sand hill; the captain leading the way, the Negro and white man following closely behind him. They had gone about halfway across the level toward the sand hummock behind which Tom Chist lay, when the white man stopped and bent over as though to tie his shoe. This brought the Negro a few steps in front of his companion.

That which then followed happened so suddenly, so unexpectedly, so swiftly, that Tom had hardly time to realize what it all meant before it was over. As the Negro passed him, the white man arose suddenly and stood silently erect; and Tom Chist saw the white moonlight glint upon the blade of a great dirk knife which he held in his hand. The white man took one, two silent, catlike steps behind the unsuspecting Negro. There was a sweeping flash of the blade in the moonlight, and a blow, the thump of which Tom could hear even from where he lay. There was an instant yell from the black man, who stumbled forward, stopped, regained his footing, and then stood for a moment as if rooted to the spot.

Meantime the pirate captain had stopped, and now he stood there watching, with his hand resting on his cane.

Then the black man started to run. The white man stood for a while glaring after him; then he started after his victim upon the run. The black man was not far from Tom when he staggered and fell. At that instant the first edge of a cloud cut across the moon, and there was a sudden darkness; but in the silence Tom heard the sound of another blow and a groan, and presently a voice calling to the pirate captain that it was all over.

Then Tom scrambled up and ran away, plunging down into the hollow of sand in the shadows below. Over the next rise and down into the next hollow, and so on over the sliding, shifting ground he ran, panting and gasping. It seemed to him that he could hear footsteps following, and in the terror that possessed him he expected every instant to feel the cold dirk blade slide between his own ribs.

So he ran on like one in a nightmare. His feet grew heavy as lead; his breath came hot and dry in his throat. But still he ran and ran until at last he found himself in front of his foster father's cottage, sobbing for breath.

As Tom opened the door and dashed into the darkened house, there was a flash of lightning, and even as he slammed the door behind him there came a peal of thunder, heavy as though a great weight had been dropped from the roof of the sky.

Tom crept into bed, trembling, shuddering, bathed in sweat; his heart beating like a triphammer, and his brain dizzy from that long race of terror.

For a long, long time he lay awake, trembling and chattering with nervous chills, and when he did fall asleep, it was only to drop into monstrous dreams.

Then came the dawning of the broad daylight, and before the rising of the sun Tom was up and out of doors to find the young day dripping with the rain of overnight. His first act was to climb the nearest sand hill and to gaze out toward the bay where the pirate ship had been the day before.

It was no longer there!

Soon afterward Tom's foster father came out and called to him to get a bite to eat, for it was time for them to be away fishing.

All that morning the recollection of the night before hung over Tom Chist like a great threatening cloud. Not for a moment was this cloud lifted, and Tom knew he must tell someone his dreadful secret. When the boat reached the shore again, he leaped scrambling to the beach, and as soon as the fish were cared for, he hurried away to find Parson Jones. He ran all the way, hardly stopping once, and when he knocked at the door, he was panting and sobbing for breath.

The good man was sitting on the kitchen doorstep, while his wife within was rattling about among the pans and dishes, preparing their supper, of which a tempting, porky smell already filled the air.

Then Tom Chist told his story, panting, hurrying, tumbling one word over another in his excitement. Parson Jones listened, breaking every now and then into an exclamation of wonder.

"I don't see why they killed that poor black man," said Tom as he finished his tale.

"Why, that is easy enough to understand," said the parson. "'Twas a treasure box they buried!"

In his agitation the parson had risen from his seat and was now clumsily pacing up and down.

"A treasure box!" Tom cried out.

"Aye, a treasure box! That was why they killed the poor black man. He was the only one, d'ye see, besides those two, who knew the place where 'twas hid, and now that they've killed him, there's nobody but themselves knows. The villains!"

"Then," said Tom, "it is indeed a wicked, bloody treasure and fit to bring a curse upon anybody who may find it!"

"'Tis more like to bring a curse upon the souls who buried it," said Parson Jones. "It may be a blessing to him who finds it. But tell me, Tom, d'ye think ye could find the place again where 'twas hid?"

"I could find the place," said Tom, "where the boat was drawn up on the beach."

"Why, then, that's something to start from," replied his friend. "If we can find that, perhaps we can find whither they went from there."

"If I were certain it was a treasure box," cried out Tom Chist, "I would rake over every foot of sand betwixt here and Henlopen to find it."

"'Tis like hunting a pin in a haystack," said the parson, "but we'll have a try at it."

The Sand Yields a Clue

The next afternoon Parson Jones and Tom Chist set off together upon their expedition. Tom carried a spade over his shoulder, and the reverend gentleman went along beside him with his cane.

As they jogged along the beach, they talked together about the only thing they *could* talk about—the treasure box. "And how big did you say 'twas?" asked the good gentleman.

"About so long," said Tom Chist, measuring off upon the spade, "and about so wide and this deep."

"What if it should be full of money, Tom!" the clergyman asked, swinging his cane in excitement of the thought as he strode along briskly.

"By Moses!" said Tom Chist, hurrying to keep up with his friend. "Then I'd buy a ship for myself, I would, and I'd trade with India and China, I would. Suppose the chest be all full of money, sir, and suppose we should find it; would there be enough in it, d'ye suppose, to buy a ship?"

"To be sure there would be enough, Tom; enough and to spare, and a good big lump over."

"And if I find it, 'tis mine to keep, is it, and no mistake?"

"Why, to be sure it would be yours!" cried the parson in a loud voice. "Whose else would it be but yours if you find it! Can you tell me that?"

"If ever I have a ship of my own," said Tom Chist, "and if ever I sail to India in her, I'll fetch ye back the very best chest of tea, sir, that ever was fetched from that land."

The parson burst out laughing. "Thankee, Tom," he said, "and I'll thankee again when I get my tea. But tell me, Tom, didst ever hear of the farmer girl who counted her chickens before they hatched?"

It was thus they talked as they hurried along up the beach together, until they came to a place at last where Tom stopped short and stood looking about him. "'Twas just here," he said, "I saw the boat last night. I know 'twas here, for I mind me that bit of wreck yonder, and that there was a tall stake in the sand just where yon stake is."

Parson Jones put on his spectacles and went over to the stake which Tom had pointed out. "Why, Tom, this hath just been driven down into the sand. 'Tis a brand-new stake of wood, and the pirates must have set it here themselves as a mark."

Tom looked closely at the stake. It was a stout piece of oak nearly two inches thick; it had been shaped with some care, and the top of it had been painted red. He shook the stake and tried to move it, but it had been driven so deeply into the sand that he could not stir it. "Aye, sir," he said, "it must have been set here for a mark, for I'm sure 'twas not here yesterday or the day before."

Tom stood looking about him to see if there were other signs of the pirates. At a little distance there was the corner of something white sticking up out of the sand. He could see that it was a scrap of paper, and he pointed to it, calling out, "Yonder is a piece of paper, sir. I wonder if they left that behind them."

It was miraculous chance that placed the paper there. There was only an inch of it showing, and if it had not been for Tom's sharp eyes, the paper would certainly have been overlooked and passed by. The next windstorm would have covered it up, and then all that afterward happened never would have occurred. "Look, sir," he said as he struck the sand from the paper. "It hath writing on it."

"Let me see it," said Parson Jones. He adjusted the spectacles a little more firmly on his nose as he took the paper in his hand and began studying it. "What's this?" he said; "a whole lot of figures and nothing else." Then he read aloud, " 'Mark— S.S.W. by S.' What d'ye suppose that means, Tom?"

"I don't know sir," said Tom. "But perhaps we can understand it better if you read on."

" 'Tis all a lot of figures," said Parson Jones, "without a grain of meaning in them so far as I can see, unless they be sailing directions." Then he began reading again, " 'Mark—S.S.W. by S. 40, 72, 91, 130, 151, 177, 202, 232, 256, 271'—d'ye see, it must be sailing directions—'299, 335, 626, 652, 676, 695, 724, 851, 876, 905, 940, 967. Peg S.E. by E. 269 foot. Peg S.S.W. by S. 427 foot. Peg. Dig to the west of this six foot.' "

"What's that about a peg?" exclaimed Tom. "What's that about a peg? And there's something about digging, too!" It was as though a sudden light began shining into his brain. He felt himself growing very excited. "Read that over again, sir," he cried. "Why, sir, you remember I told you they drove a peg into the sand, and don't they say to dig close to it? Read it over again, sir!"

"Peg?" said the good gentleman. "To be sure it was about a peg. Let's look again. Yes, here it is. 'Peg S.E. by E. 269 foot.'"

"Aye!" cried out Tom again, in great excitement, "Don't you remember what I told you, sir—269 foot? That must be what I saw 'em measuring with the line."

Parson Jones had now caught the flame of excitement that was blazing so strongly in Tom's breast. He felt as though some wonderful thing was about to happen to them. "To be sure, to be sure!" he called out, in a big voice. "They measured out 427 foot south-southwest by south, and then they drove in another peg, and then they buried the box six foot to the west of it. Why, Tom—why, Tom Chist! If—we've read this aright, thy fortune is made."

Tom stood there, staring. The harsh, insistent, jarring note of a tern echoed in his ears, but Tom heard nothing; saw nothing except the old man's face.

The parson spoke again. "What do these figures mean?" And Tom observed how the paper shook in his hand as he read, "'Mark 40, 72, 91——'"

"Mark?" cried out Tom, almost screaming. "Why, that must mean the stake yonder; that must be the mark." And he pointed to the oaken stick with its red tip blazing against the white sand behind it.

"And the 40 and 72 and 91," cried the old gentleman, in a voice equally shrill—"why, they must mean the number of steps the pirate was counting."

"To be sure that's what they mean!" cried Tom. "It can be nothing else. Oh, come, sir—come, sir; let us make haste and find it!"

"Stay! Stay!" said the good gentleman, holding up his hand. His voice was steady enough, though very hoarse, but his hand shook and trembled as if with palsy. "Stay! Stay! First of all, we must follow these measurements. And 'tis a marvelous thing," he croaked, after a little pause, "how this paper ever came to be here."

"Maybe 'twas blown here by the storm," said Tom.

"Like enough," said Parson Jones. "Like enough, after the wretches had buried the chest and killed the poor man, they were so buffeted about by the storm that the paper shook out of the man's pocket without his knowing aught of it."

"But let us find the box!" cried out Tom Chist.

"Aye, aye," said the good man, "but we must have something to measure off the feet when we find the peg. You run across to Tom Brooke's house and fetch the measuring rod he used to lay out his new barn. While you're gone, I'll pace off the distance with my pocket compass here."

When Tom returned, the parson was nowhere to be seen; but Tom followed the scuffling marks in the sand across the humps and hollows. He found the good gentleman in a spot which he at once knew as soon as he laid eyes on it. It was the open space where the pirates had driven their first peg and where Tom had seen them kill the poor black man.

Tom saw that the parson was still bending over, scraping away the sand from something he had found.

It was the first peg!

Inside of a half hour they had found the second and third pegs. Tom stripped off his coat and dug like mad. Suddenly the spade struck something hard. If it had been his own heart that he had hit, his breast could hardly have thrilled more sharply.

It was the treasure box!

Parson Jones himself leaped into the hole and began scraping away the sand with his hands as if he had gone crazy. At last, with some difficulty, they hauled the chest up to the surface, where it lay covered all over with the grit that clung to it. It was locked and fastened with a padlock, and it took a good many blows with the spade to smash the bolt. Parson Jones lifted the lid. Tom leaned forward and gazed down into the open box. It was filled with books and papers and canvas bags tied around and around with cords.

Parson Jones lifted out one of the bags, and it jingled as he did so. He cut the string and with trembling hands gave the bag to Tom, who in an ecstasy of wonder poured upon his outspread coat a cataract of money that twinkled and jingled as it fell in a shining heap.

There were two-and-twenty bags in all: ten full of silver money, eight full of gold money, three full of gold dust, and one small bag with jewels.

" 'Tis enough," cried out Parson Jones, "to make us both rich men as long as we live!"

They sat there for hours as if in a trance, with the money scattered around them. It was sundown before Parson Jones had begun to examine the books and papers in the chest. It was then, sitting there on the sand, the old gentleman reading aloud in his high, cracking voice, that they first learned from the bloody records who it was that had anchored his sloop in the bay all this time. It was the notorious pirate, Captain Kidd!

The King of the Golden River

A Stranger Comes to Treasure Valley

In a secluded mountainous part of Stiria there was, in old time, a valley of the most surprising and luxuriant fertility. It was surrounded on all sides by steep and rocky mountains which were always covered with snow. From the peaks of the mountains torrents of water descended in continuous cataracts. One of these fell westward over the face of a crag so high that when the sun had set and all below was darkness, his beams still shone upon this waterfall, so that it looked like a shower of gold. It was therefore called by the people of the valley, the Golden River.

It was strange that not one of these streams fell into the valley itself. They all flowed down the other side of the mountains and wound their way through broad plains and crowded cities. In time of drought, when all the country round about was burned up, there was still rain in the little valley. Its crops were so heavy, and its hay so high, its apples so red, its grapes so blue, and its honey so sweet, that it was called Treasure Valley.

The whole of this little valley belonged to three brothers called Schwartz, Hans, and Gluck. Now Schwartz and Hans, the two elder brothers, were very ugly men, with heavy eyebrows and small, dull eyes, which were always half shut, so that you could not see into them, yet you always fancied they saw very far into you. They lived by farming Treasure Valley, and very careful farmers they were. They killed everything that did not earn its food. They shot the blackbirds because they pecked the fruit, and they poisoned the crickets for eating the crumbs in the kitchen.

They worked their servants without wages till they would not work any more and then quarreled with them and turned them out without any pay. They generally contrived to keep their corn till it was very dear and then sell it for twice its value. They had heaps of gold lying about on their floors; yet they had never given so much as a penny or a crust of bread in charity. They never went to church and were so cruel and selfish that they came to be known far and near by the nickname of the "Black Brothers."

The youngest brother, Gluck, was completely opposite in both appearance and character. He was not above twelve years old, fair, blue-eyed, and kind to every living thing. He did not, of course, agree very well with his brothers, or rather, they did not agree with him. He was usually appointed to be the turnspit when there was any meat roasting on the spit, which was not often. For to do the brothers justice, they were hardly less sparing upon themselves than upon other people.

Things went on in this manner for a long time. At last came a very wet summer, and everything went wrong in the country around. No sooner had the hay been cut, than the haystacks were floated down to the sea by a flood; the grapevines were cut to pieces with the hail; and the corn was killed by a blight. Only in the Treasure Valley all was safe.

As it had rain when there was rain nowhere else, so it had sun when there was sun nowhere else. Everybody came to buy corn at the farm and went away pouring curses upon the Black Brothers, who asked what price they liked and got it, except from the poor, some of whom starved at their very door.

It was drawing toward winter, when one day the two elder brothers had gone out with their usual warning to Gluck, who was left to turn the roast, that he was to let nobody in and give nothing out. Gluck sat down quite close to the fire, for it was raining very hard, and the kitchen walls were by no means dry. He turned and turned, and the roast got nice and brown.

"What a pity," thought Gluck, "my brothers never ask anybody to dinner. I'm sure when they have a nice piece of mutton like this, and no one else has so much as a piece of dry bread, it would do their hearts good to share it." At that instant, there came a double knock at the door, heavy and dull—more like a puff than a knock.

"It must be the wind," said Gluck. "No one else would dare to strike double knocks at our door."

No, it wasn't the wind; there it came again very hard. Gluck went to the window, opened it, and put out his head to see who it was.

It was the most extraordinary-looking little man Gluck had ever seen. He had a very large nose, slightly brass-colored, and his cheeks were very round and very red. His eyes twinkled merrily through long, silky eyelashes; his mustaches curled twice around like a corkscrew on each side of his mouth; and his hair, of a curious mixed pepper-and-salt color, hung down to his shoulders. He was about four-feet-six in height and wore a conical hat almost as high as himself, decorated with a black feather some three feet long. His doublet was topped by an enormous black, glossy-looking cloak, which the wind whistling round the house carried out from the wearer's shoulders to about four times his own length.

Gluck was so paralyzed by the peculiar appearance of his visitor that he remained fixed without uttering a word, until the old gentleman turned round to look after his fly-away cloak. In so doing he caught sight of Gluck's bright-yellow head in the window, with his mouth and eyes wide open indeed.

"Hollo!" said the little gentleman, "that's not the way to answer the door. I'm wet; let me in."

To do the little man justice, he *was* wet. The brim of his hat was dripping like an umbrella, and from the ends of his mustaches the water began running down over his whiskers like water in a millstream.

"I beg pardon, sir," said Gluck, "but I can't."

"Can't what?" said the old gentleman.

"I can't let you in, sir—I can't indeed. My elder brothers would beat me to death, sir, if I thought of such a thing. What do you want, sir?"

"Want?" said the old gentleman irritably. "I want fire and shelter; and there's your great fire blazing, crackling, and dancing on the walls, with nobody to feel it. Let me in, I say; I only want to warm myself."

Gluck had had his head so long out of the window by this time that he began to feel it was really cold. "He does look very wet," he thought. "I'll just let him in for a quarter of an hour." Round he went to the door and opened it; and as the gentleman walked in, there came a gust of wind that made the old chimneys totter.

"That's a good boy," said the little gentleman. "Never mind your brothers. I'll talk to them."

"Pray, sir, don't," said Gluck. "I can't let you stay till they come; they'd be the death of me."

"Dear me," said the old gentleman. "I'm sorry to hear that. How long may I stay?"

"Only till the mutton's done, sir," replied Gluck, "and it's very brown."

Then the old gentleman walked into the kitchen and sat himself down by the hearth, with the top of his hat reaching up the chimney, for it was a great deal too high for the roof.

"You'll soon dry there, sir," said Gluck, and sat down again to turn the mutton. But the little old gentleman did *not* dry. He went on drip, drip, dripping among the cinders, and the fire fizzed, and sputtered, and began to look very black.

"I beg pardon, sir," said Gluck at length, after watching the water spreading in long streams over the floor. "May I take your cloak?"

"No, thank you," said the old gentleman.

"Your hat, sir!"

"I am all right, thank you," said the old gentleman rather gruffly.

"But—sir—I'm very sorry," said Gluck, "but—really, sir—you're putting the fire out."

"It'll take longer to do the mutton, then," replied his visitor.

Gluck was puzzled by the behavior of his guest; it was such a mixture of boldness and humility. He turned away at the spit musingly.

"That mutton looks nice," said the old gentleman at length. "Can't you give me a little bit!"

"Impossible, sir," said Gluck.

"I'm very hungry," continued the old gentleman. "I've had nothing to eat today. Your brothers surely couldn't miss a bit from the knuckle!"

He spoke in so melancholy a tone that he melted Gluck's heart. "They promised me one slice, sir," said he; "I can give you that, but not a bit more."

"That's a good boy," said the gentleman again.

Gluck warmed a plate and sharpened a knife. "I don't care if I do get beaten for it," he thought. Just as he had cut a large slice out of the mutton, there came a tremendous rap at the door. The old gentleman jumped from the hearth. Gluck fitted the slice into the mutton leg with desperate efforts at exactness, and ran to open the door.

"Why did you keep us waiting in the rain?" said Schwartz, throwing his umbrella in Gluck's face.

"Why, indeed, you little vagabond?" said Hans, administering a box on the ear as he followed his brother into the kitchen.

"Bless my soul!" said Schwartz when he caught sight of the stranger.

"Amen," said the little gentleman, who had taken his hat off, and was standing in the middle of the kitchen, bowing again and again.

"Who's that?" said Schwartz, catching up a rolling pin and turning to Gluck with a fierce frown.

"What's your business?" snarled Hans.

"I am a poor old man, sir," the little gentleman began, "and I saw your fire through the window; so I begged shelter for a quarter of an hour."

"Have the goodness to walk out again, then," said Schwartz. "We've quite enough water in our kitchen without making it a drying-house."

"It is a cold day to turn an old man out in, sir; look at my gray hairs."

"There are enough of them to keep you warm," said Hans. "Walk!"

"I'm very, very hungry, sir; couldn't you spare me a bit of bread before I go?"

"Bread, indeed!" said Schwartz. "Do you suppose we've nothing to do with our bread but to give it to such fellows as you?"

"A little bit?" said the old gentleman.

"Be off!" said Schwartz.

"Pray, gentlemen——"

"Off, and be hanged!" cried Hans, seizing him by the collar. But he had no sooner touched the old gentleman's collar, than away he went spinning round and round till he fell into a corner.

Then Schwartz ran at the old gentleman to turn him out; but Schwartz also had hardly touched the collar, when he went spinning after Hans, hit his head against the wall, and tumbled into the corner.

Then the old gentleman spun himself round in the opposite direction until his cloak was all wound neatly about him, gave an additional twist to his corkscrew mustaches, and said, "Gentlemen, I wish you a very good morning. At twelve o'clock tonight I'll call again. After such unkind treatment you will not be surprised if that visit is the last I ever pay you."

"If I catch you here again," muttered Schwartz; but before he could finish his sentence, the old gentleman had shut the house door behind him with a bang; and there drove past the window, at the same instant, a wreath of ragged cloud that rolled away down the valley in all manner of shapes and melted away at last in a gush of rain.

"A very pretty business, indeed, Mr. Gluck!" said Schwartz. "Dish up the mutton, sir. If ever I catch you at such a trick again—bless me, why the mutton's been cut!"

"You promised me one slice," replied Gluck.

"And you were cutting it hot, I suppose, to catch the gravy. Leave the room and wait in the cellar."

Such a night as it was! Howling wind and rushing rain! The brothers double-barred the door before they went to bed. But as the clock struck twelve, they were both awakened by a tremendous crash, and their door burst open.

"What's that?" cried Schwartz, sitting up in bed.

"Only I," said the little gentleman.

The two brothers stared into the darkness. The room was full of water; and by a misty moonbeam they could see an enormous foam globe, on which, as on a cushion, reclined the little old gentleman, hat and all.

"Sorry to inconvenience you," said their visitor. "I'm afraid your beds are dampish. Better go to your brother's room; I've left the ceiling on there."

They required no further urging, but rushed into Gluck's room in an agony of terror.

"You'll find my card on the kitchen table," the old gentleman called after them. "Remember, the *last* visit."

"Pray Heaven it may!" said Schwartz, shuddering. And the foam globe disappeared.

Dawn came at last, and the two brothers looked out of Gluck's little window in the morning. The Treasure Valley was one mass of ruin and desolation. The flood had swept away trees, crops, cattle; and left in their stead a waste of red sand and gray mud. The two brothers crept shivering and horror-struck into the kitchen. The water had gutted the entire first floor; corn, money, almost every movable thing, had been swept away, and there was left only a small white card on the kitchen table. On it, in large, breezy, long-legged letters, were the words:

Southwest Wind,
Esquire

The Brothers Change Their Occupation

Southwest Wind, Esquire, kept his word. After the momentous visit just related, he entered the Treasure Valley no more; and what was worse, neither did his relations, the other West Winds. So no rain fell in the valley from one year's end to another. Though everything remained green and flourishing in the plains below, the inheritance of the three brothers was a desert. What had once been the richest soil in the kingdom became a shifting heap of red sand; and the brothers abandoned their valueless property in despair, to seek some means of gaining a livelihood in the city. All their money was gone. They had nothing left but some curious, old-fashioned pieces of gold, the last remnants of their ill-gotten wealth.

"Suppose we turn goldsmiths?" said Schwartz to Hans as they entered the large city. "It is a good knave's trade. We can put much copper into the gold without anyone's ever finding out."

So they hired a furnace and turned goldsmiths. But two things affected their trade; first, people did not approve of coppered gold: second, the two elder brothers, whenever they sold anything, used to leave Gluck to tend the furnace and go and squander all the money in the alehouse. So they melted all their gold without making money enough to buy more. Finally they were reduced to one mug, which an uncle had given to Gluck, and which he would not have parted with for the world.

The mug was very odd to look at. The handle was formed of two wreaths of flowing golden hair so finely spun that it looked more like silk than metal. These wreaths flowed into a beard and whiskers which surrounded and decorated a fierce little face of the reddest gold imaginable. When it came to the mug's turn to be made into spoons, it half broke poor little Gluck's heart; but the brothers only laughed, tossed the mug into the melting pot, and staggered out, leaving him, as usual, to pour the gold into bars when it was melted.

When they were gone Gluck took a farewell look at his old friend in the melting pot. The flowing hair was gone; nothing remained but the red nose and the sparkling eyes. He walked dejectedly to the window and sat down to catch the fresh air and escape the hot breath of the furnace.

Now this window commanded a direct view of the mountains which overhung Treasure Valley, and more especially of the peak from which fell the Golden River. It was just at the close of day, and Gluck saw through the window the mountain tops all crimson and purple with the sunset. And the river, brighter than all, fell in a waving column of pure gold from precipice to precipice;

a double arch of a broad purple rainbow stretched across it, flushing and fading alternately in the wreaths of spray.

"Ah!" said Gluck aloud, after he had looked at it for a while, "if that river were really all gold, what a nice thing it would be."

"No, it wouldn't," said a metallic voice nearby.

"Bless me! What's that?" exclaimed Gluck, jumping up. There was nobody there. He looked round the room and under the table and behind him, but there was certainly nobody there, and he sat down again at the window. This time he did not speak, but he kept thinking that it would be very convenient if the river were really all gold.

"Not at all, my boy," said the same voice, louder than before.

"Bless me!" said Gluck again. "What *is* that?" He looked again into all the corners and cupboards and then began turning round and round as fast as he could in the middle of the room, thinking there was somebody behind him. Then the same voice struck again on his ear. It was singing now very merrily, "Lala-lira-la"—no words, only a soft melody, something like that of a kettle on the boil.

It seemed to Gluck that it sounded louder near the furnace. He ran to the opening and looked in; yes, it seemed to be coming not only out of the furnace, but out of the pot. He uncovered it and ran back in a great fright, for the pot was certainly singing! He stood in the farthest corner of the room for a minute or two with his hands up and his mouth open, when the singing stopped, and the voice became clear and distinct.

"Hollo!" said the voice.

Gluck made no answer.

"Hollo, Gluck, my boy!" said the pot again.

Gluck summoned all his energy, walked straight up to the crucible, drew it out of the furnace, and looked in. The gold was all melted, and its surface as smooth and polished as a river; but as he looked in, he saw, not the reflection of his own head, but the red nose and sharp eyes of his old friend of the mug, a thousand times redder and sharper than ever he had seen them in his life.

"Come, Gluck, my boy," said the voice out of the pot again. "I'm all right; pour me out."

But Gluck was too much astonished to obey.

"*Will* you pour me out?" said the voice sharply.

By a violent effort Gluck grasped the crucible and sloped it to pour out the gold. But instead of a liquid stream there came out, first, a pair of little yellow legs, then two coattails, then a pair of arms stuck akimbo, and finally, the well-known head of his friend the mug; all of which articles, uniting as they rolled out, stood up in the shape of a golden dwarf a foot and a half high.

"That's right!" said the dwarf, stretching out first his legs, then his arms, and then shaking his head up and down and as far around as it would go for five minutes without stopping.

Gluck looked at him in speechless amazement. He was dressed in a doublet of spun gold. Over this his hair and beard fell full halfway to the ground in waving curls so delicate that Gluck could hardly tell where they ended; they seemed to melt into air. Finally the dwarf turned his sharp eyes full on Gluck and stared at him.

"No, it wouldn't, my boy," said the little man.

This was certainly a rather abrupt mode of commencing conversation. It might refer to what Gluck had been thinking when he first heard the voice from the pot. Whatever it was, Gluck was not inclined to dispute what he said.

"Wouldn't it, sir?" said Gluck meekly.

"No," said the dwarf. "It wouldn't." And with that the dwarf pulled his cap hard over his brows and took two turns up and down the room, lifting his legs up very high and setting them down very hard. This pause gave time for Gluck to think a little, and seeing no great reason to view his diminutive visitor with dread, he ventured to ask, "Pray, sir, were you my mug?"

At this the little man drew himself up to his full height. "I," said the little man, "am the

King of the Golden River." Then he turned about again and took two more turns up and down the room in order to allow Gluck's consternation to evaporate. After this he again walked up to Gluck and stood still as if expecting a reply.

Gluck determined to say something at all events. "I hope Your Majesty is very well."

"Listen!" said the little man. "I am king of what you mortals call the Golden River. The shape you saw me in was owing to the malice of an evil king, from whose enchantments you have this instant freed me. What I have seen of your conduct toward your wicked brothers renders me willing to serve you; therefore, attend to what I tell you.

"Whoever shall climb to the top of the mountain from which you see the Golden River springing forth and shall cast into the stream at its source three drops of holy water, for him, and for him only, the river shall turn to gold. But no one failing in his first attempt can succeed in a second; and if anyone shall cast unholy water into the river, he shall become a black stone."

So saying, the King of the Golden River turned away and deliberately walked into the center of the hottest flame of the furnace. His figure became red, white—a transparent, dazzling blaze of light as he rose, trembled, and disappeared. The King of the Golden River had evaporated.

"Oh!" cried Gluck, running to look up the chimney after him; "Oh, dear, dear me! My mug! My mug!"

The Brothers Try Their Luck

The King of the Golden River had hardly made this extraordinary exit before Hans and Schwartz came into the house, roaring drunk. The discovery of the total loss of their last piece of gold made them just sober enough to be able to stand over Gluck, beating him steadily for a quarter of an hour. Then they dropped into chairs and requested to know what he had to say for himself.

Gluck told them his story, of which, of course, they did not believe a word. They beat him again till their arms were tired and staggered to bed.

Next morning, however, the steadiness with which he adhered to his story gained him some belief, and the two brothers, after wrangling for a long time about which one of them should be the first to make the journey to the Golden River, drew their swords and began fighting.

The noise of the fray alarmed the neighbors, who, when they could not pacify the brothers, sent for the constable.

Upon hearing this, Hans contrived to escape; but Schwartz was taken before the magistrate, fined for breaking the peace, and was thrown into prison till he should pay his fine.

Then Hans decided to set out immediately for the Golden River. How to get the holy water was the question. He consulted the priest, but the priest would not give any holy water to such a man. So Hans went to church for the first time in his life, and pretending to cross himself, stole a cupful of holy water and returned home in triumph.

Next morning he got up before sunrise, put the holy water into a strong flask, and two bottles of wine and some bread into a basket. These he slung over his back and, taking his staff in his hand, set off for the mountains. On his way out of town he had to pass by the prison, and as he looked in at the barred windows, whom should he see but his brother Schwartz peeping out through the bars and looking very unhappy.

"Good morning," said Hans. "Have you any message for the King of the Golden River?"

Schwartz gnashed his teeth in rage and shook the bars with all his strength; but Hans only laughed at him and, advising him to make himself comfortable till he came back again, shouldered his basket, shook the bottle of holy water in Schwartz's face, and marched off in high spirits.

Forgetting the distance he had to traverse, he set off at a rate of walking which greatly exhausted him before he had scaled the first range of hills. He was surprised on surmounting the range to find that a large glacier, which he had not seen on any previous trip up the mountain, lay between him and the source of the Golden River.

The glacier ice was slippery, and out of all its chasms came sounds of gushing water, changeful and loud, now rising into wild melody, then breaking off into sorrowful tones or sudden shrieks.

The ice was broken into a thousand shapes, and Hans thought he saw a curious expression about all their outlines—like human features, distorted and scornful. His ears grew dull and his head dizzy with the constant roar of the hidden waters. The ice crashed and yawned into fresh chasms at his feet; tottering spires nodded around him and fell thundering across his path. It was with a feeling of terror that he leaped the last chasm and flung himself, exhausted and shuddering, on firm ground.

He had been compelled to cast aside his basket of food, which had become too great a burden, and now he had no means of refreshing himself but by breaking off and eating some of the pieces of ice. This, however, relieved his thirst, and an hour's rest recruited his strength. With the unyielding spirit of greed, he resumed his journey.

His way now lay straight up a ridge of bare red rocks, without a blade of grass to ease the foot or a projecting angle to give an inch of shade from the sun. It was past noon, and the sun's rays beat fiercely upon the steep path. Burning thirst was soon added to the bodily fatigue with which Hans was now afflicted. Glance after glance he cast at the flask of water which hung at his belt.

"Three drops are enough," at last thought he. "I may at least cool my lips with it."

He opened the flask and was raising it to his lips, when his eye fell on an object lying on the rock beside him; he thought it moved. It was a small dog, apparently in the last agony of death from thirst. Its tongue was out, its jaws dry, its limbs extended lifelessly, and a swarm of black ants were crawling about its lips and throat. Its eyes moved to the bottle which Hans held in his hand. He raised it, drank, spurned the animal with his foot, and passed on. And he did not know how it was, but he thought that a strange shadow had suddenly come across the blue sky.

The path became steeper and more rugged every moment. The noise of the hill cataracts sounded like mockery in his ears, and his thirst increased every moment. Another hour passed, and he again looked down to the flask at his side. It was half empty, but there was much more than three drops. He stopped to open it, and again something moved in the path. A fair child was stretched nearly lifeless on the rock, its eyes closed, and its lips parched and burning. Hans eyed it deliberately, drank, and passed on. And a dark gray cloud came over the sun, and long, snakelike shadows crept up along the mountainsides. Hans struggled on. The sun was sinking. Its descent seemed to bring no coolness; the leaden weight of the dead air pressed upon his brow and heart, but the goal was nearer. He saw the shining cataract of the Golden River springing from the hillside, scarcely five hundred feet above him. He paused for a moment to breathe and sprang on to complete his task.

At this instant a faint cry fell on his ear. He turned and saw a gray-haired old man stretched out on the rocks. His eyes were sunken and his features deadly pale. "Water!" he cried feebly. "I am dying."

"I have none," replied Hans. "You have had your share of life."

Hans strode over the prostrate body and darted on. A flash of blue lightning rose out of the East, shaped like a sword. It shook thrice over the whole heavens and left it dark with heavy black shade. The sun was setting; it plunged toward the horizon like a red-hot ball.

The roar of the Golden River rose on Hans' ear. He stood at the brink of the chasm through which it ran. Its waves were filled with the red glory of the sunset; they shook their crests like tongues of fire, and flashes of bloody light gleamed along their foam. Their sound came mightier and mightier on his senses; his brain grew giddy with the prolonged thunder. Shuddering, he drew the flask from his girdle and hurled it into the center of the wild torrent. As he did so an icy chill shot through his limbs; he staggered, shrieked, and fell. The icy waters closed over his cry. And the moaning of the river rose wildly into the night as it gushed over—THE BLACK STONE.

Poor little Gluck waited anxiously alone in the house for Hans' return. When Hans failed to come back, Gluck was terribly frightened and went to the prison and told Schwartz what had happened. Then Schwartz was much pleased and said that Hans must certainly have been turned into a black stone, and he should have all the gold to himself. But Gluck was very sorry and cried all night.

When he got up in the morning, there was no bread in the house, nor any money; so Gluck hired himself to another goldsmith. He worked so hard and so neatly and so long every day, that he soon got money enough together to pay off his brother's fine.

Then he got Schwartz out of prison. This pleased Schwartz, and he said that Gluck should have some of the gold of the river. But Gluck only begged him to go and see what had become of Hans.

Now when Schwartz had heard that Hans had stolen the holy water, he determined to manage better. So he took more of Gluck's money and went to a bad priest, who gave him some holy water very readily for it. Schwartz got up early in the morning before the sun rose, took some bread and wine in a basket, put his holy water into a flask, and set off for the mountains. Like his brother, he was much surprised at the sight of the glacier and had great difficulty in crossing it, even after leaving his basket behind him.

The day was cloudless, but not bright; there was a heavy purple haze hanging over the sky, and the hills looked gloomy. And as Schwartz climbed the steep rock path, the thirst came upon him, as it had upon his brother, until he lifted his flask to his lips to drink. Then he saw the fair child lying near him on the rocks, and it cried to him and moaned for water.

"Water, indeed," said Schwartz. "I haven't half enough for myself," and he passed on. As he went, he thought the sunbeams grew more dim, and he saw a bank of black clouds rising out of the west. When he had climbed for another hour, the thirst overcame him again. Then he saw the old man lying on the path and moaning for water. "Water, indeed," said Schwartz. "I haven't half enough for myself." And on he went.

Then again the light seemed to fade from before his eyes. He looked up, and behold! a mist had come over the sun. The bank of black clouds, too, had risen very high, and they cast long shadows which flickered over Schwartz' path.

Schwartz climbed for another hour, and again his thirst returned. As he lifted his flask to his lips, he thought he saw Hans lying exhausted on the path before him, and, as he gazed, the figure stretched its arms to him and cried for water.

"Ha!" laughed Schwartz, "are you there, Hans? Remember those prison bars! Water, indeed—do you suppose I carried it all the way up here just for you?" He strode over the figure which seemed to have a mocking smile on its lips. When he had gone a few yards farther, Schwartz stopped and looked over his shoulder. The figure was not there.

A sudden horror came over Schwartz, and he knew not why. But the thirst for gold prevailed over his fear, and he rushed on. The sky where the sun was setting was all level, like a lake of blood; and a strong wind came out of that sky, tearing its crimson clouds into fragments and scattering them far into the darkness. And now as Schwartz stood by the brink of the Golden River, its waves were black, like thunder clouds, but their foam was like fire; and the roar of the waters below and the thunder above met as he cast the flask into the stream. As he did so, the lightning glared into his eyes; the earth gave way beneath him, and the waters closed over his cry. And the moaning of the river rose wildly into the night as it roared and gushed over—THE TWO BLACK STONES.

When Gluck found that Schwartz did not come back, he was very sorry and did not know what to do. He had no money, so he was obliged to go and hire himself again to the goldsmith, who worked him very hard and gave him very little money.

After a month or two Gluck grew tired of this and made up his mind to go and try his fortune with the Golden River.

"The little King looked kind," he mused. "I don't think he will turn me into a black stone."

So he went to the priest, and the priest gave him some holy water as soon as he asked for it.

Then Gluck put some bread in his basket, took the bottle of holy water, and set off.

If the glacier had caused a great deal of fatigue to his brothers, it was twenty times worse for him, who was neither so strong nor so practiced on the mountains. He had several bad falls, lost his basket and bread, and was very much frightened at the strange noises under the ice. When he had climbed for an hour, he became dreadfully thirsty and was going to drink as his brothers had done, when he saw an old man coming down the path.

"My son," called out the old man, "I am faint with thirst; give me some water."

"Pray don't drink it all," said Gluck. But the old man drank a great deal and gave him back the bottle two-thirds empty. Then he bade Gluck Godspeed, and Gluck started on again. The path became easier to his feet, and blades of grass appeared upon it. Some crickets began singing on the bank beside it, and Gluck thought he had never heard such merry singing.

Then he went on for another hour, and the thirst increased on him so much that he thought he should be forced to drink. As he raised the flask, he saw a little child lying panting by the roadside, and it cried out piteously for water. Gluck put the bottle to the child's lips, and it drank all but a few drops. Having done this, it smiled, got up, and ran down the hill. Gluck then turned and began climbing again. And now there were all kinds of flowers blooming on the rocks, and the sky sent down such pure light that Gluck had never felt so happy.

Yet after he had climbed for another hour, his thirst became intolerable again; and when he looked at his bottle, he saw that there were only five or six drops left in it. He dared not touch it.

But just as he was hanging the flask on his belt again, he saw a little dog lying on the rocks, gasping for breath—just as Hans had seen it.

Gluck looked at it and then at the Golden River; and he thought of the dwarf's warning that no one could succeed, except in his first attempt. He tried to pass the dog, but it whined piteously, and he stopped again.

"Poor little beast," said Gluck. "It will be dead when I come down again." Then he looked closer at it, and its eye turned on him so mournfully that he could not stand it. "Confound the King, and his gold, too," said Gluck, and he opened the flask and poured all the water into the dog's mouth.

The dog sprang up and stood on its hind legs. Its tail disappeared; its ears became long, silky, and golden; its nose became very red; its eyes became very twinkling. In three seconds the dog was gone, and before Gluck stood the King of the Golden River.

"Thank you," said the King. "Don't be frightened; it's all right. Why didn't you come before, instead of sending me those rascally brothers of yours for me to have the trouble of turning into stones?"

"Oh, dear me!" said Gluck, "have you really been so cruel?"

"Cruel!" said the dwarf. "They poured unholy water into my stream. I can't allow that."

"Why," said Gluck, "I am sure, Your Majesty, they got the water out of the church font."

"Very probably," replied the dwarf sternly, "but the water which has been refused to the cry of the weary and dying is unholy, though it had been blessed by every saint in heaven."

So saying, the dwarf stooped and plucked a lily that grew at his feet. On its white petals there hung three drops of clear dew. And the dwarf shook them into the flask which Gluck held in his hand. "Cast these into the river," he said, "and descend on the other side of the mountains into Treasure Valley. And so Godspeed."

As he spoke, the figure of the dwarf became indistinct. The colors of his robe formed themselves into a brilliant mist of dewy light. He stood for an instant veiled with them as with a belt of a broad rainbow. The colors grew faint; the mist rose into the air; the monarch had evaporated.

Gluck climbed to the brink of the Golden River; he cast the three drops of dew into the stream, and there opened where they fell a circular whirlpool, into which the waters descended with a strange noise.

Gluck stood watching it for some time, very much disappointed because not only the river did not turn into gold, but its water seemed much diminished in quantity. Yet he obeyed his friend the dwarf and went down the other side of the mountains toward Treasure Valley. As he went, he thought he heard the noise of water working its way under the ground. As he came in sight of Treasure Valley, behold, a river was springing from a new cleft in the rocks.

As Gluck gazed, fresh grass sprang beside the new streams, and creeping plants grew among the moistening soil. Flowers opened suddenly along the riverbanks as the stars leap out when twilight is deepening. And thus the Treasure Valley became a garden again, and the inheritance which had been lost by cruelty was regained by love.

And Gluck dwelt in the valley, and the poor were never driven from his door; so that his barns became full of corn, and his house of treasure. For him the river had, according to the dwarf's promise, become a River of Gold.

To this day the inhabitants of the valley point out the place where the three drops of holy dew were cast into the stream, and trace the course of the Golden River under the ground, until it emerges in Treasure Valley. And at the source of the Golden River there are still to be seen Two Black Stones round which the waters howl mournfully every day at sunset; and these stones are still called by the people of the valley—THE BLACK BROTHERS.

BOOKS TO READ
Young Americans Today

All-American and *The Iron Duke*
  John R. Tunis
Call Me Charley
  Jesse Jackson
Golden Gate
  Valenti Angelo
Gulliver Joins the Army
  Alice Dalgliesh
Homer Price
  Robert McCloskey
Melindy's Medal
  G. Faulkner and J. Becker

Rufus M.
  Eleanor Estes
Tenderfoot at Bar X
  M. M. Perdew
The Mitchells
  Hilda van Stockum
The Mule Skinners
  Myra R. Richardson
The Red Chipmunk Mystery
  Ellery Queen, Jr.
The Saturdays
  Elizabeth Enright

Early Adventures in Progress

America Was Like This
  Emma G. Sterne
Calico Bush
  Rachel Field
Gunsmith's Boy
  Herbert Best
In Calico and Crinoline
  Eleanor Sickels
Justin Morgan Had a Horse
  Marguerite Henry

Mounted Messenger
  Cornelia Meigs
Noah Webster
  Isabel Proudfit
The Long Winter
  Laura I. Wilder
The School Bell Rings
  Evelyn R. Sickels
The Wreck of the Wild Wave
  Edith Thatcher Hurd

Man-made Wonders of Today

Fly It Away and *This is Your Announcer*
  Henry B. Lent
New Wings for Women
  Sally Knapp
The Smoke Jumper
  Marjorie Hill Allee

The Story Behind Great Inventions
  E. R. Montgomery
The Story of American Aviation
  Jim Ray
Tune In for Elizabeth
  Mary Margaret McBride

Fun and Fancy

A Squirrel Called Rufus
  Richard Church
Five Golden Wrens
  Hugh Troy
Horton Hatches the Egg
  Dr. Seuss
Little Prince
  Antoine de Saint-Exupéry
Rabbit Hill
  Robert Lawson
The Fast Sooner Hound
  Arna Bontemps and Jack Conroy

The Twenty-One Balloons
  William Pène Du Bois
The Voyages of Dr. Dolittle
  Hugh Lofting
Time to Laugh
  Phyllis Fenner
Treasures Long Hidden
  Arthur Bowie Chrisman
Yankee Doodle's Cousins
  Anne Malcolmson
Yankee Thunder
  Irwin Shapiro

Publishers of these books are listed in the *Teacher's Guidebook* for *People and Progress*.

World Neighbors

Bamboo Gate
  Virginia Oakes
Chico of the Andes
  Christine Von Hagen
Jacques the Goatherd
  Cormack and Alexander
Jungle River
  Howard Pease
Pepperfoot of Thursday Market
  Robert Davis
The Cottage at Bantry Bay
  Hilda Van Stockum
Theater Shoes
  Noel Streatfeild
Wings for Nikias
  Josephine Blackstock

The World of Nature

All in a Lifetime
  Frank Buck
Animal Tales
  Ivan Sanderson
Bambi and *Forest World*
  Felix Salten
Banjo the Crow
  Theodora DuBois
Child of the Deep
  J. E. Williamson and F. J. Olcott
Misty of Chincoteaque
  Marguerite Henry
Smoky
  Will James
The Fireside Book of Dog Stories
  Jack Goodman
The Gift of the Forest
  Singh and Lownsbery
The Last of the Sea Otters
  Harold McCracken
Too Much Salt and Pepper
  Sam Campbell
Treasure of the Tortoise Islands
  Von Hagen and Hawkins

Defenders of Freedom

Against All Odds
  Marion Lansing
Daniels Boone and *Poor Richard*
  James Daugherty
Early American and *Clara Barton*
  Mildred Pace
Leader By Destiny
  Jeanette Eaton
Red Heritage
  Merritt P. Allen
The Courage and the Glory
  John J. Floherty
The Green Cockade
  Merritt P. Allen
The Matchlock Gun
  Walter Edmonds
Three Sisters
  Cornelia Spencer
Young Lafayette
  Jeanette Eaton

Stories That Never Grow Old

Arabian Nights
  Ed. by Padraic Colum
Boy's King Arthur
  Sir Thomas Malory (Lanier)
Christmas Carol
  Charles Dickens
Little Women
  Louisa M. Alcott
Merry Adventures of Robin Hood
  Howard Pyle
Odyssey
  Tr. by George Herbert Palmer
Pepper and Salt
  Howard Pyle
Stories of the Gods and Heroes
  Sally Benson
The Jungle Book
  Rudyard Kipling
The Story of Peer Gynt and *Beowulf*
  E. V. Sandys
The Three Mulla-Mulgars
  Walter de la Mare
The Wind in the Willows
  Kenneth Grahame

See also titles listed in footnotes on pages 61, 90, 114, 183, 248, and 342.

GLOSSARY

Pronunciation Key

The pronunciation of each word is shown just after the word, in this way: **ab bre vi ate** (ə brē′vi āt). The letters and signs used are pronounced as in the words below. The mark ′ is placed after a syllable with primary or strong accent, as in the example above. The mark ′ after a syllable shows a secondary or lighter accent, as in **ab bre vi a tion** (ə brē′vi ā′shən).

a	hat, cap	j	jam, enjoy	u	cup, butter
ā	age, face	k	kind, seek	u̇	full, put
ã	care, air	l	land, coal	ü	rule, move
ä	father, far	m	me, am	ū	use, music
		n	no, in		
b	bad, rob	ng	long, bring	v	very, save
ch	child, much			w	will, woman
d	did, red	o	hot, rock	y	you, yet
		ō	open, go		
e	let, best	ô	order, all	z	zero, breeze
ē	equal, see	oi	oil, voice	zh	measure, seizure
ėr	term, learn	ou	house, out		
		p	paper, cup	ə	represents:
f	fat, if	r	run, try		a in about
g	go, bag	s	say, yes		e in taken
h	he, how	sh	she, rush		i in pencil
		t	tell, it		o in lemon
i	it, pin	th	thin, both		u in circus
ī	ice, five	ŦH	then, smooth		

This pronunciation key is from *Thorndike Century Junior Dictionary, Revised Edition.*

ab bey (ab′i), the building or buildings where monks or nuns live a religious life ruled by an abbot or abbess.

ab bot (ab′ət), man who is head of an abbey of monks.

a cute (ə küt′), 1. sharp-pointed. 2. keen.

ad here (ad hēr′), stick fast (to a substance, a party, a person, an opinion).

af fect[1] (ə fekt′), 1. produce a result on. 2. touch the heart of.

af fect[2] (ə fekt′), 1. be fond of and have. She affects old jewelry and china. 2. pretend to have or feel.

a ghast (ə gast′), frightened; struck with surprise or horror.

ag ile (aj′il), moving quickly and easily; active; lively; nimble.

ag i ta tion (aj′i tā′shən), 1. a violent moving or shaking. 2. disturbance of body or mind; excitement. 3. discussion; debate.

a kim bo (ə kim′bō), with the hand on hip and the elbow bent outward.

A le ko Ka la ma to (ə lē′kō kä lä mä′tō).

Al giers (al jērz′).

A li Ta za (ä′li tä′zä).

Al lah (al′ə), Mohammedan name for God.

al li ance (ə lī′əns), 1. union formed by agreement; joining of interests. An alliance may be the joining of national interests by treaty, etc. 2. the nations, persons, etc., who belong to such a union.

al ma nac (ôl′mə nak), a calendar of days, weeks, months; often with information about the weather, sun, moon, stars, church days, etc.

am me ter (am′mē′tər or am′i tər), instrument for measuring the strength of an electric current.

am pli fi er (am′pli fī′ər), 1. one that makes greater, stronger, larger. 2. vacuum tube in a radio set for strengthening electrical impulses.

Am roo (äm rü′).

and i rons (and′ī′ərnz), a pair of metal supports for wood in a fireplace.

ap pa ra tus (ap′ə rā′təs or ap′ə rat′əs), things necessary to carry out a purpose. Tools, special instruments, and machines are apparatus. A chemical set is apparatus; so is the equipment in a gymnasium.

ap pro pri ate (ə prō′pri it for 1, ə prō′ pri āt for 2), 1. suitable; proper. Plain, simple clothes are appropriate for school. 2. take for oneself. You should not appropriate the belongings of another without permission.

Ar ab (ar′əb), a native of Arabia.

a ris to crat (ə ris′tə krat), 1. person who belongs to the ruling class. 2. person who has the tastes, opinions, and manners of the upper class.

ark (ärk), the large boat in which, according to the Bible, Noah saved himself, his family, and a pair of each kind of animals from the Flood.

Ar kan sas (är′kən sô), 1. a Southern State of the United States. 2. river flowing into the Mississippi.

ar ma dil lo (är′mə dil′ō), small burrowing animal with an armorlike shell.

as bes tos (as bes′təs), a substance which will not burn or conduct heat. Asbestos is used for mats to put under hot dishes.

a skew (ə skü′), to one side; out of the proper position; turned or twisted the wrong way. Her hat is on askew.

Ath ens (ath′inz), capital of Greece.

au di ble (ô′di bəl), that can be heard; loud enough to be heard.

aught (ôt), anything. Has he done aught to help you?

Aus tral ian (ôs trāl′yən), 1. of Australia or its people. 2. native or inhabitant of Australia.

au to mat ic (ô′tə mat′ik), 1. moving or acting of itself; as, an automatic pump. 2. done without thought or attention. Breathing is usually automatic.
a vail (ə vāl′), 1. help. Talk will not avail without work. 2. be of use or benefit to. Money will not avail you after you are dead. 3. help; use. Crying is of no avail now. 4. **Avail oneself of** means take advantage of; profit by; make use of.

barge (bärj), 1. large flat-bottomed boat for carrying freight on rivers and canals. 2. a large boat used for picnics and special occasions.
bar ri er (bar′i ər), something that stands in the way; something that stops progress or prevents approach.
bed lam (bed′ləm), uproar; confusion.
be la bor (bi lā′bər), beat hard.
Ben Has san (ben hä sän′).
Be ni to (bā nē′tō).
Ber ber (bėr′bər), 1. member of a race living in northern Africa. 2. of this race.
Berk el Lill (berk el lēl′).
bev y (bev′i), a small group.
bleak (blēk), 1. bare; swept by winds. 2. chilly; cold. 3. dreary.
Bo go tá (bō′ gō tä′).
Bo lí var (bō lē′ vär).
Bo li vi a (bō liv′i ə).
bore[1] (bōr), make a hole in anything.
bore[2] (bōr), 1. weary by tiring talk or by being dull. This book bores me. 2. a tiresome or dull person.
bore[3] (bōr), carried. The two men bore the box forward.
bow sprit (bou′sprit or bō′sprit), pole or spar projecting forward from the bow of the ship.
bri gade (bri gād′), 1. part of an army. It is usually made up of two or more regiments. 2. group of people organized for a purpose.

bro gan brō′gən), a coarse, strong shoe.
bronze (bronz), 1. brown metal of copper and tin. 2. the color of bronze; yellowish brown. 3. make or become bronze in color.
bump tious (bump′shəs), having too high an opinion of oneself.

ca liph or **ca lif** (kā′lif), ruler of a Mohammedan state.
can teen (kan tēn′), 1. small container to carry water or other drinks. 2. place where food and drink are sold to soldiers and sailors.
Ca ra cas (kə rä′kəs).
car cass (kär′kəs), dead body of an animal.
Car ta ge na (kär′tə jē′nə).
cat a ract (kat′ə rakt), 1. large, steep waterfall. 2. violent rush or downpour of water. 3. disease of the eye which causes blindness.
ca tas tro phe (kə tas′trə fi), sudden, widespread disaster.
cat boat (kat′bōt′), a sailboat with one mast set far forward.
char coal (chär′kōl′), a black substance made by partly burning wood or bones. Charcoal is used chiefly for fuel.
char i ty (char′i ti), 1. generous giving to the poor. 2. kindness in judging other people. 3. Christian love of one's fellow men.
Che lan (shē lan′), a national forest in the State of Washington.
chem i cal (kem′i kəl), a substance obtained by changing or combining other substances. Sulphuric acid, sodium bicarbonate, calcium oxide, etc., are chemicals.
Chiang Kai-shek (chyäng′ kī′shek′).
chime (chīm), 1. a set of bells tuned to the musical scale and played by hammers or simple machinery. 2. the music made by a set of tuned bells. 3. be in harmony or agreement.

460

Chi qui ta (shə kē′tə).
cinch (sinch), 1. a strong girth for a saddle or pack. 2. put on with a cinch; bind firmly. 3. a firm hold or grip. *Used in common talk.* 4. something sure and easy. *Slang.*
civ il (siv′il), 1. of a citizen or citizens. Civil war is war between two groups of citizens in the same country. 2. polite; courteous.
colo nel (kėr′nəl), officer who commands a regiment of soldiers.
col o ny (kol′ə ni), 1. a group of people who leave their own country and go to settle in another land, but who still remain citizens of their own country. 2. the settlement made by such people. 3. one of the thirteen original settlements on the Atlantic coast which later became the United States.
come ly (kum′li), 1. pleasant to look at. 2. fitting; suitable; proper.
con demn (kən dem′), 1. express strong disapproval of. We condemn cruelty and greed. 2. pronounce guilty of crime or wrong. 3. to doom; as, condemned to death.
con gress (kong′gris), 1. coming together; meeting. 2. a meeting of representatives for the discussion of some subject. 3. the national law-making body of the United States composed of the Senate and the House of Representatives, with members elected from every state.
con se quence (kon′si kwens), 1. result. 2. importance.
con ser va tion (kon′sər vā′shən), 1. a preserving from harm or decay; protecting from loss or from being used up; as, the conservation of forests. 2. official protection and care of rivers, forests, wild life, etc.
con spir a tor (kən spir′ə tər), one who plans secretly; a plotter.

con sti tu tion (kon′sti tū′shən *or* kon′sti tü′shən), the principles according to which a country, state, or society is governed.
con tact (kon′takt), 1. touch. 2. place where things touch; 3. get in touch with; make connection with. 4. connection between two conductors of electricity through which a current passes.
con ti nen tal (kon′ti nen′təl), of a continent; like a continent.
Con ti nen tal (kon′ti nen′təl), of or having to do with the American colonies during and immediately after the Revolutionary War.
con tor tion (kən tôr′shən), 1. twisting. 2. twisted condition.
con tract (kon′trakt for 1 and 2, kən tract′ for 3, 4, and 5), 1. an agreement. 2. a written agreement that can be enforced by law. 3. form; enter into; start; as, to contract a bad habit. 4. draw together; make shorter; as, to contract the brows. 5. shrink; become smaller.
con trive (kən trīv′), 1. invent; design. 2. plan; scheme; plot. 3. manage. I will contrive to be there.
con vul sive (kən vul′siv), violently disturbing.
cor dial (kôr′jəl), 1. sincere; hearty; friendly. 2. reviving; cheering.
cor mo rant (kôr′mə rənt), large, greedy sea bird with a long neck and a pouch under the beak for holding captured fish.
cor re spond ence (kor′i spon′dəns), 1. agreement. Your account of the accident has little correspondence with the story John told. 2. exchange of letters; letter writing.
cou pling (kup′ling), 1. joining together. 2. device used for joining parts of machinery. 3. device used to join two railroad cars.

hat, āge, cāre, fär; let, ēqual, tėrm; it, īce; hot, ōpen, ôrder; oil, out; cup, pùt, rüle, ūse; th, thin; ᴛʜ, then; ə represents *a* in about, *e* in taken, *i* in pencil, *o* in lemon, *u* in circus.

covey (kuv′i), 1. small flock of partridges. 2. small flock or group.
cowlick (kou′lik′), small tuft of hair that will not lie flat.
cranny (kran′i), crack; chink.
create (krē āt′), make a thing which has not been made before.
creator (krē ā′tər), person who creates. **The Creator** is another name for God.
criticism (krit′i sizm), 1. making judgments approving or disapproving. 2. faultfinding; disapproval.
crucible (krü′si bəl), pot to melt metal in.
crude (krüd), 1. in a natural or raw state. Oil, ore, and sugar are crude before being refined. 2. in the rough; lacking finish.
curry[1] (kėr′i), rub and clean a horse with brush or scraper.
curry[2] (kėr′i), 1. a peppery sauce or powder. 2. food flavored with it. 3. prepare food with curry.
cutlass (kut′ləs), a short, heavy, slightly curved sword.

deacon (dē′kən), an officer of a church who helps the minister in duties not connected with preaching.
decisive (di sī′siv), settling something beyond question.
declaration (dek′lə rā′shən), a statement; an open or public statement. The **Declaration of Independence** was a statement adopted by the American colonies July 4, 1776, declaring they were free and independent of Great Britain. **Make a declaration** means declare.
decree (di krē′), 1. something ordered or settled by authority; law. 2. order or settle by authority.
deflect (di flekt′), bend or turn aside; change the direction of.
delegate (del′i gāt), 1. one who acts for others; a representative. 2. appoint or send as a representative. I was delegated to buy flowers.

delirious (di lir′i əs), 1. out of one's senses; raving. 2. wildly excited.
deluge (del′ūj), 1. great flood. 2. heavy fall of rain. 3. to flood. 4. overwhelming rush.
Demetrios (di mē′tri əs).
democracy (di mok′rə si), 1. government that is run by the people who live under it. 2. a country or town in which the government is a democracy. The United States is a democracy. 3. treating others as one's equal.
deputy (dep′ū ti), person appointed to do the work or take the place of another.
derive (di rīv′), 1. get; obtain. He derives much pleasure from his books. 2. come into being; arise.
Dil lal Ben Ab bes (di läl′ ben ä′bes).
diminutive (di min′ū tiv), 1. small; tiny. 2. small person or thing.
dinosaur (dī′nə sôr), one of a group of reptiles no longer existing.
dismantle (dis man′təl), 1. to strip of furniture or equipment; as, to dismantle a house or ship. 2. pull down; take apart.
dispatch (dis pach′), 1. send off to some place for some purpose. 2. sending off a letter, a messenger, etc. Hurry the dispatch of this telegram. 3. a written message, such as special news or government business.
dispatcher (dis pach′ər), person who dispatches. A train dispatcher sends out trains.
disreputable (dis rep′ū tə bəl), 1. having a bad reputation. 2. not respectable; worn out and dirty.
distend (dis tend′), stretch out; swell out; expand.
distort (dis tôrt′), pull or twist out of shape; make crooked or ugly.
divan (dī′van), a long, low sofa.
Divine Providence (di vīn′ prov′i dəns), God's care and help.
Dnieper (nē′pər).

dogged

dog ged (dôg′id), stubborn; persistent.
do ry (dō′ri), a rowboat with a narrow, flat bottom and high sides.
dou blet (dub′lit), man's close-fitting jacket. Men in Europe wore doublets from 1400 to 1600.
Driss (Drēs).
drosh ky (drosh′ki), a low four-wheeled open carriage used in Russia.
drought (drout), long period of dry weather; continued lack of rain.
drub bing (drub′ing), a beating; a thorough defeat.
Drum ran ny (drum ran′i), a village on the southwest coast of Ireland.
ear shot (ēr′shot), range of hearing. We called, but he was out of earshot.
eb on y (eb′ən i), 1. hard, black wood, used for the black keys of a piano, the backs of brushes, etc. 2. like ebony; black.
ec sta sy (ek′stə si), rapture; state of very great joy.
ec stat i cal ly (ek stat′i kəl i), in a joyful manner.
ed dy (ed′i), a small whirlpool.
ef fi cient (i fish′ ənt), capable; doing things well and without waste.
E gyp tian (i jip′shən), from the country of Egypt.
e lapse (i laps′), pass; slip away.
El Ghou li (el gü′li).
ell (el), an old measure of length equal to 45 inches.
em bed (em bed′), fasten; sink in.
en dow (en dou′), 1. give money or property to provide an income for. 2. give from birth; provide with some ability or talent. Nature endowed her with beauty.
en gulf (en gulf′), swallow up. The waves engulfed the boat.

flaunt

en thu si as tic (en thü′zi as′tik), full of eager interest.
e nu mer ate (i nü′mər āt or i nü′-mər āt), 1. name one by one; give a list of. 2. count.
ep och (ep′ək), a period of time in which striking things happened.
ep och-mak ing (ep′ək māk′ing), beginning an epoch; causing important changes.
e ro sion (i rō′zhən), gradual eating or wearing away.
es quire (es kwīr′), a knight's attendant; a squire.
Es quire (es kwīr′), title of respect placed after a man's last name, instead of *Mr.* before the name.
eu re ka (ū rē′kə), Greek word meaning "I have found it." It is used to express triumph concerning a discovery.
e vac u a tion (i vak′ū ā′shən), 1. leaving empty; withdrawal from occupation or possession. 2. removal.
ev i dence (ev′i dəns), facts; proof; anything that shows or makes clear.
ex e cute (ek′si kūt), 1. carry out or do. 2. put to death according to law.
ex er tion (eg zėr′shən), effort. The exertions of the firemen saved the building.
ex ile (eg′zīl *or* ek′sīl), 1. being forced from home or country, often by law as a punishment. 2. a person forced from home or country.
ex tri cate (eks′tri kāt), release; free from entanglements, difficulties. Tom extricated the kitten from the net.
fer til i ty (fər til′i ti), bearing or abundant bearing of seeds, fruits, crops, or young.
flaunt (flônt), 1. wave proudly; as, banners flaunting in the breeze. 2. show off. 3. mention recklessly.

---

hat, āge, cãre, fär; let, ēqual, tėrm; it, īce; hot, ōpen, ôrder; oil, out; cup, put, rüle, ūse; th, thin; ᴛʜ, then; ə represents *a* in about, *e* in taken, *i* in pencil, *o* in lemon, *u* in circus.

fo gy (fō′gi), old-fashioned person; person who is behind the times.
font (font), 1. basin in a church holding water for baptism. 2. basin for holy water. 3. fountain; source.
forge[1] (fôrj), 1. place where metal is heated very hot and hammered into shape. 2. blacksmith's shop. 3. make; shape; form. 4. sign falsely (a name not one's own).
forge[2] (fôrj), move forward slowly but steadily.
forth with (fôrth′wiᴛH′), at once.
fort night (fôrt′nīt), two weeks.
For tu na ta (for tü nä′tə).
fos ter (fos′tər), 1. bring up; rear; make grow. 2. in the same family, but not related by birth. A **foster mother** is one who brings up the child of another.
frag ile (fraj′il), easily broken; delicate; frail.
fresh et (fresh′it), a flood caused by heavy rains or melted snow.
fri vol i ty (fri vol′i ti), 1. silly behavior. 2. a silly thing.

Ga lá pa gos (gə lä′pə gōs), 1. a Spanish word meaning tortoise, or giant turtle. 2. a group of islands in the Pacific Ocean 600 miles west of and belonging to Ecuador; so named because of the giant tortoises found there.
gen er al is si mo (jen′ər əl is′i mō), commander in chief of all military forces of a country.
gen er a tion (jen′ər ā′shən), 1. the people born in the same period; as, our grandmother's generation. 2. about thirty years, or the time from the birth of one generation to the birth of the next.
gen u ine (jen′ū in), 1. real; true; as, genuine leather. 2. sincere; frank; as, genuine sorrow.
Gi bral tar (ji brôl′tər), a British fortress on a high rock on the Mediterranean coast of Spain.

gin ger ly (jin′jər li), with extreme care or caution.
gla cier (glā′shər), a large mass of ice formed from snow, that moves very slowly down a mountainside.
glade (glād), a little open space in a wood or forest.
glen (glen), a small, narrow valley.
Go mes (gō′mish).
gore[1] (gōr), blood that is spilled; thick blood.
gore[2] (gōr), wound with a horn or tusk.
gore[3] (gōr), a long, three-sided piece in a skirt, sail, etc.
gorge (gôrj), 1. deep, narrow valley, usually steep and rocky. 2. to eat greedily until full.
gro tesque (grō tesk′), 1. queer; fantastic; odd or unnatural in shape, appearance, manner, etc. 2. absurd, ridiculous.
grov el (gruv′əl), lie face downward; crawl at someone's feet; humble oneself. The dog groveled before his master when he saw the whip.

hag gard (hag′ərd), wild-looking from pain, hunger, worry, etc.
ham let (ham′lit), small village; little group of houses in the country.
ham per[1] (ham′pər), get in the way; hinder.
ham per[2] (ham′pər), large basket with a cover.
har ass (har′əs or hə ras′), 1. trouble by repeated attacks. 2. disturb; worry.
hawk er[1] (hôk′ər), person who carries goods about for sale.
hawk er[2] (hôk′ər), person who hunts with a hawk.
heir (ār), person who has the right to somebody's property after that one dies.
hence (hens), 1. from here; from now. 2. from this; as a result of this; therefore.

hull (hul), 1. body or frame of a ship. 2. main body or frame of a seaplane, airship, etc. 3. outer covering of a seed. 4. remove the hull or hulls from.

hy drate (hī′drāt), substance produced when certain other chemical substances unite with water.

hy dro gen (hī′drə jən), very light, colorless gas that burns easily.

i gua na (i gwä′nə), a large lizard.

im be cile (im′bi sil), weak in mind; very stupid.

im mor tal (i môr′təl), living forever; everlasting; going on forever.

im pel (im pel′), drive; force; cause.

im pe ri al (im pēr′i əl), 1. of or pertaining to an empire or its ruler. 2. supreme; majestic; magnificent.

im pet u ous (im pech′ü əs), 1. moving with great force or speed. 2. acting hastily or rashly.

in ad e quate (in ad′i kwit), not enough; not so much as is required; lacking.

in al ien a ble (in āl′yən ə bəl), that cannot be given away or taken away. Life, liberty, and the pursuit of happiness have been called the inalienable rights of man.

in de fat i ga ble (in′di fat′i gə bəl), tireless, untiring.

In de fat i ga ble (in′di fat′i gə bəl), an island in the Galápagos group of islands in the Pacific, 600 miles west of and belonging to Ecuador.

in ex haust i ble (in′eg zôs′ti bəl), 1. that cannot be used up; abundant. 2. tireless.

in flam ma ble (in flam′ə bəl), easily set on fire.

in flict (in flikt′), 1. give or cause (a stroke, blow, or wound). 2. impose (suffering, punishment, etc.).

in ge nu i ty (in′ji nü′i ti or in′ji nü′i ti), cleverness; skill in planning.

in her it ance (in her′i təns), money, goods, or anything else received as a gift after the owner's death.

in nu mer a ble (i nü′mər ə bəl or i nü′mər ə bəl), too many to count.

in scribe (in skrīb′), write, engrave, or mark (letters, words, etc.) on paper, metal, stone, etc.

in sist ent (in sis′tənt), 1. keeping firmly to some demand, statement, or position. 2. compelling attention or notice; pressing; urgent.

in sti tute (in′sti tūt or in′sti tüt), set up; establish; begin.

in tense (in tens′), 1. very much; very great; very strong; as, intense pain, intense happiness, intense light; full of vigorous activity, strong feeling, etc. 2. having or showing strong feeling; as, an intense person, an intense face.

in tol er a ble (in tol′ər ə bəl), unbearable; hard to be endured.

Iz da Ta za (iz′dä tä′zä).

jack boot (jak′büt′), large, strong boot reaching above the knee.

Ja mai ca (jə mā′kə), island in the West Indies, south of Cuba.

jet sam (jet′səm), goods which are thrown overboard to lighten a ship in distress and are often washed ashore.

jo ey (jō′i), a name given to young kangaroos by the Australians.

ju bi lant (jü′bi lənt), rejoicing; exulting.

ju jube (jü′jüb), 1. small tablet of gummy candy. 2. datelike fruit of a shrub or tree which is used to sweeten this candy.

Kho lod ny (ko lôd′nyə).

knave (nāv), 1. tricky, dishonest person; rogue; rascal. 2. a male servant; man of humble birth.

---

hat, āge, cāre, fär; let, ēqual, tėrm; it, īce; hot, ōpen, ôrder; oil, out; cup, pút, rüle, üse; th, thin; ᴛʜ, then; ə represents *a* in about, *e* in taken, *i* in pencil, *o* in lemon, *u* in circus.

knoll

knoll (nōl), a small hill; a mound.
Kung (kung).
Kyr Mi ha le (kir mē′hä li).
La fay ette (lä′fā et′).
la goon (lə gün′), 1. pond connected with a larger body of water. 2. shallow water separated from the sea by sandbanks.
Lan Ying (län′ ying′).
la va (lä′və), 1. melted rock flowing from a volcano. 2. rock formed by the cooling of this melted rock.
lee (lē), side sheltered from the wind.
live li hood (līv′li hůd), means of living.
liv er y (liv′ər i), 1. any special uniform provided for servants or members of other groups or professions. 2. stable where horses are cared for and hired out for pay.
lla no (lä′nō), treeless plain.
lux u ri ant (lug zhůr′i ənt), 1. growing thick and green. 2. producing abundantly. 3. rich in ornament.
ma caw (mə kô′), a large parrot.
Mag da le na (mäg dä lā′nä).
mag is trate (maj′is trāt), 1. an officer of the government who has power to apply the law and put it in force. The President is the chief magistrate of the United States. 2. a judge. A justice of the peace is a magistrate.
main tain (mān tān′), keep; keep up; carry on; uphold. One may maintain one's hold on a rope, maintain a family or a household, maintain peace, or maintain an opinion.
mal ice (mal′is), spite; active ill-will; wish to hurt or make suffer.
ma neu ver (mə nü′vər), 1. a planned movement of troops or warships. 2. perform maneuvers. 3. to plan skillfully; use clever tricks. 4. to scheme. 5. to force or drive.
Ma nit za (mä′ni tsä), Greek word meaning grandmother.

minstrel

Ma noel (mun wel′).
Ma ri a (mə rē′ə).
ma rine (mə rēn′), 1. of the sea; found in the sea; produced by the sea. Seals and whales are marine animals. 2. shipping; fleet; as, our merchant marine. 3. of shipping; of the navy; for use at sea. 4. soldier serving on sea and land.
mar mo set (mär′mə zet), a very small monkey with soft, thick fur.
ma roon[1] (mə rün′), put (a person) ashore and leave (him) on a desert island or in a desolate place.
ma roon[2] (mə rün′), very dark red.
mar quis (mär′kwis), nobleman ranking below a duke.
Med i ter ra ne an (med′i tə rā′ni ən), sea between Europe and Africa.
med ley (med′li), 1. a mixture of things that do not belong together. 2. a piece of music made up of other pieces.
me nag er ie (mə naj′ər i), 1. collection of wild animals kept in cages for exhibition. 2. place where such animals are kept.
me thod i cal (mi thod′i kəl), done according to a method.
mi li tia (mi lish′ə), a military force; army of citizens partly trained for war. Every State has a militia called the National Guard.
min a ret (min′ə ret′), high, slender tower attached to a Mohammedan church from which a crier calls the people to prayer.
Min is ter of State (min′is tər əv stāt), a high official who represents his government.
min strel (min′strəl), 1. singer or musician in the household of a lord in the Middle Ages. 2. singer or musician who went about and sang or recited poems, often of his own making. 3. member of a company of actors giving songs, music, and jokes supposed to have come from the Negroes.

mis sion (mish/ən), errand; sending or being sent on some special work.
mode (mōd), 1. the manner, way or fashion in which a thing is done. 2. the style or custom that is in use.
Mo ham med (mo ham/id), founder and prophet of a religion widely accepted in Asia and Africa.
mon arch (mon/ərk), king, queen, emperor, ruler, etc.
monk (mungk), a man who gives up everything for religion and goes to stay in a monastery (building where a group of monks live).
mo not o nous (mə not/ə nəs), 1. continuing in the same tone. 2. not varying. 3. wearying because of its sameness; as, monotonous work.
Mon ti cel lo (mon/ti sel/ō), the home of Thomas Jefferson, near Charlottesville, Virginia.
moor (mür), put or keep (a ship, etc.) in place by means of ropes or chains fastened to the shore or to anchors.
Mos cow (mos/kou or mos/kō), capital of the Soviet Union, in Russia.
mu ti ny (mū/ti ni), open rebellion against lawful authority, especially by soldiers or sailors against their officers.
mu tu al (mū/chü əl), done, said, felt by each toward the other; given and received; as mutual promises.
myr i ad (mir/i əd), a great number.

naph tha (naf/thə), a liquid made from petroleum, coal tar, etc., used as fuel and to remove spots from clothing.
Naz a rene (naz/ə rēn/), person born in Nazareth or living in Nazareth, a town in Palestine where Jesus lived in childhood. Jesus is often called "the Nazarene."
nib (nib), 1. pen point. 2. the point of anything. 3. a bird's bill.
Ni ki as (nē/ki əs).
no to ri ous (nō tō/ri əs), well known, especially because of something bad; having a bad reputation.
Nour Ed den (nür e dēn/).

ob nox ious (əb nok/shəs), offensive; very disagreeable; hateful; as an obnoxious person.
on slaught (on/slôt/), strong attack.
out skirts (out/skėrts), outer parts or edges of a town, district, etc.
ox y gen (ok/si jən), a gas without color or odor that forms about one fifth of the air.

pal sy (pôl/zi), paralysis; loss of power to feel, to move, or to control motion in any part of the body.
Pa pous (pä/pous), Greek word meaning grandfather.
par ka (pär/kə), fur jacket with a hood worn in Arctic regions.
par ry (par/i), turn aside; ward off.
Pe nel o pe (pi nel/ə pi).
pen e trate (pen/i trāt), 1. get into or through. 2. pierce through. 3. soak through. 4. see into; understand.
per am bu la tor (pər am/bū lā tər), a small carriage in which a baby is pushed about.
per pet u al (pər pech/ü əl), 1. lasting forever; lasting throughout life. 2. continuous; never ceasing; as, perpetual pain.
per se cu tion (pėr/si kū/shən), being treated badly; being harmed again and again.
per son age (pėr/sən ij), 1. an important person. 2. person.
phi los o pher (fi los/ə fər), a lover of wisdom; person who has a system for guiding life.

---

hat, āge, cāre, fär; let, ēqual, tėrm; it, īce; hot, ōpen, ôrder; oil, out; cup, put, rūle, ūse; th, thin; ᴛʜ, then; ə represents *a* in about, *e* in taken, *i* in pencil, *o* in lemon, *u* in circus.

phosphorus

phos pho rus (fos′fə rəs), a substance that burns slowly and shines in the dark.
pic tur esque (pik chər esk′), vivid; interesting.
plait (plat), braid.
pla toon (plə tün′), 1. group of soldiers acting as a unit. 2. a small group.
poach[1] (pōch), 1. trespass on another's land, especially to hunt. 2. take (game or fish) without any right.
poach[2] (pōch), cook (an egg) by breaking it into boiling water.
poise (poiz), balance. She has perfect poise both of mind and body and never seems embarrassed.
po lit i cal (pə lit′i kəl), having to do with citizens or government.
pom mel (pum′əl), 1. the part of a saddle that sticks up at the front. 2. strike; beat with the fists.
pom pous (pom′pəs), fond of display; acting proudly; trying to seem magnificent. The leader of the band bowed in a pompous manner.
pon der (pon′dər), consider carefully.
pon der ous (pon′dər əs), 1. very heavy. 2. heavy and clumsy. 3. dull; tiresome. The speaker talked in a ponderous way.
pop u lace (pop′ū lis), the common people.
pos tern (pōs′tərn), a back door or gate.
post haste (pōst′hāst′), in great haste.
prec i pice (pres′i pis), very steep place.
pres er va tion (prez′ər vā′shən), 1. preserving; keeping from harm or change; keeping safe. 2. being protected.
priv i lege (priv′i lij), special right; advantage or favor.
pro found (prō found′), 1. very deep; as, a profound sleep. 2. deeply felt; very great.

resolute

prone (prōn), 1. inclined. We are prone to think evil of people we don't like. 2. lying face down.
proph et (prof′it), 1. a person who tells what will happen. 2. one who preaches what he thinks has been revealed to him. Every religion has its prophets.
pros trate (pros′trāt), 1. lay down flat; cast down. 2. lying flat.
pro trude (prō trüd′), thrust forth; stick out.
prov ince (prov′ins), 1. a part of a country at a distance from the capital. 2. a big division of a country. Canada is divided into provinces instead of into States.

queue (kū), a braid of hair hanging down the back. 2. line of persons, automobiles, etc.

Rab ka (räb′kä).
Ra fa el (rä′fā el).
reb el (reb′əl for 1 and 2, ri bel′ for 3), 1. person who resists or fights against authority instead of obeying. The rebels fought against the government. 2. defying law or authority; as, the rebel army. 3. feel a great dislike or opposition. We rebelled at having to stay home.
re bel lion (ri bel′yən), a fight against government; revolt; rebelling.
re in force (rē′in fōrs′), strengthen with new force or materials; as, to reinforce an army or a fleet.
re li ance (ri lī′əns), trust; dependence.
re luc tant (ri luk′tənt), unwilling; slow to act because unwilling.
rem nant (rem′nənt), small part left.
re pub lic (ri pub′lik), nation or state in which the citizens elect representatives to manage the government.
res o lute (rez′ə lüt), bold; determined; firm.

res o lu tion (rez ə lü′shən), 1. thing decided on. 2. power of holding firmly to a purpose. 3. a statement of opinion.
re solve (ri zolv′), 1. make up one's mind; determine; decide. 2. firmness in carrying out a purpose.
rev o lu tion (rev ə lü′shən), 1. a complete change in government. The American Revolution (1775-1783) gave independence to the colonies. 2. complete change. 3. a moving round some point in a circle.
rid i cule (rid′i kūl), 1. laugh at; make fun of. 2. words or actions that make fun of somebody or something.
rig ging (rig′ing), ropes, chains, etc., used to support and work the masts, yards, sails, etc., on a ship.
rig id (rij′id), stiff; firm.
rout[1] (rout), 1. flight of a defeated army in disorder. 2. put to flight. 3. complete defeat.
rout[2] (rout), 1. dig (out); get by searching. 2. put (out); force (out).
rue ful (rü′fəl), sorrowful; unhappy.

Sam ar cand (sam ər kand′), a city in western Asia, north of Afghanistan.
San Mar tín (sän mär tēn′).
São Paulo (soung pou′lō).
sat u rate (sach′ủ rāt), soak through and through.
Sche nec ta dy (ski nek′tə di).
schoon er (skün′ər), 1. a ship with two or more masts and fore-and-aft sails. 2. prairie schooner, a large covered wagon used in crossing the plains of North America before the railroads were built.
scull (skul), 1. an oar worked with a side twist over the end of a boat to make it go. 2. act of propelling (a boat) by a scull. 3. a boat propelled by a scull or by sculls.

scut tle[1] (skut′əl), a kind of bucket for carrying coal.
scut tle[2] (skut′əl), scamper; scurry.
S. E., southeast; halfway between south and east.
se clude (si klüd′), keep apart from company; shut off from others.
sedge (sej), a grasslike plant that grows in wet places.
Se lim (sē′lim).
sem a phore (sem′ə fôr), device for signaling.
sem blance (sem′bləns), likeness; appearance.
Shang hai (shang′hī′), a large seaport in eastern China.
sheer (shēr), 1. very thin. 2. complete. She fainted from sheer weariness. 3. straight up and down. From the top of the wall was a sheer drop of 100 feet to the water below.
shil ling (shil′ing), a British coin worth about 24 cents in United States money.
Shu ra Tre kach (shü′rä trä kach′).
Si an (sē′än′), city in north central China.
Si be ri an (sī bēr′i ən), of or pertaining to Siberia, a region in northern Asia.
Si di Ah med (sē′di ä′med).
sil hou ette (sil′ü et′), 1. outline portrait cut out of black paper or filled in with a single color. 2. **In silhouette** means shown in outline. 3. show in outline. The mountain was silhouetted against the sky.
silt (silt), earth, sand, etc., carried by moving water and deposited.
Si món (sē mōn′).
si moom (si müm′), hot, sand-laden wind of the deserts of Arabia, Syria, and northern Africa.
singe (sinj), burn a little.
sin is ter (sin′is tər), 1. threatening; showing ill will. 2. bad; evil.

hat, āge, cāre, fär; let, ēqual, tėrm; it, īce; hot, ōpen, ôrder; oil, out; cup, put, rüle, ūse; th, thin; ᴛʜ, then; ə represents *a* in about, *e* in taken, *i* in pencil, *o* in lemon, *u* in circus.

sloop (slüp), a sailboat having one mast, a mainsail, a jib, and sometimes other sails.
Soong (sŭng).
sour dough (sour′ dō′), prospector or pioneer in Alaska or Canada.
spat ter dash (spat′ər dash′), long leggings or gaiters worn to keep the stockings from being splashed.
spav in (spav′in), a disease of horses in which a bony swelling forms at the leg joint, causing lameness.
spec i fi ca tion (spes′i fi kā′shən), 1. definite mention. 2. a detailed description of the dimensions, materials, etc., for a building, road, dam, boat, etc.
spec tac u lar (spek tak′ū lər), making a great display.
spec u late (spek′ū lāt), 1. reflect; consider; think; wonder. 2. buy or sell when there is a large risk.
squire (skwīr), 1. in England, a chief landowner in a district. 2. in the United States, a justice of the peace.
S. S. W., south southwest; halfway between south and southwest.
star board (stär′bərd), the right side of a ship, looking forward.
state ly (stāt′li), having dignity.
states man (stāts′mən), man skilled in the management of public or national affairs.
sti let to (sti let′ō), a dagger with a long, narrow blade.
strand[1] (strand), 1. shore; land bordering a river, sea, or lake. 2. run aground. 3. bring into a helpless position.
strand[2] (strand), one of the threads, strings, or wires that are twisted together to make a rope.
strat e gy (strat′i ji), 1. the science or art of war; the planning and directing of military movements and operations. 2. skillful planning.
sub lime (səb līm′), lofty; noble; majestic; grand.

sub side (səb sīd′), 1. sink to a lower level. After the rain stopped, the water subsided. 2. grow less; die down. 3. settle.
sub tle (sut′əl), 1. faint; mysterious. 2. having a keen, quick mind; discerning; acute. 3. sly; crafty; tricky. 4. skillful; clever; expert.
sub urb (sub′ėrb), district lying outside a city or town.
Su lie man (sü′lē män).
su per flu ous (sü pėr′flü əs), needless; more than is needed.
sur mount (sər mount′), 1. rise above. 2. be on top of. 3. overcome. 4. go up and across.
swath (swôth), the space covered by a single cut of a scythe; one cut of a mowing machine.
sym bol (sim′bəl), something that stands for or represents something else.

tac tics (tak′tiks), 1. the art of placing military or naval forces in action. 2. procedures to gain advantage or success.
ta pir (tā′pər), large piglike animal that has a long snout.
tense (tens), stretched tight; strained; as, a tense rope, tense nerves, a tense moment.
tern (tėrn), sea bird like a gull.
Tha li a (thə lē′ə).
tide (tīd), 1. the rise and fall of the ocean about every twelve hours. 2. stream; current; flood. 3. season; time; as, Christmastide. 4. **Tide over** means help along.
ti dings (tī′dingz), news.
till er (til′ər), person who tills (farms) land; a farmer.
tim or ous (tim′ər əs), easily frightened; timid.
tou can (tü kän′), a tropical bird.
trac tion (trak′shən), 1. drawing or pulling; being drawn. 2. friction. Wheels slip on ice because there is too little traction.

trag ic (traj′ik), very sad; dreadful.
trans par ent (trans pār′ənt), easily seen through.
trav erse (trav′ərs or trə vėrs′), pass across; go across.
treach er ous (trech′ər əs), 1. not to be trusted, not faithful. 2. deceiving; not reliable; having a false appearance of security. Thin ice is treacherous.
trea son (trē′zən), falseness to one's country or one's ruler.
Tre kach (tre käch′).
Trip′o li (trip′ə li).
truce (trüs), a stop in fighting; peace for a short time.
Tu nis (tū′nis or tü′nis).
tur bine (tėr′bin), an engine or motor in which a wheel with vanes is made to revolve by the force of water, steam, or air.
tur bu lent (tėr′bū lənt), 1. disorderly; unruly; violent. 2. greatly disturbed; as, turbulent water.
tur moil (tėr′moil), commotion; disturbance; tumult.
turn spit (tėrn′spit′), one that turns a roast of meat on a sharp-pointed rod or bar over a fire.

u nan i mous ly (ū nan′i məs li), with complete agreement; without a single opposing vote.
un ap peas a ble (un ə pēz′ə bəl), not able to be satisfied or calmed.
un can ny (un kan′i), strange and mysterious.
un du la tion (un′jü lā′shən), 1. waving motion. 2. wavy form. 3. one of a series of wavelike bends.
un par al leled (un par′ə leld), having no equal; matchless.
un seem ly (un sēm′li), 1. not suitable. 2. improperly.

vag a bond (vag′ə bond), wanderer; idle wanderer; tramp.
ven dor (ven′dər), seller; peddler.
Ven e zue la (ven′i zwē′lə).
ven i son (ven′i zən), deer meat; the flesh of a deer, used for food.
ves try (ves′tri), room in a church where meetings are held, supplies kept, etc.
vi zier or **vi zir** (vi zēr′), a high official in Mohammedan countries; a minister of state.
vo lu mi nous (və lü′mi nəs), of great size; very bulky.

waif (wāf), 1. person without home or friends; homeless or neglected child. 2. anything without an owner; stray thing, animal, etc.
weird (wērd), unearthly; mysterious; wild; strange.
where fore (hwăr′fōr), 1. for what reason; why. 2. therefore; so.
whit (hwit), very small bit.
wield (wēld), hold and use; manage; control.

Xen o phon (zen′ə fən).

yacht (yot), boat for pleasure trips or for racing.
Yang tze (yäng′tse′).
yeo man (yō′mən), 1. a servant or attendant of a lord or king. 2. in England, a person who owns land, but not a large amount. 3. in the United States Navy, a petty officer who has charge of supplies or accounts.
yew (ū), 1. an evergreen tree of Europe and Asia. 2. the wood of this tree.
You-Seff (yü sef′).
Ys o bel (ē′sə bel or iz′ə bel).

---

hat, āge, cāre, fär; let, ēqual, tėrm; it, īce; hot, ōpen, ôrder; oil, out; cup, pùt, rüle, ūse; th, thin; ᴛн, then; ə represents *a* in about, *e* in taken, *i* in pencil, *o* in lemon, *u* in circus.

TO THE TEACHER

People and Progress follows *Days and Deeds* and is designed for use at the sixth-grade level. The accompanying *Teacher's Guidebook* and *Think-and-Do Book* (workbook) provide the methodology and materials for a developmental skill-building program in reading.

VOCABULARY LIST

This vocabulary list contains the 1540 words introduced in *People and Progress*. The following forms of known words are not counted as new: variants formed by adding or dropping the endings *s, es, d, ed, ing, n, en,* and *er, est* of comparison (including those formed by changing *y* to *i* or *f* to *v*, dropping the final *e*, or doubling the final consonant in the root word); possessives; derivatives formed by adding prefixes *a-, dis-, en-, fore-, im-, re-,* or *un-* and the suffixes *-en, -ful, -ish, -ly, -ness, -y, -less, -like, -er* and *-or* (of agent), *-teen* and *-th* (when suffixed to numerals); compounds; contractions. Homographs, for example *close* (klōz) and *close* (klōs), are not counted as separate words. Proper names that are visual combinations of known word forms and the following foreign words are not counted: *dinar, hu akbar, bismillah, jellaba, behime, Hadj, mishwee, verdura, vassoura, gallinha, gourda, peixe, camarão, abacaxi, milreis, senhor, senhora, senhorita, mon général, de, soroche*. Words italicized in the Vocabulary List are pronounced or defined in the glossary.

UNIT I
7 ....
8 Ronnie
   Beth
   roan
   Sprint
   gopher
9 triumphantly
   Dude
10 *curry*
   jubilantly
11 applauded
12 circular
13 smothered
14 ....
15 grudgingly
   cinched
   overtake
   stately
   stork
   chickadees
16 gesture
   halters
17 Marion
   Andrews
   enthusiastic
   carnival
18 pyramids
   spectacular

Daniels
personally
19 *poised*
   comedy
20 indistinct
21 paralyzed
   suspended
22 examination
23 hospital
   medical
   treatment
   congratulate
   flush
   heroine
24 Jenkins
   Centerville
   fireflies
   weird
   skeleton
25 *created*
   guaranteed
   carved
   notified
   membership
26 Claude
   Spencer
   chimed
   golf
   Stan

27 obtain
   faded
28 crescent
29 collided
   pell-mell
30 racket
   conspirators
   unanimously
31 smudge
32 *Arkansas*
   Proctor
   Tad
   craft
   hencoop
   bedraggled
33 plumb
   Susie
   capered
34 levee
   pshaw
   mooring
   protruding
   riverward
35 northward
   motto
   observations
36 shantyboat
   Noah
   ark

Negro
deluge
capsize
37 ....
38 Mister
   persisted
   title
   wreckage
39 pivoted
   lee
   marooned
   bronzed
   salmon
40 *prophet*
   famished
   erected
   supervisor
   medal
41 McMahon
   Dover
   Frankville
   stake
42 harum-scarum
   uncanny
   persistent
   handicap
   prospect
43 per cent
   opinion
   sissies

472

44 namby-pamby
   million
45 notion
   grim
   efficient
46 *wielded*
   energetically
   jab
47 utmost
   demonstrate
   whetted
   exertion
   trooped
48 muffins
   cordially
   bashful
49 emphasis
50 unison

UNIT II
51 ....
52 Gazette
   Timothy
   apprentice
   editor
   contract
   colonies
53 Nellie
   convention
   Philadelphia
54 *declaration*
   subscribers
   cantered
   scissors
   delegates
   independent
55 *treason*
   revolution
   reliable
   Towser
   Jenny
   bombarded
56 ....
57 apprenticeship
   jelly
   scoffed
   patriot
58 ....
59 revived
   whippoorwill
60 item
   token
   heir
   embarrassment
61 Yankee

clipper
Adams
Humphrey
Reynolds
rigging
hardtack
62 mallet
   chisel
   voyages
   dingy
   clutter
   hull
   yacht
63 musing
   thunderous
   congress
   specifications
   design
64 *bowsprit*
   revolutionary
   affair
   comment
   withstand
65 *Mediterranean*
   pirates
   tribute
   Algiers
   Tripoli
   Tunis
   dispatches
   masts
66 *evidence*
   Gibraltar
67 *minister*
   Arab
   appropriate
   inspection
   tour
68 pursuit
   British
   groveling
69 sluggish
   becalmed
   bore
   Maryland
70 Albany
   Derek
   demon
   DeWitt
   Clinton
   Schenectady
71 draped
   accommodate
   trod

72 fashionably
   sketching
   artist
   plied
   pencil
   historic
   precisely
   Dexter
73 plush
   voluminous
   wheezed
   trapeze
   belched
74 jets
   smoldered
   resolutely
75 singed
   tattered
   agile
   applied
   repetition
76 balked
   volunteer
   worst
   consolingly
   cured
77 refreshments
   nation
   absence
   deacon
   dawdled
   gingerbread
78 truant
   silhouette
   exhibit
   original
   queried
79 Cyrus
   cradle
   Virginia
   reaping
80 McCormick
   perspiration
   swath
   stubble
   devices
   sickle
   whittled
81 drudgery
   prosperous
   forges
   anvil
   cider
82 ....
83 mess
   sow

84 *doggedly*
   centuries
85 revolving
   reel
   crank
   gears
86 shimmering
   jointed
   crudely
87 public
   exhibition
   Lexington
   calloused
88 humbug
   jeered
   ridicule
89 contraption
   academy
   twilight
90 newfangled
   Nan
   Dana
   stitches
   Marshall
   maintained
91 expression
92 *contrived*
93 implored
94 lavender
   taffeta
   gingerly
95 *ruefully*
   posthaste
   complicated
96 ....
97 ....
98 thoroughly
   drenched
   sympathetically
   fidgety
   livery
99 riddle
   veranda
   parlor
   mackintoshes
100 labeled
101 Kokomo
    Indiana
    Haynes
    continually
102 machinery
    pistons
    Apperson
    ingenuity
    patriotic

473

103 *enumerate*
   mildly
   Paris
104 compete
   Michigan
   connection
   Hollins
   depot
   No.
   dray
   traction
105 ancestor
106 *deputy*
   agent
   barbecue
   inalienable
   liberty
107 *fogies*
   Indianapolis
   Wayne
   beads
   objections
108 . . . .
109 tumult
110 spouting
   poetry
   starched
   accomplishment
111 *preservation*
   explosion
   reluctantly
112 . . . .

UNIT III
113 . . . .
114 Brewster
   starboard
   Curt
   Sprong
   cargoes
   shuttling
   barges
115 complex
   pattern
   catboat
   acknowledge
   inlets
116 surfboat
117 *contact*
   preserver
118 compartment
119 shucks
120 *Chelan*
   Rex
   Boyd

   zipped
   ankles
   material
121 mask
   mesh
   'chute
122 estimating
   correction
   billowed
   descent
123 kit
   canteen
   vigorously
   landscape
   telescope
124 *profound*
   extricate
125 McClary
   midcontinent
   Ivorsen
   jewelry
   parkas
   Sourdough
   ceremonies
   Gus
126 phonograph
   MacDonald
   Caruthers
   Akers
   inserted
127 portable
   ecstatically
   mike
   issued
   Tex
   Jensen
128 establish
129 *bleak*
   organize
   severity
130 antenna
   clogged
   alder
   sheer
   torture
131 *saturated*
   pried
   foil
   embers
   fangs
132 boost
   solitude
   nightmare
   panel
   earphones
   jovial

133 *intense*
   atmosphere
134 *Siberians*
   unreality
   muddled
135 verse
   discord
   amplifier
136 *ammeter*
   drained
137 blurred
   distorted
   magnified
   babbling
138 okay
   genuine
139 Galesburg
   Potts
   tranquil
   Harrison
   stoker
   Pullman
140 Altona
   semaphore
   prolonged
   schedule
   straggling
141 hulking
   naphtha
   continuous
   caboose
   coupling
   automatically
   indicator
142 collision
   rival
   detached
143 agonized
   confidence
   begrimed
   method
   wavered
144 mechanical
   separation
145 *inflammable*
   jangled
   rhythm
   clamoring
   tense
   elapsed
146 . . . .
147 importance
148 Donohue
   squad
   fads
   frills

   impetuous
   hydrogen
   oxygen
149 *chemicals*
   scientific
   pulmotor
   drill
   asbestos
   burglar
   explosives
   dynamite
150 devil
   mop
   hydrant
   stifling
151 nozzle
   valve
   interior
   bedlam
152 calcium
   oxide
   quicklime
   hydrate
153 *outskirts*
   sodium
   bicarbonate
   overtaxed
   sulphuric
   perilous
   admiration
154 hurtle
   oozing
   horrifying
155 curb
   veteran
156 cement
   ambulance

UNIT IV
157 . . . .
158 *Caliph*
   Chunder-abad-dad
   divan
   Selim
   Vizir
159 *subsided*
   elastic
   spatterdashes
   superiority
160 adopt
   stingy
   attachment
   unparalleled
   cuckoo
   merits
   install

161 *forthwith*
    proclamation
    henceforth
    imperial
    pendulum
    vibrate
162 *Allah*
    plague
    altered
163 *almanac*
164 tock
    thrice
    nightingale
165 buckwheat
    argument
166 contradict
    oasis
    quantities
    scuttling
    populace
    snack
167 extraordinary
    medley
    beetles
    spattering
    Roman
    perpetual
    Samarcand
168 *simoom*
    postern
    minarets
    Sheba
    crevice
169 deceiving
    oath
    imbecile
    fortnight
    corridor
170 bing
    spang
    aghast
171 lustily
    unappeasable
172 passeth
    cometh
    superfluous
    swaggered
    mustache
    modestly
173 hath
    miser
    pence
    genius
    pompously
    Sulieman

    otherwise
    frivolity
174 Simon
    Smug
    enthusiasm
175 rockery
    poet
176 poem
    hippopotamus
    nibs
    rumpled
    scribbles
177 advertisement
    shilling
    refunded
178 flitted
    gutter
179 scrawled
    illustration
    inconvenient
180 gravy
    perchance
181 deftly
    receipts
    caterpillar
182 fertilizer
    charming
183 M.D.
    marsh
    lawn
184 hedgehog
    Jip
    Polynesia
    rheumatism
    Oxenthorpe
    personage
    squire
    parson
185 ....
186 vets
    Theodosia
    scholar
    reference
    ain't
187 ....
188 ....
189 altogether
    pugs
    poodles
    spavins
    pills
190 mustard
    plaster
    booby
191 ....

192 moles
    badgers
193 ....
194 career
    lamented
    patron
    historians
    achievements
    fund
195 justice
    Bathsheba
    Xenophon
    Ysobel
    Zenas
    vestry
    Christ
    sermons
196 encounter
    delirious
    rind
197 scientist
    statesman
    philosopher
    disreputable
198 ....
199 critical
    chestnut
200 junk
    dormouse
    pincers
201 *andirons*
202 *eureka*
    rye
    tankard
    ale
    angle
    London
    thereby
203 derived
    convulsive
    contraction
    rebellion
    omit
    epoch
    tingling
204 *unseemly*
    sensations
    strictly
    investigation
    disclosed
205 series
    investigate
    electrical
    moreover
    resigned

206 foundations
    liquid
    phosphorus
207 sulphur
    visible
    befallen
208 *apparatus*

UNIT V
209 ....
210 *Driss*
    waif
    Sidi Ahmed
    charcoal
    Berber
    Ali Taza
211 *jujube*
212 *Fortunata*
    clink
    dove
    wax
    fuzzy
    clipped
213 *Egyptian*
    Nazarene
    Izda Taza
    Amroo
214 *You-Seff*
    weaned
    Rabka
215 puckered
    accord
216 existed
    barley
217 tanner
    lagged
    carpet
    pilgrim
    pilgrimage
    holy
    Mecca
218 saunter
    blissfully
219 doughnut
    mutton
    flourish
220 cutlet
    razor
    shave
    Mohammed
    mystified
    Nour Edden
    Ben Hassan
    example

221 tampering
 Dillal Ben Abbes
222 digested
 inactive
 noticeable
 raid
 vicious
223 belly
 El Ghouli
 Berk El Lill
224 rogue
 creased
 summit
 radiance
225 *Moscow*
 Kholodny
 crinkled
 Shura
 Trekach
 wistfully
226 proposal
 memory
 treacherous
 Dnieper
 concrete
 spans
 Europe
 symbol
227 students
 standard
 sympathetic
 discussion
 council
228 Stalinsky
 qualify
229 satisfactory
230 superintendent
 catastrophe
 invaded
 barrier
231 *evacuation*
232 evacuating
 turbines
 construction
 jumble
 transplant
233 *dismantling*
 wheelbarrows
 perambulators
 droshkies
234 makeshift
 salvaged
 draperies

contents
bulbs
structure
turbulent
doom
235 *brigade*
 encampment
 destruction
236 *Nikias*
 Demetrios
 regiment
 Greece
 Kyr Mihale
237 *Penelope*
 Theo
 almond
 mincemeat
238 *Thalia*
239 *Manitza*
 ravine
 Athens
240 reflected
241 revolvers
 Greek
242 cockerel
 Benito
 Rafael
 quest
243 ....
244 balsams
245 agony
246 bandaged
 propped
 brogans
 wallet
 Papous
247 outflank
 Aleko Kalamato
 colonel
248 *Manoel*
 accidentally
 Chiquita
 Gomes
 São Paulo
 Maria
 Brazil
 Brazilian
249 canaries
 parakeets
 armadillo
 tapir
 macaws
 toucans
250 conferring
 Amazon

251 *vendors*
 spools
 hawker
 shrimps
252 advantage
 menagerie
 strung
253 residential
 suburbs
 cobblestones
 leopard
 acquire
254 engage
 marmoset
 flounced
255 boulevard
 cooing
256 ornamental
 shrubbery
257 *Lan Ying*
 Yangtze
 tides
258 hillock
 hamlet
259 minnows
 sliver
 companionable
 coveys
 askew
260 *sculls*
261 ....
262 pouted
 pondered
 rinse
263 differ
 clod
264 *inexhaustible*
 gorges
265 canals
 engulfed
266 *generations*
267 Lobo
268 ....
269 surlily
270 abate
271 steadfastly
272 ribs
 gruel
273 ....
274 ....

UNIT VI
275 ....

276 Chut
 orphan
 Henton
 innumerable
 moths
 spider
 Australian
 invisible
277 bleached
 kangaroo
 undulation
 thighs
 joeys
 exception
278 conversational
 muscular
 semblance
 security
 ebony
 rebelled
 reproving
 pinafore
279 cowlick
 coral
 absurdly
 posture
 grappled
 despised
280 nubbled
 overwhelming
 russet
 barbed
 twittered
 draggled
281 drunk
 soothe
 somersault
 Jove
282 scruff
 instinctively
 enclosed
283 mellow
 sizzling
 attuned
 jests
 clanging
 homestead
284 *pommel*
 bulging
285 accompanier
 bumptious
 arch
 sociably
 resounding

476

286 *persecution*
hefty
nubby
christened
287 Zodie
dewy
miraculously
288 entice
adored
foster
bullying
289 hunk
coward
fatal
sacred
290 falcon
schooner
Doug
Indefatigable
San Francisco
Galápagos
dory
291 stow
knapsack
sheath
hatchet
hike
292 *lava*
chasm
purling
iguana
293 daubs
grotesque
volcanic
attentively
inhabited
dinosaurs
294 vegetarian
momentary
emboldened
refuge
crannies
295 male
combat
combatants
arena
bevy
female
withdraw
296 dangled
seascape
platoons
crabs
jetsam
297 sparred
telescopic

298 *stiletto*
resumed
tennis
299 finches
sparrows
description
lagoon
coarse
vegetation
300 conical
flamingos
301 webbed
302 *contortions*
tropics
303 admonished
304 scrabbling
blurted
305 metallic
horde
306 gnashing
enlarged
cells
307 *rout*
defeated
tantalized
resisted
vats
amber
308 sentries
309 distinguish
cutlass
communicate
hymn
majestic
tactics
310 defiantly
defense
311 mangled
shrank
sacrifice
312 skyward
murdered
host
313 tragic
314 *erosion*
silt
superb
stranded
havoc
dappled
eddy
gill
315 surging
abundant

freshet
rotten
fringing
316 yearling
fingerlings
squawfish
marine
studio
hobby
317 tourist
318 scanned
capable
conservationist
science
craved
exulted
319 streamlining
filmed
speckled
aristocrat
poach
battering
flabby
320 exposed
cramped
321 blank
underexposure
slats
322 *transparent*
defensive
323 courageous
befriended
treachery
324 haunted
captivity
deprived
resort
photographic
contestant
325 dumbly
conservation
326 crags
previous
slain
Drumranny
Irish
327 cormorants
ringlets
328 brine
comely
subtle
acute
shun
sprout
glen
fragile

329 bracelets
infancy
gloating
earshot
maneuvered
distended
330 sagged
331 *consequence*
groove
resistance
332 *knoll*
audible
333 secrecy
rapped
334 *parried*
335 *deflected*
fiendish
overpower
hampered
fretful
336 rigidly
onslaught
timorous
pantomime
myriads
infant
tumultuous
seamed
337 undulating
methodically
sinister
lather
confined
strategy
338 . . . .
339 *embedded*
gored
penetrated
340 *carcass*
precipice
Cahir

UNIT VII

341 . . . .
342 azaleas
iris
Monticello
bridle
343 elegant
jostling

344 Massachusetts
   Richard
   exclamation
   Spain
   allies
   Continental
   militia
345 numerous
   leisure
   correspondence
   flaunted
   unavoidable
346 *resolution*
   resolved
   voting
   postponed
   Sherman
347 govern
   obnoxious
   violin
348 *inadequate*
   political
   entitles
   decent
   mankind
   impel
   strife
   sublime
349 *endowed*
   privilege
   instituted
   minced
   reliance
   divine
   providence
   mutually
350 whither
   dome
   canopy
351 torment
   bewigged
   submitted
   compose
   Thompson
   criticism
352 embark
   democracy
   ponderous
   perspire
   wigs
   flack
   Hancock
353 signature
   mockingly

354 fro
   Hopkins
   indifferent
   inscribed
355 *Lafayette*
   Carolina
   enrolled
356 mansion
   buff
   Excellency
   Marquis
   athletic
   affected
357 *picturesque*
   blushed
   accent
358 hereafter
   Delaware
   Germantown
   Gilbert
   oppose
   defy
   Trenton
359 attired
   aides
   Nathanael
   Greene
   Alexander
   Hamilton
   Brandywine
360 hardships
361 disease
   devotion
   dwindling
   unit
362 *alliance*
363 *Bolívar*
   liberator
   Caracas
   capital
   Venezuela
   republic
   exile
   provinces
364 *Cartagena*
   Granada
   Magdalena
365 *haggard*
366 skirmishes
   Spaniard
367 reception
   reinforced
   inflicted
   disastrous
   portion
   Jamaica

368 Panama
   representatives
   Orinoco
   campaigns
   constitution
   cape
   expelled
369 conference
   skulls
370 *llanos*
   harass
   compel
   Rooke
   Patagonia
   swollen
371 eternal
   remnant
   enlisted
   decisive
372 victorious
   Bogotá
   San Martín
   Peru
   Bolivia
   Pan-American
373 Madame
   Chiang
   Kai-shek
   Shanghai
   Generalissimo
374 *Sian*
   rebellious
   mutiny
   turmoil
375 bombers
   civil
   condemn
376 discouragement
   education
   Christian
   religion
   Soong
   educated
   Mayling
   endangers
377 telegram
   Kung
   urgent
   despite
378 *truce*
   mission
   wintry
   mutinous
   Donald
   captors

379 serene
   hostess
   courtesy
   mutineer
380 lair
   Jehovah
381 *executed*
   military
   discipline
   imprisonment
   Japan
   rank
   misunderstood
   reforms
382 apologetic
   repentant
   confided
   pneumonia
383 . . . .
384 typewriter
   recommend
385 forgave
   agricultural
   poultry
386 orphanages
   association
   zones
   sum

UNIT VIII
387 . . . .
388 outlaw
   decree
   glades
   Sherwood
   clad
389 *yew*
   minstrel
   yeoman
   domain
   quoth
   thou
390 thyself
   whit
   wouldst
   naught
   darest
   belaboring
   nigh
   clouted

478

391 cudgel	406 ye	425 *secluded*	439 alternately
hast	whence	mountainous	melody
drubbing	407 hummocks	Stiria	440 distinct
wherefore	*monotonous*	*luxuriant*	*crucible*
Stutely	408	*fertility*	*akimbo*
thwacked	409 *sedge*	426 drought	441 *mode*
ado	410 peg	grapes	*diminutive*
restrained	stead	Schwartz	442 consternation
392 chortled	411 dune	Hans	*malice*
ell	412 *speculating*	Gluck	enchantments
avail	413 dirk	wages	443 exit
cavorting	414 sweat	*charity*	*adhered*
thee	triphammer	427 *turnspit*	wrangled
pranks	415 monstrous	428 corkscrew	fray
393 *tiller*	recollection	*doublet*	pacify
sheriff	416 *agitation*	429 hollo	*magistrate*
Nottingham	villains	430 irritably	444 consulted
394 sworn	417 betwixt	431 fizzed	priest
foul	Henlopen	mixture	flask
395 *prone*	clue	humility	*traverse*
tidings	reverend	432 knuckle	*surmounting*
396	418 clergyman	melancholy	445 *glacier*
397	Moses	433 *vagabond*	recruited
398 *monk*	India	administering	446 spurned
abbot	thankee	amen	rugged
399 *abbeys*	didst	434 gush	mockery
venison	419 yon	435 reclined	447 *prostrate*
400 garland	420 S.S.W.	436 inconvenience	448 giddy
401 tweaked	S.E.	desolation	449 ....
smite	421 *insistent*	gutted	450 prevailed
402	tern	*Esquire*	fragments
403 yearned	422 palsy	437 occupation	451 obliged
404 *sloop*	measurement	momentous	452 piteously
Chist	*aught*	relations	*intolerable*
bail	Brooke	*inheritance*	453 confound
Matt	scuffling	property	*font*
405 Kidd	423 grit	*livelihood*	454 veiled
naked	padlock	knave	*monarch*
petticoat	424 *ecstasy*	squander	cleft
bandanna	*cataract*	438 imaginable	455 cruelty
plaited	trance		inhabitants
queue	*notorious*		
jackboots			

ILLUSTRATORS

The pictures for this book were made by the following artists: John Merryweather (cover, pp. 1, 3, 7, 8-16, 51, 79-89, 113, 125-157, 194-209, 275, 341, 387; I. B. Hazelton 17-23, 32-40; Robert Weisman 24-31, 41-50; Rafaello Busoni 52-60, 210-274; Harve Stein 61-69, 114-124, 388-455; David Hendrickson 70-78, 90-112; Hugh Lofting 183-193; Charlotte Becker 158-182; Robert Kuhn 276-289, 313-340; Else Bostleman 290-312; Gregory Orloff 342-354, 363-386; Milo Winter 355-362.

ACKNOWLEDGMENTS

Grateful acknowledgment is made to the following authors and publishers for permission to adapt and use copyrighted material: To Belle Coates for "Ronnie and the Mystery Horse" from "Old Dude the Mystery Horse"; to Charles Finger for "Highwater in Arkansas," *Story Parade;* to Eleanor Hammond for "Who's Scared of Bears?" *Wee Wisdom;* to Chesley Kahmann for "The Junior Team's Bargain" from "The Junior Team Tackles Something"; to the Century Company for "Marion Andrews, Lifesaver" from "The Greater Part" by Mildred Augustine, *St. Nicholas;* to Frances Cavanah for "News for the Gazette" from "Timothy's Ride," and to Jeanette C. Nolan for "All Aboard," *Child Life;* for "The Horseless Carriage" from "Terry Randall Goes Riding" in *America Was Like This* by Emma Gelders Sterne, copyright, 1941, by Dodd, Mead and Company, Inc.; to Margaret Curtis McKay for "Smoke Jumper" from "Smoke Jumper for Uncle Sam," reprinted by permission from the *American Junior Red Cross News;* to Frederic N. Litten for "Miracle of the Air" from "Birthday for Jen Ivorsen"; to Callaghan and Company for Howard M. Brier's "A Fireman's Bag of Tricks" from "Devil Wagon"; to Ray Stannard Baker for "The Night Express" from "How Potts Saved the Night Express"; to John Bennett for "The Caliph's Clock" from *The Pig Tail of Ah Lee Ben Loo*, Longmans, Green; for "Rhyming Ink" from *Fifteen Tales for Lively Children*, by Margaret and Mary Baker, copyright, 1939, by Dodd, Mead and Company, Inc.; for "Can't a Machine Do It?" from *Children of Necessity* by Grace Humphrey, copyright, 1925, used by special permission of the publishers, The Bobbs-Merrill Co.; for *Ben and Me* by Robert Lawson, reprinted by permission of Little, Brown and Company; to Holiday House for "Pepperfoot Earns His Name" from *Pepperfoot of Thursday Market* by Robert Davis; to Ruth Epperson Kennell for "The Immortal Railroad"; to Josephine Blackstock for "A Letter for Nikias" from *Wings for Nikias*, G. P. Putnam's Sons; for "The Good River" from *The First Wife and Other Tales*, copyright, 1933, by Pearl S. Buck, published by the John Day Company, Inc.; to Julian Messner, Inc., for "Adventures of Chut" from *Wilderness Orphans* by Dorothy Cottrell; to Appleton for "Sharp Wits in Bronze Armor" from *Cities of Wax* by Julie Closson Kenly; for "The Enchanted Island" from *Treasure of the Tortoise Islands* by Victor W. Von Hagen and Quail Hawkins, copyright, 1940, by Harcourt, Brace and Company, Inc.; to Hubert Evans for "The Shining Gateway"; to Liam O'Flaherty for "The Wild Goat's Kid"; to Jeanette Eaton for "Lafayette Meets His Hero"; for "Simon Bolivar, Liberator" adapted from *Against All Odds* by Marion F. Lansing, copyright, 1942, by Doubleday, Doran and Co., Inc.; to Basil Matthews for "First Lady of China" from *Wings Over China*, Friendship Press; for "Tom and the Treasure Chest" from "Tom Chist and the Treasure Box" from *The Book of Pirates* by Howard Pyle.

1 11 12 13 14 15 16 17 18 19 20 21 22 23 24 25 55 54 53